THE MOST COMPLETE AND INEXPENSIVE BOOK OF MATHEMATICAL TABLES AVAILABLE IN PAPERBACK!

Here in one handy volume are all the mathematical tables you need for school, home, or office. Also included are a clear, concise description of how to use the tables and a brief refresher course in basic mathematical operations.

MATHEMATICS TABLES AND HOW TO USE THEM

THE ONE INDISPENSABLE BOOK
FOR EVERYONE WHO HAS TO USE MATH!

BANTAM SCIENCE AND MATHEMATICS

THE ATOM AND BEYOND
by E. Sheldon Smith

•

THE CHANGING EARTH
by Judith Viorst of Science Service, Inc.

•

GREAT IDEAS IN MODERN SCIENCE
by Robert W. Marks

•

MATHEMATICS TABLES AND HOW TO USE THEM
edited by Bradley V. Smith

•

THE NEW MATHEMATICS DICTIONARY AND HANDBOOK
by Robert W. Marks

•

THE NEW PHYSICS AND CHEMISTRY DICTIONARY
AND HANDBOOK
by Robert W. Marks

•

150 SCIENCE EXPERIMENTS STEP-BY-STEP
by Judith Viorst of Science Service, Inc.

•

ONE TWO THREE . . . INFINITY
by George Gamow

•

PROFILES OF THE FUTURE
by Arthur C. Clarke

•

RATS, LICE AND HISTORY
by Hans Zinsser

•

THE SEARCH FOR LIFE ON OTHER WORLDS
by David C. Holmes

•

WEATHER
by Armand N. Spitz

Mathematics Tables and How to Use Them

Edited by Bradley V. Smith

MATHEMATICS TABLES AND HOW TO USE THEM

Bantam Matrix edition published September 1964
Bantam Science and Mathematics edition published April 1967

Most of the tables in this book are reprinted, with permission of The Macmillan Company, from LOGARITHMIC AND TRIGONOMETRIC TABLES *by Earle Raymond Hedrick. Copyright, 1913, 1920, by The Macmillan Company; Renewed 1941 by Grace G. Kenyon and Stanley Ingold, 1948 by Helen B. Hedrick.*

The first chapter of this book is closely based on Chapter 1 of Air Force Manual Number 52-8, published by the Air Training Command; for sale by the Superintendent of Documents, U.S. Government Printing Office, Washington 25, D. C.

Library of Congress Catalog Card Number: 64-17894

Published simultaneously in the United States and Canada

Bantam Books are published by Bantam Books, Inc., a subsidiary of Grosset & Dunlap, Inc. Its trade-mark, consisting of the words "Bantam Books" and the portrayal of a bantam, is registered in the United States Patent Office and in other countries. Marca Registrada. Bantam Books, Inc., 271 Madison Avenue, New York, N.Y. 10016.

PRINTED IN THE UNITED STATES OF AMERICA

PREFACE

The Bantam *Mathematics Tables and How to Use Them* has been designed to provide the student, engineer, and professional with a concise, authoritative, conveniently arranged manual of the mathematical reference data most often used. The book is sufficiently compact to be carried in the pocket, sufficiently comprehensive to meet all general needs. Because of its moderate cost, a student can readily avail himself of several copies—one to be kept on his desk, others to be used in the laboratory, shop, or field. This factor also makes it practicable to detach pages for ready reference; thus quick access can be had to data in regular use such as area and volume formulas, compound interest rates, decimal equivalents of fractions, or roots and powers of numbers.

For readers who may have forgotten some of the basic mathematical operations, an extensive refresher section has been included. This treats in detail the essential principles of algebra and trigonometry, with emphasis on exponents, radicals, complex numbers, and the theory and use of logarithms. In addition, simple rules are given for interpolating values of logarithms and trigonometric functions intermediate to those listed in the tables.

The publishers hope that this handbook will fill a long-felt need for a reference text that is authoritative, concise, and extensive in scope, and provides maximum usefulness at minimum cost.

B.V.S.

CONTENTS

Introduction to the Use of the Tables:
A Review of Basic Mathematical Operations . . 9

TABLE

I. Important Mathematical Formulas
- Algebra 49
- Plane Geometry 54
- Solid Geometry 54
- Analytic Geometry 55
- Trigonometry 58

II. Powers, Roots, and Reciprocals 62
III. Common Logarithms of Numbers 80
IV. Natural Trigonometric Functions 99
V. Logarithms of Trigonometric Functions 123
VI. Compound Interest 169
VII. Weights and Measures: Conversion Ratios . . . 170
VIII. Decimal Equivalents of Common Fractions . . 184
IX. Greek Alphabet; Roman Numerals 185

Introduction to the Use of the Tables:

A Review of Basic Mathematical Operations

ALGEBRA

Definitions

An *algebraic expression* is any combination of signs, numerals, and letters used for numbers, written according to the rules of algebra. For example, $a + b$, l, lw, and $-\frac{x}{2Y}$ are algebraic expressions. Numbers represented by letters are called *literal* numbers. Thus a, b, l, w, x, and y are literal numbers. Signs may indicate whether the numbers are positive or negative, or they may indicate operations such as addition, subtraction, multiplication, division, extracting a root, or raising to a power.

Multiplication of two algebraic numbers need not be indicated by the symbols for multiplication, the times sign ($\times$) or the dot ($\cdot$). Just putting them together indicates multiplication. Thus, the product of a and b may be written ab. In the expression ab, a and b are called *factors* of the product. Likewise 6, a, and b are factors of $6ab$.

Each factor of a product is the *coefficient* of the other factors. In the algebraic expression $6ab$, 6 is the coefficient of ab, $6a$ of b, and $6b$ of a. In this expression, 6 is called the *numerical* coefficient and b the *literal* coefficient of a. The word "coefficient" is usually restricted to mean only the numerical, or arithmetic, coefficient.

The size, or magnitude, of a number is called its *absolute value*. Absolute value refers only to the magnitude with no consideration for the sign preceding the number. For example, the absolute value of $+7$ is 7, and the absolute value of -9 is 9. Both $+3$ and -3 have the same absolute value, 3.

An *exponent* is a number or letter which indicates the power to which a quantity is to be raised, or the number of times the quantity (called the base) is multiplied by itself. For example, 4^3 is read 4 *to the third power*, and means $4 \times 4 \times 4$. The expression e^x is read *e to the x power*, and means that e is multiplied by itself x times.

Any arithmetic or literal number, or the product or the quotient of these numbers, is called a *term*. For example, 4, x, y, $25b$, ab, $\frac{x}{y}$, and $\frac{3a^2b}{c}$ are terms.

Terms that have the same literal parts are called *similar* or *like* terms. Thus a, $7a$, and $12a$ are like terms. Terms such as x^2, y, and lh, which do not have the same literal parts, are called *unlike* terms.

You can add or subtract two or more numbers if they are like terms. For example, you can add $4x$ to $5x$ to produce the sum $9x$. Likewise, you can add $5x^2$ to $10x^2$, since the literal parts x^2 are alike. (Literal numbers raised to the same power are like terms.) The sum of numbers such as $4x$ and $5m^2$ must be indicated as $4x + 5m^2$ since x and m^2 are not like terms.

An algebraic expression containing two or more terms joined together by a plus or minus sign is called a *polynomial*. Thus, the expressions $a + b - c$ and $ab - ac + \frac{a}{c}$ are polynomials. A polynomial with just two terms, such as $5x + y$, is a *binomial*. A polynomial with only three terms is a *trinomial*. The expression $5x^2 + ab + c$ is a trinomial. A single term, such as a, x, or $10x^2y$, is a *monomial*.

Algebraic Addition and Subtraction

To add two numbers having the same sign, add their absolute values and prefix the common sign. Thus:

$+6$ added to $+3$ equals $+9$
-6 added to -3 equals -9
$+6a^2$ added to $+3a^2$ equals $+9a^2$
$-6m^2n$ added to $-3m^2n$ equals $-9m^2n$

To add two numbers having opposite signs, take the difference between their absolute values and prefix the sign of the number with the larger absolute value. Thus:

$+6$ added to -3 equals $+3$
-6 added to $+3$ equals -3
$+6a^2$ added to $-3a^2$ equals $+3a^2$
$-3m^2n$ added to $+6m^2n$ equals $+3m^2n$

The process of subtraction is the opposite of the process of addition. To subtract one quantity from another, change the sign of the quantity to be subtracted; then add the quantities, following the rules of addition. Example:

$$(-6) - (-3) = (-6) + (+3) = -3$$
$$(-3) - (-6) = (-3) + (+6) = +3$$
$$(+6) - (-3) = (+6) + (+3) = +9$$
$$(+6) - (+3) = (+6) + (-3) = +3$$

Polynomials are added and subtracted in the same way as single terms (monomials). For example:

ADDITION	SUBTRACTION
$- 4a^2 + 3az - 3y$	$3m^2 - 6n^2$
$3a^3 \quad - 2az + 5y$	$-3m^2 - 8n^2$
$3a^3 - 4a^2 + az + 2y$	$6m^2 + 2n^2$

Note in these examples that the plus sign is omitted before $3a^3$, $3m^2$ and $6m^2$. Algebraic practice permits the omission of the sign before the first term of an expression if it is positive. Likewise, the numerical coefficient 1 is omitted before a literal number, as before az in the answer to the addition problem.

Signs of Grouping

Certain symbols, called *signs of grouping*, tie, or group together, several quantities affected by the same operation. The most commonly used symbols of groupings are *parentheses* ( ), *braces* { }, *brackets* [ ], and the *vinculum* $\overline{\quad}$. All these symbols indicate that the quantities affected by them are to be treated as single quantities. For example, the expression $(4a^2 - 3ab) - (3a^2 + 2ab)$ means that the quantity $3a^2 + 2ab$ is to be subtracted from the quantity $4a^2 - 3ab$. To perform this operation, change the signs of the expression $3a^2 + 2ab$, and add algebraically:

$$\begin{array}{r} 4a^2 - 3ab \\ -3a^2 - 2ab \\ \hline a^2 - 5ab \end{array}$$

In removing a sign of grouping preceded by a minus sign, change the signs of all terms included by the symbol. When one symbol of grouping occurs within another, remove the innermost symbol first. You may remove both symbols at the same time if you are quite careful, but this practice can easily lead to errors of sign. Therefore, it is best to remove only one symbol at a time. The following example illustrates the procedure for removing a symbol of grouping occurring within another and combining like terms:

$$\begin{array}{l} 3a^2 - [2am - (2a^2 + 5am) + a^2] \\ 3a^2 - [2am - 2a^2 - 5am + a^2] \\ 3a^2 - 2am + 2a^2 + 5am - a^2 \\ 4a^2 + 3am \end{array}$$

Multiplication

In the multiplication of algebraic terms, there are three things to consider—the sign, the exponent, and the coefficient.

The product of two terms with like signs is positive. The product of two terms with unlike signs is negative.

The *exponent* of any letter in the product is the sum of the exponents of the factors with the same base. Thus:

$$x^2 \times x^3 = x^{(2+3)}, \text{ or } x^5$$

Likewise:

$$y^3 \times y^7 = y^{10}$$

The arithmetic *coefficient* of the product is the product of the absolute values of the coefficients of the terms being multiplied. Thus:

$$6x^2 \times 2x^3 = 12x^5$$

Likewise:

$$3y^3 \times 3y^7 = 9y^{10}$$

More examples:

$$\begin{array}{l} (3a^2) \times (5a^3) = 15a^5 \\ (2ax) \times (-3a^2xy) = -6a^3x^2y \end{array}$$

$$(m^2n) \times (-7mn^2) = -7m^3n^3$$
$$(4xy) \times (-xy^3) = -4x^2y^4$$
$$(-a) \times (-5a^3) = 5a^4$$

A literal quantity with no written exponents means the quantity is to the first power; that is, it has an exponent of 1.

Multiplication of polynomials is similar to the multiplication of numbers consisting of several digits in arithmetic. Multiply each term of the multiplier by every term of the multiplicand and add the partial products. Thus, in multiplying $2e^2 - 3e - 5$ by $-4e + 7$, proceed as follows:

$$\begin{array}{r} 2e^2 - 3e - 5 \\ -4e + 7 \\ \hline -8e^3 + 12e^2 + 20e \\ + 14e^2 - 21e - 35 \\ \hline -8e^3 + 26e^2 - \quad e - 35 \end{array}$$

Division

In the division of one term by another, the sign, the coefficient, and the exponent must be considered in obtaining the quotient.

The quotient of two positive or two negative quantities is positive; the quotient of a positive and a negative quantity is negative. Division by zero is excluded.

The quotient of powers having like bases has the same base as the given powers, and an exponent which is the difference of the exponents of the given powers. Thus:

$$\frac{x^4}{x^2} = x^2$$

Likewise:

$$\frac{x^{10}}{x^3} = x^7$$

To obtain the coefficient of the quotient, divide the absolute value of the coefficient of the dividend by the absolute value of the coefficient of the divisor. Thus:

$$\frac{6x^4}{3x^2} = 2x^2$$

Likewise:

$$\frac{8x^{10}}{2x^3} = 4x^7$$

In division there is the possibility of zero and negative exponents, as the following examples indicate:

$$\frac{a^5}{a^5} = a^{(5-5)} \text{ or } a^0$$

$$\frac{a^4}{a^5} = a^{-1}$$

$$\frac{a^3}{a^5} = a^{-2}$$

Any quantity with a zero exponent is equal to 1. Thus:

$$\frac{a^5}{a^5} = a^0 = 1$$

Likewise:

$$\frac{x^3}{x^3} = x^0 = 1$$

Any quantity with a negative exponent is equal to the reciprocal of that quantity with the corresponding positive exponent. Thus:

$$\frac{a^3}{a^5} = a^{-2} = \frac{1}{a^2}$$

Likewise:

$$\frac{1}{x^{-3}} = x^3$$

Any factor can be moved from the numerator to the denominator of a fraction, or vice versa, without changing the value of the fraction if the sign of the exponent is changed. Thus:

$$\frac{3x^2y}{a^3b} = \frac{3x^2ya^{-3}}{b}$$

Division of one polynomial by another is similar to long division in arithmetic. One difference is that the dividend, divisor, and the remainder (if there is one) must be arranged in order of ascending or descending powers of some letter.

Example: Divide $30c^4 + 3 - 82c^2 - 5c + 11c^3$ by $3c^2 - 4 + 2c$.

Solution:

$$\begin{array}{r|l}
 & \phantom{30c^4 + 11c^3 - {}} 10c^2 - 3c - 12 \\
\hline
3c^2 + 2c - 4 & 30c^4 + 11c^3 - 82c^2 - 5c + 3 \\
 & 30c^4 + 20c^3 - 40c^2 \\
 & \quad - 9c^3 - 42c^2 - 5c \\
 & \quad - 9c^3 - 6c^2 + 12c \\
 & \qquad\quad - 36c^2 - 17c + 3 \\
 & \qquad\quad - 36c^2 - 24c + 48 \\
 & \qquad\qquad\qquad 7c - 45 \text{ remainder}
\end{array}$$

Solution of Equations

Any equation is a statement that two quantities are equal. To solve an equation means to find the value, or values, of the literal numbers for which the equation holds true. In solving an equation, you will have to use *axioms*, statements accepted as true without proof. Here are a few of the more commonly used axioms:

1. If the same number is added to, or subtracted from, both sides of an equation, the result is still an equation.

2. If both sides of an equation are multiplied by the same quantity or divided by the same quantity (not zero), the result is still an equation.

3. If like roots or powers are taken of both sides of an equation, the result is still an equation.

Other processes that are based upon these axioms and that are often applied in the solution of equations are *transposition*, *changing signs*, and *cancellation*. Transposition is the transferring of a term from one side of an equation to the other and the changing of its sign. This is merely another way of saying that the term was added to, or subtracted from, both sides (Axiom 1). Changing signs of terms on both sides of an equation is merely another way of multiplying or dividing both sides by -1 (Axiom 2). Cancellation is the means of collecting terms, or transposing and collecting terms.

Example 1: Given $x - 5 = 3$; find x.

Solution: Add 5 to both sides of the equation (Axiom 1):

$$x - 5 + 5 = 3 + 5$$

Then collect terms:

$$x = 8$$

Example 2: Given $5x - 4 = 21$; find x.

Solution: Add 4 to both sides of the equation (Axiom 1):

$$5x - 4 + 4 = 21 + 4$$

Then collect terms on both sides:

$$5x = 25$$

Divide both sides by 5 (Axiom 2):

$$x = 5$$

Example 3: Given $\frac{1}{3}x + 5 = 8$; find x.

Solution: Subtract 5 from both sides of the equation (Axiom 1):

$$\frac{1}{3}x + 5 - 5 = 8 - 5$$

Collect terms:

$$\frac{1}{3}x = 3$$

Then multiply both sides of the equation by 3 (Axiom 2):

$$x = 9$$

Example 4: Given $\frac{4}{5}x + 5 = 25 - 1\frac{1}{5}x$; find x.

Solution: Subtract 5 from both sides of the equation (Axiom 1):

$$\frac{4}{5}x = 20 - 1\frac{1}{5}x$$

Then add $1\frac{1}{5}x$ to both sides (Axiom 1):

$$\frac{4}{5}x + 1\frac{1}{5}x = 20 - 1\frac{1}{5}x + 1\frac{1}{5}x$$

Collect terms:

$$2x = 20$$

Divide both sides by 2 (Axiom 2):

$$x = 10$$

Example 5: Given $16 - 5(x + 3) = 4(2x + 1) - 9\frac{1}{2}$; find x.

Solution: Remove the parentheses:

$$16 - 5x - 15 = 8x + 4 - 9\frac{1}{2}$$

Collect terms:

$$1 - 5x = 8x - 5\frac{1}{2}$$

Subtract 1 from both sides (Axiom 1):

$$-5x = 8x - 6\frac{1}{2}$$

Subtract $8x$ from both sides (Axiom 1):

$$-13x = -6\frac{1}{2}$$

Then divide both sides by -13 (Axiom 2):

$$x = \frac{1}{2}$$

Example 6: Given $\sqrt{x} + 2 = 4$; find x.

Solution: Subtract 2 from both sides of the equation:

$$\sqrt{x} = 2$$

Then square both sides (Axiom 3):

$$x = 2^2 = 4$$

Example 7: Given $z^2 = r^2 + x^2$; find r.

Solution: Subtract x^2 from both sides of the equation:

$$z^2 - x^2 = r^2$$

Take the square root of both sides of the equation (Axiom 3):

$$\pm\sqrt{z^2 - x^2} = r$$

or

$$r = \pm\sqrt{z^2 - x^2}$$

Monomial Squares and Square Roots

When a monomial is multiplied by itself, the product is the *square* of the coefficient multiplied by each literal quantity with its exponent doubled. Examples:

$$(3a^2)^2 = 9a^4$$
$$(-5mn^3)^2 = 25m^2n^6$$

The square root of a monomial is the square root of the coefficient times each literal number with its exponent halved. There are two roots—a negative root and a positive root. This is true because the sign of the product of two negative quantities or of two positive quantities is positive. Examples:

$$\sqrt{64a^4} = \pm 8a^2$$

(The symbol $\pm$ means that it could be either $+8a^2$ or $-8a^2$.)

$$\sqrt{50a^3} = \pm 7.07a^{1.5}$$

Special Products and Factoring

Factoring is the process of finding two or more quantities, each called a factor, whose product is equal to a given quantity. The simplest form of polynomial factoring is finding the common monomial factor. The expression $5x + 5y$ is a polynomial in which 5 is a factor common to both monomials. Factor this expression by dividing $5x + 5y$ by 5. Write the result as $5(x + y)$.

Examples:

$$ax + ab - az = a(x + b - z)$$
$$4mx - 8my + 2mz = 2m(2x - 4y + z)$$
$$5a^3b - 10a^2b^2 - 15ab^3 = 5ab(a^2 - 2ab - 3b^2)$$

A frequently encountered product has the form

$$(x + a)(x + b)$$

which, when multiplied, gives $x^2 + x(a + b) + ab$. This relationship can be stated as a rule: The product of two binomials having a common term is the square of the common term, plus the product of the common term times the algebraic sum of the unlike terms, plus the algebraic product of the unlike terms.

Examples:

$$(a+3)(a+4) = a^2 + a(3+4) + (3 \times 4)$$
$$= a^2 + 7a + 12$$
$$(a-5)(a-3) = a^2 - 8a + 15$$
$$(a-7)(a+3) = a^2 - 4a - 21$$
$$(x+7)(x-9) = x^2 - 2x - 63$$

A trinomial such as $x^2 + x(a+b) + ab$ is often expressed in the general form $x^2 + mx + n$ in which m represents the sum of the unlike terms and n, their product. Factoring, or finding the binomial factors, in trinomials of this form involves finding two quantities whose sum equals m and whose product equals n. After you determine these quantities, write the binomial factors by algebraically adding these quantities to the square root of the first term of the trinomial. Thus, for example, in $b^2 - 9b + 14$, the numbers -7 and -2 must be part of the binomial factors, for their sum is -9 and their product is $+14$. This means that the binomial factors are $(b-7)$ and $(b-2)$.

Examples:

$$e^2 - 9e + 20 = (e-5)(e-4)$$
$$r^2 + 11r - 42 = (r+14)(r-3)$$
$$p^2 - p - 42 = (p-7)(p+6)$$
$$t^2 + 11t + 24 = (t+3)(t+8)$$

When the product is of the form $(x+a)\,(x+a)$ or $(x+a)^2$, the middle term of the product is $2ax$, and the final term is a^2. Thus, $(x+a)^2 = x^2 + 2ax + a^2$.

Expressed in rule form, this relation is: The square of a binomial is the sum of the squares of the two terms added to twice their algebraic product. Examples:

$$(r+t)^2 = r^2 + 2rt + t^2$$
$$(k-2j)^2 = k^2 - 4kj + 4j^2$$
$$(3e-d)^2 = 9e^2 - 6ed + d^2$$

Factoring polynomials of the type $x^2 + 2ax + a^2$, called perfect trinomial squares, depends largely on your ability to recognize them as such. A trinomial is a perfect square if two of its terms are perfect squares and the third term is twice the product of their square roots. Examples:

$$g^2 + 2gk + k^2 = (g + k)^2$$
$$p^2 + 2pq + q^2 = (p + q)^2$$
$$r^2 - 10r + 25 = (r - 5)^2$$

The product of binomials of the type $mx + a$ and $nx + b$ is $mnx^2 + x(na + mb) + ab$; little time is saved by following a rule. However, knowing the rule for such multiplication may make it easier for you to factor the product of binomials of this type.

Rules for multiplying any two binomials are:

1. To find the first term of the product, multiply the first terms of the binomials by each other.

2. To find the second term of the product, obtain the product of the outer terms of the binomials and the product of the inner terms of the binomials and add them algebraically.

3. To find the third term of the product, multiply the second terms of the binomials by each other.

Thus, to find the product of $(2e - 3)(3e + 4)$, proceed as follows:

First term: $2e \times 3e$, or $6e^2$.

Second term: $(2e \times 4) + (-3 \times 3e) = 8e - 9e$ or $-e$.

Third term: -3×4, or -12.

The final product is: $6e^2 - e - 12$.

Factoring trinomials of the form $mnx^2 + (mb + na)x + ab$ usually involves a trial-and-error method. As you saw in the rule just given, the factors must be such that the product of the first terms of the binomials equals the first term of the trinomial; the product of the second terms of the binomials equals the third term of the trinomial; and the algebraic sum of the cross products is the second term of the trinomial. The usual procedure is to try two binomials that satisfy the first and second conditions; then check to see if they also satisfy the third condition.

With practice you can eliminate some elements in guessing the right combination. For example, you can tell by the signs of the trinomial whether the signs of the binomials will be both plus, both minus, or one plus and one minus. You should remove monomial factors from the trinomial before extracting the binomial factors. Then you should not use a binomial factor that contains a monomial factor, because there are no monomial factors left in the trinomial.

Example: Factor $6a^2 - 17a + 12$.

TRIAL FACTORS		PRODUCT
	(No monomials are present in the trinomial.)	
$(6a - 1)(a - 12)$		$6a^2 - 73a + 12$ Wrong; middle term incorrect.
$(6a - 12)(a - 1)$	6 is a factor of $(6a - 12)$;	do not use.
$(6a - 3)(a - 4)$	3 is a factor of $(6a - 3)$;	do not use.
$(6a - 4)(a - 3)$	2 is a factor of $(6a - 4)$;	do not use.
$(3a - 2)(2a - 6)$	2 is a factor of $(2a - 6)$;	do not use.
$(3a - 6)(2a - 2)$	3 is a factor of $(3a - 6)$ and 2 is a factor of $(2a - 2)$;	do not use.
$(3a - 3)(2a - 4)$	3 is a factor of $(3a - 3)$ and 2 is a factor of $(2a - 4)$;	do not use.
$(3a - 4)(2a - 3)$		$6a^2 - 17a + 12$ Right.

Fractions and Fractional Equations

A fraction is an indicated division in which the *numerator* (number above the line) is the dividend and the *denominator* (number below the line) is the divisor. The ratio of two quantities (the value of the fraction) is unchanged if they are both multiplied or divided by the same number (not zero). Dividing both numerator and denominator by the same integer is called *reduction to lower terms*. Sometimes it is easier to solve problems if you write them in factored form first. Examples:

$$\frac{14}{21} = \frac{14 \div 7}{21 \div 7} = \frac{2}{3}$$

$$\frac{6ax}{9a} = \frac{(2x)(3a)}{(3a)(3a)} = \frac{2x}{3a}$$

$$\frac{a^2 - b^2}{a^2 - 2ab + b^2} = \frac{(a + b)(a - b)}{(a - b)(a - b)} = \frac{a + b}{a - b}$$

Note that a quantity can be used as a divisor only if it is a factor of the *complete* numerator and *complete* denominator.

$$\frac{e^2 - 14e - 51}{e^2 - 2e - 15} = \frac{(e - 17)(e + 3)}{(e - 5)(e + 3)} = \frac{e - 17}{e - 5}$$

To change a given fraction to an equivalent fraction with a specific denominator, multiply both numerator and denominator by a number which will make the new denominator the desired value. For example, to change $\frac{1}{5}$ to 25ths, multiply both the denominator and numerator by 5. The equivalent fraction is $\frac{5}{25}$.

Example 1: Given $\frac{2a}{5b} = \frac{?}{10ab}$, find the equivalent numerator.

Solution: Dividing $10ab$ by $5b$ gives $2a$, so both terms of the fraction must be multiplied by $2a$ to change to the desired denominator. Thus:

$$\frac{2a}{5b} \times \frac{2a}{2a} = \frac{4a^2}{10ab} \text{ and } \frac{2a}{5b} = \frac{4a^2}{10ab}$$

Example 2: Given:

$$\frac{2m + 1}{3m - 5} = \frac{?}{6m^2 - 7m - 5}$$

Solution:

The factors of $6m^2 - 7m - 5$ are $(3m - 5)(2m + 1)$.

$$\frac{(6m^2 - 7m - 5)}{(3m - 5)} = (2m + 1)$$

Multiplying:

$$\frac{2m+1}{3m-5} \times \frac{2m+1}{2m+1} = \frac{(2m+1)(2m+1)}{(3m-5)(2m+1)}$$
$$= \frac{4m^2+4m+1}{6m^2-7m-5}$$

Fractions may be combined (added or subtracted) only if they have the same common denominator. When you need to combine fractions with different denominators, first change them to equivalent fractions with the same denominator (called *common denominator*). The *least common denominator* (LCD) is best since the use of any other denominator necessitates further reduction of the answer to lower terms. When dealing with polynomial denominators, factor each denominator as far as possible. The least common denominator is then the product of all the factors of the denominators, taking each factor the greatest number of times it occurs in any one denominator.

Example 1: Combine:

$$\frac{x}{4} + \frac{3x}{5} - \frac{2x}{6}$$

Solution:

$$\text{LCD} = 2 \times 2 \times 5 \times 3 = 60$$

$$\frac{(15)x + (12)3x - 10(2x)}{60} = \frac{15x + 36x - 20x}{60} = \frac{31x}{60}$$

Example 2: Combine:

$$\frac{3}{4xy} - \frac{2}{3x^2}$$

Solution:

$$\text{LCD} = 12x^2y$$

$$\frac{(3x)3 - (4y)2}{12x^2y} = \frac{9x - 8y}{12x^2y}$$

Example 3: Combine:

$$\frac{1}{R^2-1} + \frac{3}{R^2-2R+1}$$

Solution:

$$\frac{1}{(R+1)(R-1)} + \frac{3}{(R-1)(R-1)}$$

$$= \frac{1(R-1) + 3(R+1)}{(R-1)(R-1)(R+1)}$$

$$= \frac{R - 1 + 3R + 3}{(R-1)(R-1)(R+1)}$$

$$= \frac{4R + 2}{(R-1)^2(R+1)}$$

Example 4: Combine:

$$3R + 5 - \frac{5}{2R+1}$$

Solution:

$$\frac{3R+5}{1} - \frac{5}{2R+1} = \frac{(3R+5)(2R+1) - 5}{2R+1}$$

$$= \frac{6R^2 + 13R + 5 - 5}{2R+1} = \frac{6R^2 + 13R}{2R+1}$$

The expression combined in Example 4 is known as a *mixed expression* and the answer as an *improper fraction*. Handle them as mixed numbers and improper fractions are handled in arithmetic.

The product of two fractions consists of the product of the numerators divided by the product of the denominators. Frequently it is possible to reduce the result to lower terms by dividing out factors common to both numerator and denominator. This is sometimes called *cancellation of common factors* or merely *cancellation*. To divide one fraction by another, invert the second fraction (or divisor) and multiply. Factoring of polynomial numerators and denominators is advisable in order to eliminate common factors from the result.

Example 1: Perform the indicated operations:

$$\frac{4a}{3b} \times \frac{6ab}{2a^2} \div \frac{7ac}{9c^2}$$

Solution:

$$\frac{4\cancel{a}}{\cancel{3}\cancel{b}} \times \frac{\overset{2}{\cancel{6}}\cancel{a}\cancel{b}}{\cancel{2}\underset{a}{\cancel{a^2}}} \times \frac{9\overset{c}{\cancel{c^2}}}{7a\cancel{c}} = \frac{36c}{7a}$$

Note the use of cancellation in this example. Wherever fractions are being multiplied, you can cancel out like terms. Note in the example that an a above the division line is canceled and that a^2 below is replaced by an a. Remember,

$$\frac{a}{a^2} = \frac{a}{aa} = \frac{a}{a} \times \frac{1}{a} = \frac{1}{a}$$

Therefore, when you see an a above and a^2 below, you can mentally do the steps outlined, leaving in this case an a below the line. Since there is an a above the line in the first fraction, this left-over a can be canceled into it. Further cancellation removes practically two-thirds of the fraction.

Example 2: Multiply:

$$\frac{m^2 + 5m + 6}{m^2 - 4} \times \frac{m^2 - 6m + 8}{m^2 - 9}$$

Solution:

$$\frac{\cancel{(m+2)}\cancel{(m+3)}}{\cancel{(m+2)}\cancel{(m-2)}} \times \frac{\cancel{(m-2)}(m-4)}{\cancel{(m+3)}(m-3)} = \frac{m-4}{m-3}$$

Example 3: Perform the indicated operations:

$$\frac{5t^2 + 8t + 3}{2t^2 - 6t} \times \frac{6t^2 - 18t}{5t^2 - 2t - 3} \div \frac{t^2 + 5t + 4}{t^2 + 3t - 4}$$

Solution:

$$\frac{5t^2 + 8t + 3}{2t^2 - 6t} \times \frac{6t^2 - 18t}{5t^2 - 2t - 3} \times \frac{t^2 + 3t - 4}{t^2 + 5t + 4}$$

$$= \frac{\cancel{(5t+3)}\cancel{(t+1)}}{2t\cancel{(t-3)}} \times \frac{6t\cancel{(t-3)}}{\cancel{(5t+3)}\cancel{(t-1)}} \times \frac{\cancel{(t-1)}\cancel{(t+4)}}{\cancel{(t+1)}\cancel{(t+4)}}$$

$$= \frac{6t}{2t} = 3$$

Complex fractions are fractions whose numerator, denominator, or both, contain fractions. They can be simplified by treating them as division problems.

Example: Simplify:

$$\frac{R_1\left(\dfrac{R_2R_3}{R_2 + R_3}\right)}{R_1 + \dfrac{R_2R_3}{R_2 + R_3}}$$

(The numbers 1, 2, 3 below and to the right of the R's are subscripts. They indicate that the R's are different quantities and are to be treated as if they were different letters.)

Solution:

$$R_1\left(\frac{R_2R_3}{R_2 + R_3}\right) \div \left(R_1 + \frac{R_2R_3}{R_2 + R_3}\right)$$

$$= \frac{R_1R_2R_3}{R_2 + R_3} \div \frac{R_1R_2 + R_1R_3 + R_2R_3}{R_2 + R_3}$$

$$= \frac{R_1R_2R_3}{\cancel{R_2 + R_3}} \times \frac{\cancel{R_2 + R_3}}{R_1R_2 + R_1R_3 + R_2R_3}$$

$$= \frac{R_1R_2R_3}{R_1R_2 + R_1R_3 + R_2R_3}$$

The solution of fractional equations is not so difficult as you might think, for you can multiply both sides of an equation by the same number (Axiom 2). Multiplying all the fractions by the lowest common denominator, you obtain an equation involving whole numbers, which you can then solve as previously outlined.

Example 1: Solve for a in the equation:

$$\frac{6a}{7} - \frac{1}{3} = \frac{5a}{14} + \frac{13}{6}$$

Solution: 42 is the lowest common denominator. Multiply both sides by 42:

$$36a - 14 = 15a + 91$$

Add 14 to both sides:

$$36a = 15a + 105$$

Subtract $15a$ from both sides:

$$21a = 105$$

Divide both sides by 21:

$$a = 5$$

Example 2: Solve for x in the equation:

$$\frac{8}{x} + \frac{1}{2} = 2 - \frac{7}{x}$$

Solution: Multiply both sides by $2x$:

$$16 + x = 4x - 14$$

Subtract 16 from both sides:

$$x = 4x - 30$$

Subtract $4x$ from both sides:

$$-3x = -30$$

Divide both sides by -3:

$$x = 10$$

Example 3: Solve for m in the equation:

$$\frac{2m + 1}{4m + 1} = \frac{2m + 5}{4m + 7}$$

Solution: Multiply both sides by $(4m + 1)(4m + 7)$:

$$(2m + 1)(4m + 7) = (2m + 5)(4m + 1)$$
$$8m^2 + 18m + 7 = 8m^2 + 22m + 5$$

Subtract $8m^2$ from both sides:

$$18m + 7 = 22m + 5$$

Subtract 7 from both sides:

$$18m = 22m - 2$$

Subtract $22m$ from both sides:

$$-4m = -2$$

Divide both sides by -4:

$$m = 0.5$$

Example 4: Solve for r_t in the equation:

$$\frac{1}{r_t} = \frac{1}{r_1} + \frac{1}{r_2} + \frac{1}{r_3}$$

Solution: Multiply both sides by $(r_t)(r_1)(r_2)(r_3)$:

$$r_1r_2r_3 = r_2r_3r_t + r_1r_3r_t + r_1r_2r_t$$

Factor the right-hand member:

$$r_1r_2r_3 = r_t(r_2r_3 + r_1r_3 + r_1r_2)$$

Divide both sides by $(r_2r_3 + r_1r_3 + r_1r_2)$:

$$\frac{r_1r_2r_3}{r_2r_3 + r_1r_3 + r_1r_2} = r_t$$

or

$$r_t = \frac{r_1r_2r_3}{r_2r_3 + r_1r_3 + r_1r_2}$$

Simultaneous Linear Equations

As long as equations contain only one unknown, the simple rules for solution apply, but when an equation has two unknowns, *simultaneous linear equations* must be used.

Simultaneous linear equations are two or more equations that contain only first powers of the unknown quantities and no products of unknowns. They are true for certain values of the unknowns. Among the various methods for finding the values of the unknowns are solution by graphing, elimination by addition or subtraction, elimination by substitution, and the use of determinants. Of these, the most common method is elimination by addition or subtraction. Therefore, it is well to understand this method.

If the unknown you wish to eliminate has the same coefficient (disregarding sign) in the two equations, merely add (or subtract) the two equations. If the coefficients are different, you can make them the same by multiplying both members of each equation by the right number, as you can see in this example: Solve for e and i in the following pair of equations:

$$2e + 10i = 25 \quad (1)$$
$$5e - 8i = 46 \quad (2)$$

Solution: Multiply Equation (1) by 4:

$$8e + 40i = 100 \quad (3)$$

Multiply Equation (2) by 5:

$$25e - 40i = 230 \quad (4)$$

Add Equation (4) to Equation (3):

$$33e = 330 \quad (5)$$

Divide both sides of Equation (5) by 33:

$$e = 10 \quad (6)$$

Substitute 10 for e in Equation (1):

$$20 + 10i = 25 \quad (7)$$

Subtract 20 from both sides of Equation (7):

$$10i = 5 \quad (8)$$

Divide both sides of Equation (8) by 10:

$$i = 0.5 \quad (9)$$

In this example, the coefficients of i were made equal by multiplying Equation (1) by 4, and Equation (2) by 5. You could have eliminated the e's by multiplying Equation (1) by 5, and Equation (2) by 2. While equations are not always in the form of (1) and (2), you can put them in such a form by simplifying and transposing.

If you have three equations with three unknown quantities, follow the same procedure of elimination. Eliminate one unknown by combining one pair of equations, then eliminate the same unknown from another pair of equations. This results in two equations with two unknowns, which you can solve as explained before.

Example:

$$9i_1 - 4i_2 - 7i_3 = 4 \quad (1)$$
$$5i_1 + 3i_2 - 10i_3 = 3 \quad (2)$$
$$2i_1 - 5i_2 + 9i_3 = 2 \quad (3)$$

Solution: First, eliminate i_3 between (1) and (2). Multiply Equation (1) by 10:

$$90i_1 - 40i_2 - 70i_3 = 40 \quad (4)$$

Multiply Equation (2) by 7:

$$35i_1 + 21i_2 - 70i_3 = 21 \quad (5)$$

Subtract Equation (5) from Equation (4):

$$55i_1 - 61i_2 = 19 \quad (6)$$

Next, eliminate i_3 from (1) and (3). Multiply Equation (1) by 9:

$$81i_1 - 36i_2 - 63i_3 = 36 \quad (7)$$

Multiply Equation (3) by 7:

$$14i_1 - 35i_2 + 63i_3 = 14 \quad (8)$$

Add Equation (7) and Equation (8):

$$95i_1 - 71i_2 = 50 \quad (9)$$

Now you have two equations with two unknowns—Equations (6) and (9).

$$55i_1 - 61i_2 = 19 \quad (6)$$
$$95i_1 - 71i_2 = 50 \quad (9)$$

Eliminate i_1. Multiply Equation (6) by 19:

$$1045i_1 - 1159i_2 = 361 \quad (10)$$

Multiply Equation (9) by 11:

$$1045i_1 - 781i_2 = 550 \quad (11)$$

Subtract Equation (11) from Equation (10):

$$-378i_2 = -189 \quad (12)$$

Divide Equation (12) by -378:

$$i_2 = 0.5$$

Substitute 0.5 for i_2 in Equation (6):

$$55i_1 - 30.5 = 19 \tag{13}$$

Add 30.5 to both sides of Equation (13):

$$55i_1 = 49.5$$

Divide by 55:

$$i_1 = 0.9$$

Substitute 0.5 for i_2 and 0.9 for i_1 in Equation (1):

$$8.1 - 2.0 - 7i_3 = 4$$

Collect terms:

$$6.1 - 7i_3 = 4$$

Subtract 6.1:

$$-7i_3 = -2.1$$

Divide by -7:

$$i_3 = 0.3$$

Check by substituting in Equations (1), (2), and (3):

$$\begin{aligned} 8.1 - 2.0 - 2.1 &= 4 \\ 4 &= 4 \\ 4.5 + 1.5 - 3.0 &= 3 \\ 3 &= 3 \\ 1.8 - 2.5 + 2.7 &= 2 \\ 2 &= 2 \end{aligned}$$

Exponents, Radicals, and Complex Numbers

You have already noted that a number raised to the zero power is equal to 1, and a number raised to a negative exponent is the same as the reciprocal of the quantity to that same exponent with a plus sign. Now consider the significance of a fractional exponent. Squaring the quantity $x^{\frac{1}{2}}$ gives $(x^{\frac{1}{2}})(x^{\frac{1}{2}})$. By adding the exponents $x^{(\frac{1}{2}+\frac{1}{2})}$, as in any other multiplication with exponents, you find that the result is x^1, or x. By this reasoning, you can see that $x^{\frac{1}{2}}$ is the square root of x. In like manner, $x^{\frac{1}{3}}$ is the cube root of x, and $x^{\frac{1}{4}}$ is $\sqrt[4]{x}$. The expression

$x^{\frac{2}{3}}$ is read "x to the two-thirds power." This means that x is raised to the power of the numerator of the fractional exponent, and reduced by the root of the denominator. Thus, $x^{\frac{2}{3}}$ is the cube root of x squared, or $\sqrt[3]{x^2}$.

Sometimes it is necessary to simplify an expression involving *radicals* (square roots, cube roots, etc.) without changing its value. Sometimes you can divide the quantity under the radical (called the *radicand*) into two factors, and take the indicated root of one of the factors.

Examples:

$$\sqrt{80} = \sqrt{16 \cdot 5} = 4\sqrt{5}$$
$$\sqrt{54} = \sqrt{9 \cdot 6} = 3\sqrt{6}$$
$$\sqrt[3]{16m} = \sqrt[3]{8 \cdot 2m} = 2\sqrt[3]{2m}$$

When the quantity under the radical sign is a fraction, multiply both numerator and denominator by a quantity which will make it possible to take the indicated root of the denominator.

Examples:

$$\sqrt{\tfrac{2}{3}} = \sqrt{\tfrac{2}{3} \cdot \tfrac{3}{3}} = \sqrt{\tfrac{6}{9}} = \sqrt{\tfrac{1}{9} \cdot 6} = \tfrac{1}{3}\sqrt{6}$$
$$\sqrt[3]{\frac{40}{x^2}} = \sqrt[3]{\frac{40}{x^2} \cdot \frac{x}{x}} = \sqrt[3]{\frac{40x}{x^3}} = \sqrt[3]{\frac{8}{x^3} \cdot 5x} = \frac{2}{x}\sqrt[3]{5x}$$

You may combine (add or subtract) radicals if they differ only in the coefficient, that is, if they have the same radicand and root.

Examples:

$$4\sqrt{x} + 3\sqrt{x} - 2\sqrt{x} = 5\sqrt{x}$$
$$\sqrt{4x} + 5\sqrt{x} = 2\sqrt{x} + 5\sqrt{x} = 7\sqrt{x}$$
$$\sqrt[3]{40} + \sqrt[3]{16\tfrac{7}{8}} = \sqrt[3]{40} + \sqrt[3]{\tfrac{135}{8}}$$
$$= \sqrt[3]{8 \cdot 5} + \sqrt[3]{\tfrac{27}{8} \cdot 5} = 2\sqrt[3]{5} + \tfrac{3}{2}\sqrt[3]{5}$$
$$= 3\tfrac{1}{2}\sqrt[3]{5}$$

You can multiply two radicals together provided they have the same index (indicated root). You can do this by multiplying the coefficients together for the coefficient of the product and multiplying the radicands together for the radicand of the product.

Examples:

$$(2\sqrt{3})(3\sqrt{2}) = 6\sqrt{6}$$
$$(7\sqrt{x})(2\sqrt{y}) = 14\sqrt{xy}$$
$$(2\sqrt{x})(3\sqrt{x}) = 6\sqrt{x^2} = 6x$$
$$a\sqrt{b}\,(2\sqrt{3} + 4) = 2a\sqrt{3b} + 4a\sqrt{b}$$

$$(5\sqrt{3} + 2\sqrt{6})(5\sqrt{3} + 4\sqrt{6})$$

Multiply out:

$$\begin{array}{l} 5\sqrt{3} + 2\sqrt{6} \\ \underline{5\sqrt{3} + 4\sqrt{6}} \\ 25\sqrt{9} + 10\sqrt{18} \\ \underline{\qquad\qquad 20\sqrt{18} + 8\sqrt{36}} \\ 25\sqrt{9} + 30\sqrt{18} + 8\sqrt{36} \\ = 25 \cdot 3 + 30\sqrt{9 \cdot 2} + 8 \cdot 6 \\ = 75 + 30 \cdot 3\sqrt{2} + 48 \\ = 123 + 90\sqrt{2} \end{array}$$

To divide expressions containing radicals, use the opposite process; that is, divide coefficient by coefficient and radicand by radicand. In many cases the result of this process is an expression with a radical in the denominator. The radical can be eliminated by a special process called *rationalizing the denominator*. This process changes the denominator to a whole number, a fraction, or a mixed number.

You can rationalize the denominator by multiplying both the numerator and the denominator by a quantity that will eliminate radicals from the denominator. In the case of monomials this is quite simple, and is the same process as discussed previously under *simplification of fractional radicands*.

Example:

$$\frac{\sqrt{5}}{\sqrt{6}} = \sqrt{\tfrac{5}{6}} = \sqrt{\tfrac{5}{6} \cdot \tfrac{6}{6}} = \sqrt{\tfrac{30}{36}} = \sqrt{\tfrac{1}{36} \cdot 30} = \tfrac{1}{6}\sqrt{30}$$

When the denominator is a binomial, rationalize by multiplying both the numerator and the denominator by the binomial with the sign between terms changed. This changed binomial is called the *conjugate* of the denominator.

Examples:

$$\frac{5}{3-\sqrt{2}} = \frac{5}{3-\sqrt{2}} \cdot \frac{3+\sqrt{2}}{3+\sqrt{2}} = \frac{15+5\sqrt{2}}{9-\sqrt{4}}$$

$$= \frac{15+5\sqrt{2}}{9-2} = \frac{15+5\sqrt{2}}{7}$$

Here the denominator was $3-\sqrt{2}$ and the conjugate was $3+\sqrt{2}$.

$$\frac{x}{\sqrt{x}+a} = \frac{x}{\sqrt{x}+a} \cdot \frac{\sqrt{x}-a}{\sqrt{x}-a} = \frac{x\sqrt{x}-ax}{\sqrt{x^2}-a^2}$$

$$= \frac{x\sqrt{x}-ax}{x-a^2}$$

$$\frac{4-\sqrt{m}}{2+\sqrt{m}} = \frac{4-\sqrt{m}}{2+\sqrt{m}} \cdot \frac{2-\sqrt{m}}{2-\sqrt{m}} = \frac{8-6\sqrt{m}+\sqrt{m^2}}{4-\sqrt{m^2}}$$

$$= \frac{8+m-6\sqrt{m}}{4-m}$$

$$\frac{\sqrt{r}-\sqrt{s}}{\sqrt{r}+2\sqrt{s}} = \frac{\sqrt{r}-\sqrt{s}}{\sqrt{r}+2\sqrt{s}} \cdot \frac{\sqrt{r}-2\sqrt{s}}{\sqrt{r}-2\sqrt{s}}$$

$$= \frac{\sqrt{r^2}-3\sqrt{rs}+2\sqrt{s^2}}{\sqrt{r^2}-4\sqrt{s^2}} = \frac{r+2s-3\sqrt{rs}}{r-4s}$$

Note that in each of the foregoing examples the final result has no radicals in the denominator.

Thus far you have dealt with roots of positive quantities. We say that P is a square root of B if $P^2 = B$. If B is positive, it has exactly two square roots, one positive and one negative, denoted by $\pm\sqrt{B}$. If a negative number $-A$ has R as square root, then $R^2 = -A$. But, if R is *either* positive or negative, R^2 is positive and cannot equal $-A$. Therefore, $-A$ has *no positive or negative square root.* In order for $-A$ to have square roots, the symbol $\sqrt{-1}$, with the property that

$$\sqrt{-1}\sqrt{-1} = -1$$

is introduced. $\sqrt{-1}$ is *defined* as a new variety of number, called an *imaginary number*. The letter i stands for $\sqrt{-1}$ in mathematics. (In electrical work the symbol j is used instead of i because the letter i is used to represent current.)

Now the indicated square roots of negative numbers can be treated as follows: $\sqrt{-x} = \sqrt{x} \cdot \sqrt{-1} = i\sqrt{x}$; $\sqrt{-3} = \sqrt{3} \cdot \sqrt{-1} = i\sqrt{3}$. In each case, i stands for the imaginary quantity, the square root of -1.

Since $i = \sqrt{-1}$, then $i^2 = -1$. Operations of addition, subtraction, multiplication, and division may be applied to combinations of i and real numbers as if i were an ordinary real number.

Real and imaginary quantities can be graphically represented by four positions of a unit vector, as shown in Figure 1. Positive real numbers are plotted to the right of the origin, and negative real numbers to the left along the horizontal axis, which is known as the *axis of reals*. Imaginaries that have positive signs are plotted above the origin and those that have negative signs, below the origin along the vertical axis, which is known as the *axis of imaginaries*.

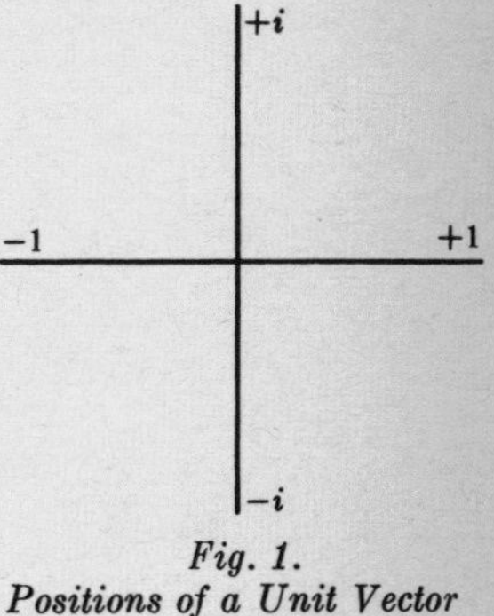

Fig. 1.
Positions of a Unit Vector

Real and Imaginary Numbers

A *complex number* is the sum or difference of a real quantity and an imaginary quantity. For example, $5 - bi$ and $3 + 2i$ are complex numbers. The term complex number is really inappropriate because the system is not complex at all: *rectangular notation* would be a better designation. It is not difficult to apply the fundamental processes to this special notation, for two or more complex numbers can be combined by combining the real portions and imaginary portions separately.

Examples. Addition:

$$\begin{array}{r} 5+3i \\ 2-2i \\ \hline 7+i \end{array} \qquad \begin{array}{r} 6-4i \\ -5-3i \\ \hline 1-7i \end{array}$$

Subtraction:

$$\begin{array}{r} 5+3i \\ 2-2i \\ \hline 3+5i \end{array} \qquad \begin{array}{r} 6-4i \\ -5-3i \\ \hline 11-i \end{array}$$

To multiply complex numbers, use the same procedure as with binomials except that, where i^2 occurs in the final result, you replace it by its equivalent, -1.

Example: Multiply $5 + 3i$ by $2 - 2i$:

$$\begin{array}{rrr} 5 + & 3i & \\ 2 - & 2i & \\ \hline 10 + & 6i & \\ & -10i & -6i^2 \\ \hline 10 - & 4i & -6i^2 \end{array}$$

$$= 10 - 4i - (6)(-1) = 10 - 4i + 6 = 16 - 4i$$

Divide one rectangular quantity (complex number) by another by rationalizing the denominator, then dividing the real number into the numerator. Remember that you rationalize the denominator by multiplying both numerator and denominator by the conjugate of the denominator.

Example 1: Divide $5 + 3i$ by $2 - 2i$.

Solution:

$$\frac{5+3i}{2-2i} \cdot \frac{2+2i}{2+2i} = \frac{10+16i+6i^2}{4-4i^2} = \frac{10+16i-6}{4+4}$$

$$= \frac{4+16i}{8} = \frac{4(1+4i)}{8} = \frac{1+4i}{2} \text{ or } 0.5 + 2i$$

Example 2: Divide $6 - 4i$ by $(-5 - 3i)$.

Solution:

$$\frac{6-4i}{-5-3i} \cdot \frac{-5+3i}{-5+3i} = \frac{-30+38i-12i^2}{25-9i^2}$$

$$= \frac{-30+38i+12}{25+9} = \frac{-18+38i}{34} = \frac{-9+19i}{17}$$

Quadratic Equations

The degree of an equation in which the unknown has only positive integral exponents and does not appear in the denominator of a fraction is the same as its term of highest degree. The degree of a term in a letter means its exponent in that term. To illustrate, the degree of the term $4x^2y^3$ in x is the second. The equation $ax^2 + bx + c = 0$ is a second degree or quadratic equation in x. The following discusses the solution of equations of this form.

There are several methods you can use to solve a quadratic equation, such as graphing, completing the square, factoring, and using a formula derived from the general form $ax^2 + bx + c = 0$ by the completion of the square method. The formula is $x = \dfrac{-b \pm \sqrt{b^2 - 4ac}}{2a}$ where a, b, and c are, respectively, the coefficient of x^2, of x, and of the term which does not contain x. Before applying the formula, always put the equation in the standard form $ax^2 + bx + c = 0$. The following examples illustrate the process for solving quadratic equations by formula.

Example 1: Solve for x in the equation $3x^2 + 8x - 10 = 0$.

Solution: By the formula:

$$x = \frac{-8 \pm \sqrt{64+120}}{6}$$

$$= \frac{-8 \pm \sqrt{184}}{6} = \frac{-8 \pm 13.56}{6}$$

$$= \frac{5.56}{6} \text{ or } \frac{-21.56}{6}$$

$$= 0.93 \text{ or } -3.59$$

Example 2: Solve for a in the equation $2a = 3a^2 - 8$.

Solution: Subtract $3a^2$ from both sides:

$$-3a^2 + 2a = -8$$

Add 8 to both sides:

$$-3a^2 + 2a + 8 = 0$$

By formula

$$a = \frac{-2 \pm \sqrt{4 + 96}}{-6} = \frac{-2 \pm \sqrt{100}}{-6}$$

$$= \frac{-2 \pm 10}{-6}$$

$$= \frac{8}{-6} \text{ or } \frac{-12}{-6} = -1.33 \text{ or } 2$$

Example 3: Solve for R in the equation:

$$\frac{R^2}{R + 5} = \frac{R}{3} + \frac{5}{6}$$

Solution:

$$6R^2 = 2R(R + 5) + 5(R + 5)$$
$$6R^2 = 2R^2 + 10R + 5R + 25$$
$$6R^2 = 2R^2 + 15R + 25$$
$$4R^2 - 15R - 25 = 0$$
$$R = \frac{15 \pm \sqrt{225 + 400}}{8}$$
$$= \frac{15 \pm \sqrt{625}}{8} = \frac{15 \pm 25}{8}$$
$$= \frac{40}{8} \text{ or } \frac{-10}{8} = 5 \text{ or } -1.25$$

The quantity $b^2 - 4ac$ which appears under the radical in the formula is called the *discriminant*. It indicates the type of roots. If $b^2 - 4ac$ is positive, there are two real and unequal roots; if $b^2 - 4ac$ is negative, the roots are imaginary and unequal; if $b^2 - 4ac$ equals zero, the roots are real and equal.

LOGARITHMS

The *logarithm* of a quantity is the exponent (or the power) to which a given number (called the base) must be raised to equal that quantity. To illustrate, in the equation $3^2 = 9$, the exponent, 2, is called the logarithm of 9 to the base 3. This relation is usually written $\log_3 9 = 2$. Any positive number greater than 1 might serve as a base. Two numbers have been selected, resulting in two systems of logarithms. One base, e (approximately 2.718), is used in the *natural* logarithm system. The other base is 10; it is used in the *common* system of logarithms. In the common system, the base 10 is usually omitted in the logarithmic expression. Thus $\log_{10} 1{,}000 = 3$ is usually written $\log 1{,}000 = 3$. In the natural system the logarithm of x to the base e may be written $\ln x$.

In the common system, logarithms that are exact powers of 10 are integers. Thus:

$$
\begin{aligned}
\log 10{,}000 &= 4, & \text{since } 10^4 &= 10{,}000\\
\log 1{,}000 &= 3, & \text{since } 10^3 &= 1{,}000\\
\log 100 &= 2, & \text{since } 10^2 &= 100\\
\log 10 &= 1, & \text{since } 10^1 &= 10\\
\log 1 &= 0, & \text{since } 10^0 &= 1\\
\log 0.1 &= -1, & \text{since } 10^{-1} &= 0.1\\
\log 0.01 &= -2, & \text{since } 10^{-2} &= 0.01
\end{aligned}
$$

For numbers not exact powers of 10, the logarithm consists of two parts, an integral part (whole number) and a decimal part. The integral part is called the *characteristic* and the decimal part the *mantissa*. Thus, for example, $\log 595 = 2.77452$ (this means, the logarithm of 595 is 2.77452), the characteristic is 2, and the mantissa is .77452. The characteristic is found by inspection and the mantissa from the Table of Common Logarithms (p. 80ff.).

You can determine the characteristic by the following rules:

1. The characteristic of the logarithm of a number greater than 1 is positive and is one less than the number of digits to the left of the decimal point. For example, in the case of log 595, the characteristic is 2, and for the log of 59.5, the characteristic is 1.

2. The characteristic of the logarithm of a positive number less than 1 is negative, and its absolute value is equal to one more than the number of zeros immediately to the right of the decimal point. For example, for log .0595, the characteristic is -2, and for log .00595, the characteristic is -3.

When the characteristic is negative, do not put the minus sign in front of the logarithm, since it applies only to the characteristic and not to the mantissa. Instead, add 10 to the negative characteristic and indicate the subtraction of 10 at the end of the logarithm.

Thus the characteristic -2 is written, 8.(mantissa) $- 10$, and the characteristic -3 is written, 7.(mantissa) $- 10$.

Another method of indicating that the characteristic is negative is to place the minus sign above the characteristic. For example:

$$\bar{2}.\text{(mantissa)}$$
$$\bar{3}.\text{(mantissa)}$$

The mantissa must be found from Table of Common Logarithms. Numbers which have the same figures in the same order and differ only in the position of the decimal point have the same mantissa in their logarithms. For example, the mantissa of 595 is .77452; the mantissa of 59.5 is also .77452.

To Find the Logarithm of a Number

1. Determine by inspection the characteristic of the number.

2. Find the mantissa from the Table of Common Logarithms. The mantissa of the number is independent of the position of the decimal point, so you can disregard the decimal point in the number when finding the mantissa. The mantissas in the table are the decimal part of the logarithm and therefore should be preceded by the decimal point.

In five-place logarithm tables, the first column in the table contains the first three digits of the numbers whose mantissas are given in the table, and the top row contains the fourth digit. Thus, to find the mantissa of 5,956, find 595 in the left-hand column and 6 at the top. In the column under 6, and opposite 595, is 77495, the mantissa. The logarithm of 5,956 is then 3.77495. (See p. 90.)

3. To find the logarithm of a quantity with more than four digits, use the proportional parts columns in the right-hand margins of the Table of Common Logarithms. Suppose you want to find log 59,563. The mantissa of 59,560 is .77495; the mantissa of 59,570 is .77503. The digit difference is 8, so use the proportional parts column headed 8. Look for the entry opposite 3 (the fifth digit): it is 2.4. Add .000024 to the mantissa of 59,560, which is .77495; the sum is .774974. Adding the characteristic, 4, gives the logarithm: log 59,563 = 4.774974.

For sixth and additional digits, interpolate between entries in the proportional parts columns. Thus, for log 595,635, interpolate $\frac{5}{10}$ of the way from 2.4 (fifth digit 3) to 3.2 (fifth digit 4), giving 2.8. Continue as above.

The number corresponding to a given logarithm is called the *antilogarithm* of that number. It is written antilog or $\log^{-1}$. To find the antilog, reverse the process for finding logarithms.

Example 1: Find the antilog ($\log^{-1}$) of 1.89883.

Solution: Look in the Table of Common Logarithms (p. 94) and locate the mantissa .89883. It is in line with the number 792 and under the column headed 2. Thus the number corresponding with the mantissa .89883 has the digits 7922.

To determine the location of the decimal point, reverse the rule for finding a characteristic. If the characteristic were zero, the decimal point would be placed after the first digit (7.922). Since the characteristic is 1, count one place to the right and place the decimal point after the 9. Thus the antilog of 1.89883 is 79.22.

Example 2: Find the antilog ($\log^{-1}$) of 2.43091.

Solution: You will have to use the proportional parts column. The mantissa of 2697 is .43088; the mantissa of 2698 is .43104. (Note the asterisks in the Table, which indicate that the first two digits of the mantissa, 42, have changed to 43 in the middle of the line.) The digit difference between the mantissas is 43104 − 43088 = 16, so use the proportional parts column headed 16.

The given mantissa, .43091, is a digit difference of 3 greater than .43088, so look for the entry under 16 that is closest to 3.

The closest entry, 3.2, is opposite 2 in the left-hand column; therefore, 2 is the fifth digit of the antilog.

The antilog is 26972—but you must still place the decimal point. Since the characteristic is 2, the number of digits to the left of the decimal point is one *more* than 2, or 3. Thus $\log^{-1} 2.43091 = 269.72$.

Computations with Logarithms

To *multiply two quantities*, add their logarithms and find the antilog of the result.

Example: Find the product of 6,952 and 437.

Solution:

$$\log (6{,}952 \times 437) = \log 6{,}952 + \log 437$$
$$\log 6{,}952 = 3.84211$$
$$\log 437 = 2.64048$$
$$\log 6{,}952 + \log 437 = 6.48259$$

Find antilog 6.48259.

$$\text{antilog } 6.48259 = 3{,}038{,}000$$

Actual multiplication of 6,952 by 437 would give the result 3,038,024. Thus the logarithmic calculation was accurate to five places.

To *divide two quantities*, subtract the logarithm of the divisor from the logarithm of the dividend and find the antilog of the result.

Example: Divide 6,952 by 437.

Solution:

$$\log (6{,}952 \div 437) = \log 6{,}952 - \log 437$$
$$\log 6{,}952 = 3.84211$$
$$\log 437 = 2.64048$$
$$\log 6{,}952 - \log 437 = 1.20163$$

Find antilog 1.20163.

$$\text{antilog } 1.20163 = 15.909$$

To *raise a quantity to any power*, multiply the logarithm of the quantity by the exponent, or the power, and find the antilog of the result.

Example 1: Find the value of $(5.2)^6$.

Solution:

$$
\begin{aligned}
\log (5.2)^6 &= 6 \log 5.2 \\
\log 5.2 &= 0.71600 \\
\log (5.2)^6 &= 6(0.71600) = 4.29600 \\
\text{antilog } 4.29600 &= 19{,}770
\end{aligned}
$$

Therefore, $(5.2)^6 = 19{,}770$.

Example 2: Find the value of $(3.7)^{\frac{1}{5}}$. (Exponent is fractional.)

Solution:

$$
\begin{aligned}
\log (3.7)^{\frac{1}{5}} &= \tfrac{1}{5} \log 3.7 \\
\log 3.7 &= 0.56820 \\
\log (3.7)^{\frac{1}{5}} &= \tfrac{1}{5}(0.56820) = 0.11364 \\
\text{antilog } 0.11364 &= 1.2991
\end{aligned}
$$

Therefore, $(3.7)^{\frac{1}{5}} = 1.2991$.

Example 3: Find the value of $(45.6)^{-4}$. (Exponent is negaive.)

Solution:

$$
\begin{aligned}
\log (45.6)^{-4} &= -4 \log 45.6 \\
\log 45.6 &= 1.65896 \\
\log (45.6)^{-4} &= -4(1.65896) = -6.63584
\end{aligned}
$$

Since logarithm tables list only positive values of mantissa, ewrite -6.63584 as $3.36416 - 10$, or $\overline{7}.36416$.

$$
\begin{aligned}
\text{antilog } (\overline{7}.36416) &= 0.00000023129 \\
(45.6)^{-4} &= 0.00000023129
\end{aligned}
$$

To *find the root of a quantity*, treat the radical as a fractional exponent.

Example: Find the value of $\sqrt[3]{1.572}$.

Solution:

$$\log \sqrt[3]{1.572} = \log (1.572)^{\frac{1}{3}} = \tfrac{1}{3} \log 1.572$$
$$\log 1.572 = 0.19645$$
$$\tfrac{1}{3} \log 1.572 = 0.065483$$
$$\text{antilog } 0.065483 = 1.1627$$
$$\sqrt[3]{1.572} = 1.11627$$

TRIGONOMETRIC FUNCTIONS

Several special relationships, called *trigonometric functions*, hold true in a right triangle. In Figure 2, θ is the angle ZOR. OR is the projection of OZ on the horizontal axis; OX is the projection of OZ on the vertical axis. The length ZR is equal to the length XO, and is perpendicular to the horizontal axis, making ZRO a right triangle. The letters r, x, and z represent the lengths of OR, ZR, and OZ.

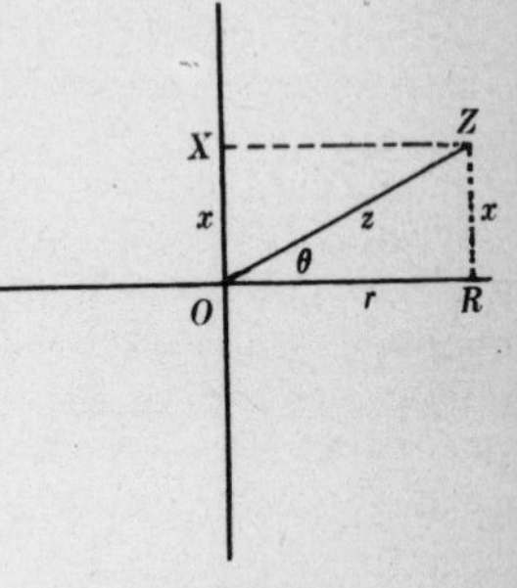

Fig. 2.
Trigonometric Functions

There are six ratios associated with the three sides of a right triangle. Each ratio has been given a name. By definition, in a right triangle ZRO with the right angle at R (Figure 2):

$$\text{sine of } \theta = \sin \theta = \frac{\text{side opposite the angle } \theta}{\text{hypotenuse}} = \frac{x}{z}$$

$$\text{cosine of } \theta = \cos \theta = \frac{\text{side adjacent to the angle } \theta}{\text{hypotenuse}} = \frac{r}{z}$$

$$\text{tangent of } \theta = \tan \theta = \frac{\text{side opposite the angle } \theta}{\text{side adjacent to the angle } \theta} = \frac{x}{r}$$

$$\text{cotangent of } \theta = \text{ctn } \theta = \frac{\text{side adjacent to the angle } \theta}{\text{side opposite the angle } \theta} = \frac{r}{x}$$

$$\text{secant of } \theta = \sec \theta = \frac{\text{hypotenuse}}{\text{side adjacent to the angle } \theta} = \frac{z}{r}$$

$$\text{cosecant of } \theta = \csc \theta = \frac{\text{hypotenuse}}{\text{side opposite the angle } \theta} = \frac{z}{x}$$

Notice that $\sin \theta$ is the reciprocal of $\csc \theta$, $\cos \theta$ is the reciprocal of $\sec \theta$, and $\tan \theta$ is the reciprocal of $\text{ctn } \theta$.

If you assume that in Figure 2, OZ has a unit length of 1 and is rotated in a counterclockwise direction beginning with angle θ at a value of 0° and continuing until it is 90°, then the functions will vary within the following limits:

$\sin \theta$ increases from 0 to 1
$\cos \theta$ decreases from 1 to 0
$\tan \theta$ increases from 0 to ∞
$\text{ctn } \theta$ decreases from ∞ to 0
$\sec \theta$ increases from 1 to ∞
$\csc \theta$ decreases from ∞ to 1

(∞ represents an *infinitely large* number.)

When θ varies between the values of 90° and 180° (second quadrant), the projection r is negative and the functions which involve r become negative. Thus, $\cos \theta$ and $\tan \theta$ are negative in this quadrant. In the third quadrant, both r and x are negative. Therefore, $\sin \theta$ and $\cos \theta$, which involve only one or the other, are negative, while $\tan \theta$, which involves both r and x, is positive. In the fourth quadrant, r is positive, but x is still negative. For this reason, $\sin \theta$ and $\tan \theta$ are negative in the fourth quadrant, while $\cos \theta$ is positive. When $\sin \theta$, $\cos \theta$, or $\tan \theta$ is negative, its reciprocal is negative.

Variations in Value of Functions

	sin θ		*cos θ*		*tan θ*	
Quadrant	*from*	*to*	*from*	*to*	*from*	*to*
I (0°–90°)	0	1	1	0	0	∞
II (90°–180°)	1	0	0	−1	$-\infty$	0
III (180°–270°)	0	−1	−1	0	0	∞
IV (270°–360°)	−1	0	0	1	$-\infty$	0

Trigonometric tables give functions up to 90° only. Therefore you will need to use special rules for finding values of functions of angles in the other quadrants.

In quadrant II: $\theta = 180°$ minus some acute angle which is designated α (alpha).

$$\sin(180° - \alpha) = \sin\alpha$$
$$\cos(180° - \alpha) = -\cos\alpha$$
$$\tan(180° - \alpha) = -\tan\alpha$$

In quadrant III: $\theta = 180° + \alpha$

$$\sin(180° + \alpha) = -\sin\alpha$$
$$\cos(180° + \alpha) = -\cos\alpha$$
$$\tan(180° + \alpha) = \tan\alpha$$

In quadrant IV: $\theta = 360° - \alpha$

$$\sin(360° - \alpha) = -\sin\alpha$$
$$\cos(360° - \alpha) = \cos\alpha$$
$$\tan(360° - \alpha) = -\tan\alpha$$

To find values of functions of acute angles, use the Table of Natural Trigonometric Functions (p. 99 ff.).

Example 1: Find sin 29°.

Solution: $\sin 29° = 0.48481$.

Example 2: Find cos 129° 16′.

Solution: $\cos 129°\ 16' = \cos(180° - 50°\ 44')$. From the Table, $\cos 50°\ 44' = 0.63293$. (Note that angles over 45° are read up from the bottom, in the Table.) But

$$\cos(180° - 50°\ 44') = -\cos 50°\ 44'$$

as above. Therefore, $\cos 129°\ 16' = -0.63293$.

Interpolations can be made for seconds. (60 seconds = 1 minute, or $60'' = 1'$.)

The angle corresponding to a given function is called the *inverse trigonometric function*. The expression *arc sin h,* read "arc sine h," means "an angle whose sine is h." By definition, then, these equations are equivalent:

$$h = \sin\theta$$
$$\theta = \text{arc}\sin h$$

Similar equations can be set up for each of the trigonometric functions. Another way of writing the inverse function is $\sin^{-1} h = \theta$.

There are two angles corresponding to any given function. For example, arc sin 0.7071 is 45° or 135°. To avoid confusion, certain values of arc sin, arc cos, arc tan, etc., are designated the principal values and are the values meant unless otherwise indicated. For arc sin and arc tan the principal values are in the first or fourth quadrants; for arc cos the principal values are in the first or second quadrants. Therefore, arc sin 0.7071 = 45°.

In finding the function of an angle, or its inverse, note that the functions repeat themselves every 360°. Thus

$$\sin 400° = \sin (400° - 360°) = \sin 40° = 0.64279$$

You can say that a negative angle is equivalent to a positive angle which is 360° plus the negative angle. To illustrate, $-50° = 360° + (-50°) = 310°$. Hence

$$\sin (-50°) = \sin 310° = -0.76604$$

Angles in the fourth quadrant are frequently expressed as negative angles.

The Table of Natural Trigonometric Functions (Table IV) lists the sines, cosines, tangents, and cotangents of angles from 0° to 90°. To find these functions for angles less than 45°, read down the page; degrees are indicated at the top of each page, minutes in the column at the left of the page. To find the functions of angles greater than 45°, read up the page; degrees are indicated at the bottom of each page, minutes in the column at the right.

In extensive computation with trigonometric functions, where multiplication, division, or combined multiplication and division of functions is required, time and effort can be saved by using logarithms of the functions. Multiplication of one function by another is thus reduced to the operation of adding logarithms of the functions (then finding the antilogarithm); similarly, division is reduced to finding the difference of the logarithms of the functions. Obviously, the logarithm of a function can be found by determining (from Table IV) the value of the natural trigonometric function, then (from Table III) determining the logarithm of this number. This operation, how ever, requires the separate use of two tables. The Table o Logarithms of Trigonometric Functions (Table V) gives th required value directly.

It should be noted that the sines and cosines of all acut angles, the tangents of acute angles less than 45°, and th cotangents of acute angles greater than 45° are proper fractions Their logarithms, consequently, should terminate with −1 (Example: log sin 68° 25′ = 9.96843 −10). The −10 is no printed in the table, but is to be appended to the listed values

POWERS, ROOTS, AND RECIPROCALS

The Table of Powers, Roots, and Reciprocals (Table II) is s arranged that for any number n, with three significant digits the square, cube, square root, cube root, or reciprocal of n ca be read directly to five decimal places. Thus, to find $\sqrt{1.17}$ read 1.08167 in the $\sqrt{n}$ column, opposite 1.17. Similarly, t find $\sqrt[3]{1.17}$, read 1.05373 in the $\sqrt[3]{n}$ column on the same line It is to be noted that a shift in the decimal point in n produce in n^2, n^3, and $1/n$ a shift in the position of the decimal point i the result; there is no alteration, however, in the resultin digits. Example $(1.9)^2 = 3.61$; $(19)^2 = 361$.

I. Important Mathematical Formulas

ALGEBRA

Identities

$$(a + b + c)^2 \equiv a^2 + b^2 + c^2 + 2ab + 2bc + 2ac$$

$$(a^2 + b^2 + c^2)(f^2 + g^2 + h^2) - (af + bg + ch)^2$$
$$\equiv (bh - cg)^2 + (cf - ah)^2 + (ag - bf)^2$$

$$(a + b)^3 \equiv a^3 + 3a^2b + 3ab^2 + b^3$$

$$a^3 + b^3 \equiv (a + b)(a^2 - ab + b^2)$$

Natural Numbers

$$1 + 2 + 3 + \ . \ . \ . + n = \tfrac{1}{2}n(n + 1)$$

$$1^2 + 2^2 + 3^2 + \ . \ . \ . + n^2 = \tfrac{1}{6}n(n + 1)(2n + 1)$$

$$1^3 + 2^3 + 3^3 + \ . \ . \ . + n^3 = \tfrac{1}{4}n^2(n + 1)^2$$

Arithmetic Progression

$$a + (a + d) + (a + 2d) + \ . \ . \ . + [a + (n - 1)d]$$
$$= \frac{n}{2}[2a + (n - 1)d]$$

Arithmetic mean of n quantities $a_1, a_2, \ . \ . \ . \ a_n$

$$= \frac{a_1 + a_2 + a_3 + \ . \ . \ . + a_n}{n}$$

Geometric Progression

$$a + ar + ar^2 + \ . \ . \ . + ar^{n-1} = a\frac{1 - r^n}{1 - r}$$

If r^2 is less than 1 the sum to infinity is $\frac{a}{1 - r}$.

Geometric mean of n quantities $a_1, a_2, \ . \ . \ . \ a_n$

$$= \sqrt[n]{a_1a_2a_3 \ . \ . \ . \ a_n}$$

Harmonic Progression

$$\frac{1}{a}, \frac{1}{a+d}, \frac{1}{a+2d}, \ldots \frac{1}{a+(n-1)d}$$

Harmonic mean of n quantities $a_1, a_2, \ldots a_n$

$$= \frac{n}{\left(\frac{1}{a_1} + \frac{1}{a_2} + \ldots + \frac{1}{a_n}\right)}$$

Binomial Coefficients

The coefficient of x^r in $(1+x)^n$ is

$$\frac{n(n-1)(n-2)\ldots(n-r+1)}{r!} = C_r^n$$

when n is a positive integer.

Properties of C_r^n:

$$C_r^n = C_{n-r}^n = \frac{n!}{r!(n-r)!}$$
$$C_0^n = C_n^n = 1$$
$$C_r^{n+1} = C_r^n + C_{r-1}^n$$
$$C_{r+1}^{n+1} = C_r^n + C_r^{n-1} + C_r^{n-2} + \ldots + C_r^r$$
$$C_r^{m+n} = C_r^m C_0^n + C_{r-1}^m C_1^n + C_{r-2}^m C_2^n + \ldots + C_1^m C_{r-1}^n + C_0^m C_r^n$$

Complex Numbers

$a + ib$ where $i = \sqrt{-1}$ is called a complex number, a and b being real.

$i^2 = -1$, $i^3 = -i$, $i^4 = 1$, $i^5 = i$ and so on.

If $a_1 + ib_1 = a_2 + ib_2$, then $a_1 = a_2$, $b_1 = b_2$.

$$(a_1 + ib_1)(a_2 + ib_2) = (a_1a_2 - b_1b_2) + i(a_1b_2 + a_2b_1)$$
$$(a + ib)^2 = a^2 - b^2 + 2iab$$
$$\frac{a_1 + ib_1}{a_2 + ib_2} = \frac{a_1a_2 + b_1b_2}{a_2^2 + b_2^2} + i\,\frac{a_2b_1 - a_1b_2}{a_2^2 + b_2^2}$$
$$\ln(a + ib) = \frac{1}{2}\ln(a^2 + b^2) + i\left(\tan^{-1}\frac{b}{a} + 2n\pi\right)$$

where n is any positive or negative integer.

If $a = r\cos\theta$, $b = r\sin\theta$, so that $r^2 = a^2 + b^2$, $\tan\theta = \frac{b}{a}$, then

$$a + ib = r(\cos\theta + i\sin\theta) = re^{i\theta},$$

$$(a+ib)^{\frac{p}{q}} = r^{\frac{p}{q}}\left(\cos\frac{p}{q}(2n\pi+\theta) + i\sin\frac{p}{q}(2n\pi+\theta)\right)$$

where p and q are integers and $n = 0, 1, 2, \ldots q-1$

Determinants

$$\begin{vmatrix} a_1 & a_2 \\ b_1 & b_2 \end{vmatrix} = a_1b_2 - a_2b_1$$

$$\begin{vmatrix} a_1 & a_2 & a_3 \\ b_1 & b_2 & b_3 \\ c_1 & c_2 & c_3 \end{vmatrix} = a_1\begin{vmatrix} b_2 & b_3 \\ c_2 & c_3 \end{vmatrix} - a_2\begin{vmatrix} b_1 & b_3 \\ c_1 & c_3 \end{vmatrix} + a_3\begin{vmatrix} b_1 & b_2 \\ c_1 & c_2 \end{vmatrix}$$

$$= a_1(b_2c_3 - b_3c_2) - a_2(b_1c_3 - b_3c_1) + a_3(b_1c_2 - b_2c_1)$$

Linear Equation

If $a_1x + a_2y + a_3 = 0 \qquad b_1x + b_2y + b_3 = 0$

then

$$\frac{x}{\begin{vmatrix} a_2 & a_3 \\ b_2 & b_3 \end{vmatrix}} = \frac{-y}{\begin{vmatrix} a_1 & a_3 \\ b_1 & b_3 \end{vmatrix}} = \frac{1}{\begin{vmatrix} a_1 & a_2 \\ b_1 & b_2 \end{vmatrix}}$$

If

$$a_1x + a_2y + a_3z + a_4 = 0$$
$$b_1x + b_2y + b_3z + b_4 = 0$$
$$c_1x + c_2y + c_3z + c_4 = 0$$

then

$$\frac{x}{\begin{vmatrix} a_2 & a_3 & a_4 \\ b_2 & b_3 & b_4 \\ c_2 & c_3 & c_4 \end{vmatrix}} = \frac{-y}{\begin{vmatrix} a_1 & a_3 & a_4 \\ b_1 & b_3 & b_4 \\ c_1 & c_3 & c_4 \end{vmatrix}} = \frac{z}{\begin{vmatrix} a_1 & a_2 & a_4 \\ b_1 & b_2 & b_4 \\ c_1 & c_2 & c_4 \end{vmatrix}} = \frac{-1}{\begin{vmatrix} a_1 & a_2 & a_3 \\ b_1 & b_2 & b_3 \\ c_1 & c_2 & c_3 \end{vmatrix}}$$

Cubic Equation

The general cubic equation $ax^3 + bx^2 + cx + d = 0$ can be reduced to one of the following forms by dividing by a and putting $x = y - \frac{b}{3a}$.

(i) $x^3 + px \pm q = 0$

The only real root is $\mp \sqrt{\frac{4p}{3}} \sinh \theta$ where $\sinh 3\theta = \sqrt{\frac{27q^2}{4p^3}}$

(ii) $x^3 - px \pm q = 0$

If $27q^2 > 4p^3$ the only real root is $\mp \sqrt{\frac{4p}{3}} \cosh \theta$ where $\cosh 3\theta = \sqrt{\frac{27q^2}{4p^3}}$

But if $27q^2 < 4p^3$ the three real roots are

$$\mp \sqrt{\frac{4p}{3}} \cos \theta,\ \mp \sqrt{\frac{4p}{3}} \cos (\theta + 120°),\ \mp \frac{4p}{3} \cos (\theta + 240°)$$

$$\text{where } \cos 3\theta = \sqrt{\frac{27q^2}{4p^3}}$$

Binomial Equation

If $x^n = a$
then

$$x = a^{\frac{1}{n}} \left(\cos \frac{2k\pi}{n} + i \sin \frac{2k\pi}{n} \right) \qquad k = 0, 1, 2, \ldots n - 1$$

If $x^n = -a$
then

$$x = a^{\frac{1}{n}} \left(\cos \frac{(2k + 1)\pi}{n} + i \sin \frac{(2k + 1)\pi}{n} \right)$$

$$k = 0, 1, 2, \ldots n - 1$$

Newton's Method of Approximation

If a is an approximate root of the equation $f(x) = 0$, then $x_1 = a - \frac{f(a)}{f'(a)}$ is in general a closer approximation. Similarly $x_2 = x_1 - \frac{f(x_1)}{f'(x_1)}$ is a still closer approximation, and so on. Here $f'(x)$ is the derivative of $f(x)$.

Resolution into Partial Fractions

Let $f(x)$, $F(x)$ be two polynomials of which $f(x)$ is of lower degree than $F(x)$.

(i) If $F(x) = (x - a)(x - b) \ldots (x - k)$ where $a, b, c, \ldots k$ are different, then

$$\frac{f(x)}{F(x)} \equiv \frac{f(a)}{F'(a)} \frac{1}{x-a} + \frac{f(b)}{F'(b)} \frac{1}{x-b} + \ldots + \frac{f(k)}{F'(k)} \frac{1}{x-k}$$

(ii) If $F(x) = (x - a)^r (x - b)^s \ldots (x - k)^u$

Assume

$$\frac{f(x)}{F(x)} \equiv \frac{A_1}{x-a} + \frac{A_2}{(x-a)^2} + \ldots + \frac{A_r}{(x-a)^r} + \frac{B_1}{x-b} + \frac{B_2}{(x-b)^2} + \ldots + \frac{B_s}{(x-b)^s} + \ldots$$

Multiply both sides by $F(x)$ and determine $A_1, A_2, \ldots B_1, B_2, \ldots$ by equating coefficients.

(iii) If $F(x) = (x - a)^r \ldots (x^2 + bx + c)^s$

Assume

$$\frac{f(x)}{F(x)} \equiv \frac{A_1}{x-a} + \frac{A_2}{(x-a)^2} + \ldots + \frac{A_r}{(x-a)^r} + \ldots + \frac{P_1 x + Q_1}{x^2 + bx + c} + \frac{P_2 x + Q_2}{(x^2 + bx + c)^2} + \ldots + \frac{P_s x + Q_s}{(x^2 + bx + c)^s}$$

Multiply both sides by $F(x)$ and determine $A_1, A_2, \ldots P_1, P_2, \ldots Q_1, Q_2, \ldots$ by equating coefficients.

PLANE GEOMETRY

The following notation is used in the formulas of plane geometry:

a = apothem	h = height, altitude
A = area	p = perimeter
a, b, c = sides of $\triangle ABC$	r = radius
b, b' = bases	s = semiperimeter of $\triangle ABC$; that is, $s = \frac{1}{2}(a + b + c)$
C = circumference	π = approximately 3.14159.
d = diameter	

Formulas for Lines

right triangle	$a^2 + b^2 = c^2$
circle	$C = 2\pi r$
	$C = \pi d$
radius of circle	$r = \dfrac{C}{2\pi}$
equilateral triangle	$h = \frac{1}{2}b\sqrt{3}$
side of square	$b = \sqrt{A}$

Areas of Plane Figures

rectangle	$A = bh$
parallelogram	$A = bh$
triangle	$A = \frac{1}{2}bh$
	$A = \sqrt{s(s - a)(s - b)(s - c)}$
equilateral triangle	$A = \frac{1}{4}b^2\sqrt{3}$
trapezoid	$A = \frac{1}{2}h(b + b')$
regular polygon	$A = \frac{1}{2}ap$
circle	$A = \frac{1}{2}rC$
	$A = \pi r^2$

SOLID GEOMETRY

In addition to the symbols indicated above the following are used in the formulas of solid geometry:

B = area of base	L = lateral area
e = element, lateral edge	M = area of midsection
E = spherical excess	S = area of curve surface
l = slant height	V = volume

Areas of Solid Figures

prism	$L = ep$
regular pyramid	$L = \frac{1}{2}lp$
frustum of regular pyramid	$L = \frac{1}{2}l(p + p')$
cylinder of revolution	$S = 2\pi rh$
cone of revolution	$S = \frac{1}{2}lC$
	$S = \pi rl$
frustum of cone of revolution	$S = \frac{1}{2}l(C + C')$
sphere	$S = 4\pi r^2$
spherical polygon	$S = \frac{1}{180}E\pi r^2$
zone	$S = 2\pi rh$

Volumes

parallelepiped	$V = Bh$
prism or cylinder	$V = Bh$
cylinder of revolution	$V = \pi r^2h$
pyramid or cone	$V = \frac{1}{3}Bh$
cone of revolution	$V = \frac{1}{3}\pi r^2h$
frustum of pyramid or cone	$V = \frac{1}{3}h(B + B' + \sqrt{BB'})$
frustum of cone of revolution	$V = \frac{1}{3}\pi h(r^2 + r'^2 + rr')$
prismoid	$V = \frac{1}{6}h(B + B' + 4M)$
sphere	$V = \frac{4}{3}\pi r^3$
	$V = \frac{1}{6}\pi d^3$

ANALYTIC GEOMETRY

Distance Between Two Points

$$d = \sqrt{(x_2 - x_1)^2 + (y_2 - y_1)^2}$$

Slope of Line Joining Two Points

$$m = \frac{y_2 - y_1}{x_2 - x_1}$$

Midpoint Formulas

$$x = \frac{x_1 + x_2}{2}, \quad y = \frac{y_1 + y_2}{2}$$

Point Dividing a Segment in a Given Ratio

$$x = \frac{x_1 + rx_2}{1 + r}, \quad y = \frac{y_1 + ry_2}{1 + r}$$

Angle Between Two Lines

Condition for parallelism $\quad m_1 = m_2$

Condition for perpendicularity $\quad m_1 m_2 = -1$

$$\tan \theta = \frac{m_1 - m_2}{1 + m_1 m_2}$$

Equation of a Straight Line

Point-slope form: $\quad y - y_1 = m(x - x_1)$

Slope-intercept form: $\quad y = mx + b$

Two-point form: $\quad \dfrac{y - y_1}{x - x_1} = \dfrac{y_2 - y_1}{x_2 - x_1}$

Intercept form: $\quad \dfrac{x}{a} + \dfrac{y}{b} = 1$

Distance from a Line to a Point

$$d = \frac{y_1 - mx_1 - b}{\sqrt{m^2 + 1}}$$

Equations of Curves

Circle with center (h, k) and radius r:

$$(x - h)^2 + (y - k)^2 = r^2$$

Parabola with vertex at the origin and with focus on the x-axis:

$$y^2 = 2px$$

Ellipse with center at the origin and with foci on the x-axis:

$$\frac{x^2}{a^2} + \frac{y^2}{b^2} = 1$$

Hyperbola with center at the origin and with foci on the x-axis:

$$\frac{x^2}{a^2} - \frac{y^2}{b^2} = 1$$

Equilateral hyperbola with center at the origin and with the coordinate axes for asymptotes:

$$xy = C$$

Other Curves with Historical Names

catenary

$$y = \frac{a}{2}\left(e^{\frac{x}{a}} + e^{-\frac{x}{a}}\right)$$

cissoid

$$y^2(2a - x) = x^3$$

conchoid

$$x^2y^2 = (y + a)^2(b^2 - y^2)$$

cubical parabola

$$y = ax^3$$

cycloid

$$x = a(\theta - \sin\theta), \quad y = a(1 - \cos\theta)$$

folium

$$x^3 + y^2 - 3axy = 0$$

hypocycloid of four cusps

$$x^{\frac{2}{3}} + y^{\frac{2}{3}} = a^{\frac{2}{3}}$$

lemniscate

$$(x^2 + y^2)^2 = a^2(x^2 - y^2)$$

parabola

$$\sqrt{x} + \sqrt{y} = \sqrt{a}$$

probability curve

$$y = e^{-x^2}$$

semicubical parabola

$$y^2 = ax^3$$

strophoid

$$(a - x)y^2 = (a + x)x^2$$

witch

$$y = \frac{8a^3}{x^2 + 4a^2}$$

Radius of Curvature

$$R = \pm\frac{(1 + y'^2)^{\frac{3}{2}}}{y''}$$

TRIGONOMETRY

$$\sin^2 x + \cos^2 x = 1 \quad \sec^2 x = 1 + \tan^2 x \quad \csc^2 x = 1 + \cot^2 x$$

$$\sin x = \frac{2 \tan \frac{x}{2}}{1 + \tan^2 \frac{x}{2}} \quad \cos x = \frac{1 - \tan^2 \frac{x}{2}}{1 + \tan^2 \frac{x}{2}} \quad \tan x = \frac{2 \tan \frac{x}{2}}{1 - \tan^2 \frac{x}{2}}$$

$$\sin^2 x = \tfrac{1}{2}(1 - \cos 2x) \qquad \cos^2 x = \tfrac{1}{2}(1 + \cos 2x)$$

$$\sin 2x = 2 \sin x \cos x \qquad \cos 2x = \cos^2 x - \sin^2 x$$

$$= 2 \cos^2 x - 1 = 1 - 2 \sin^2 x$$

$$\sin 3x = 3 \sin x - 4 \sin^3 x \qquad \cos 3x = 4 \cos^3 x - 3 \cos x$$

$$\tan 2x = \frac{2 \tan x}{1 - \tan^2 x} \qquad \tan 3x = \frac{3 \tan x - \tan^3 x}{1 - 3 \tan^2 x}$$

$$\sin (A + B) = \sin A \cos B + \cos A \sin B$$

$$\sin (A - B) = \sin A \cos B - \cos A \sin B$$

$$\cos (A + B) = \cos A \cos B - \sin A \sin B$$

$$\cos (A - B) = \cos A \cos B + \sin A \sin B$$

$$\tan (A + B) = \frac{\tan A + \tan B}{1 - \tan A \tan B}$$

$$\tan (A - B) = \frac{\tan A - \tan B}{1 + \tan A \tan B}$$

$$2 \sin A \cos B = \sin (A + B) + \sin (A - B)$$

$$2 \cos A \sin B = \sin (A + B) - \sin (A - B)$$

$$2 \cos A \cos B = \cos (A + B) + \cos (A - B)$$

$$2 \sin A \sin B = \cos (A - B) - \cos (A + B)$$

$$\sin A + \sin B = 2 \sin \frac{A + B}{2} \cos \frac{A - B}{2}$$

$$\sin A - \sin B = 2 \cos \frac{A + B}{2} \sin \frac{A - B}{2}$$

$$\cos A + \cos B = 2 \cos \frac{A + B}{2} \cos \frac{A - B}{2}$$

$$\cos A - \cos B = -2 \sin \frac{A + B}{2} \sin \frac{A - B}{2}$$

Plane Triangle

$$\frac{a}{\sin A} = \frac{b}{\sin B} = \frac{c}{\sin C} = 2R = \frac{abc}{2\Delta}$$

$$a^2 = b^2 + c^2 - 2bc \cos A \qquad \cos A = \frac{b^2 + c^2 - a^2}{2bc}$$

$$\tan \frac{B - C}{2} = \frac{b - c}{b + c} \operatorname{ctn} \frac{A}{2} \qquad a = (b - c) \sec \theta$$

$$\text{where } \tan \theta = \frac{2\sqrt{bc}\sin \frac{A}{2}}{b - c}$$

$$a = b \cos C + c \cos B \qquad b = a \cos C + c \cos A$$

$$c = a \cos B + b \cos A$$

$$\text{area} = \Delta = \sqrt{s(s - a)(s - b)(s - c)} = \tfrac{1}{2}ab \sin C$$

$$\text{where } s = \frac{a + b + c}{2}$$

$$r = \frac{\Delta}{s} = \sqrt{\frac{(s - a)(s - b)(s - c)}{s}}$$

$$\tan \frac{A}{2} = \frac{r}{s - a} \qquad \tan \frac{B}{2} = \frac{r}{s - b} \qquad \tan \frac{C}{2} = \frac{r}{s - c}$$

$$\sin \frac{A}{2} = \sqrt{\frac{(s - b)(s - c)}{bc}} \qquad \cos \frac{A}{2} = \sqrt{\frac{s(s - a)}{bc}}$$

$$\tan \frac{A}{2} = \sqrt{\frac{(s - b)(s - c)}{s(s - a)}}$$

Spherical Triangle

$$\frac{\sin a}{\sin A} = \frac{\sin b}{\sin B} = \frac{\sin c}{\sin C}$$

$$\cos a = \cos b \cos c + \sin b \sin c \cos A$$

$$\sin a \cos B = \cos b \sin c - \sin b \cos c \cos A$$

$$\sin a \sin B = \sin b \sin A$$

$$\cos A = \frac{\cos a - \cos b \cos c}{\sin b \sin c}$$

$$\cos a = \frac{\cos A + \cos B \cos C}{\sin B \sin C}$$

$$\sin A \operatorname{ctn} B = \sin c \operatorname{ctn} b - \cos c \cos A$$

$$\sin \frac{A}{2} = \sqrt{\frac{\sin (s - b) \sin (s - c)}{\sin b \sin c}} \qquad \cos \frac{A}{2} = \sqrt{\frac{\sin s \sin (s - a)}{\sin b \sin c}}$$

$$\tan \frac{A}{2} = \sqrt{\frac{\sin (s - b) \sin (s - c)}{\sin s \sin (s - a)}} \qquad \text{where } s = \frac{a + b + c}{2}$$

$$\tan \frac{A}{2} = \frac{r}{\sin (s - a)} \qquad \tan \frac{B}{2} = \frac{r}{\sin (s - b)}$$

$$\tan \frac{C}{2} = \frac{r}{\sin (s - c)}$$

where

$$r = \sqrt{\frac{\sin (s - a) \sin (s - b) \sin (s - c)}{\sin s}}$$

$$\text{area} = (A + B + C - 180°) \frac{\pi R^2}{180}$$

where R is the radius of the sphere

Napier's Analogies

$$\tan \tfrac{1}{2}(a + b) = \frac{\cos \frac{1}{2}(A - B)}{\cos \frac{1}{2}(A + B)} \tan \tfrac{1}{2}c$$

$$\tan \tfrac{1}{2}(a - b) = \frac{\sin \frac{1}{2}(A - B)}{\sin \frac{1}{2}(A + B)} \tan \tfrac{1}{2}c$$

$$\tan \tfrac{1}{2}(A + B) = \frac{\cos \frac{1}{2}(a - b)}{\cos \frac{1}{2}(a + b)} \operatorname{ctn} \tfrac{1}{2}C$$

$$\tan \tfrac{1}{2}(A - B) = \frac{\sin \frac{1}{2}(a - b)}{\sin \frac{1}{2}(a + b)} \operatorname{ctn} \tfrac{1}{2}C$$

Delambre's Analogies or Gauss's Equations

$$\cos \tfrac{1}{2}c \sin \tfrac{1}{2}(A + B) = \cos \tfrac{1}{2}C \cos \tfrac{1}{2}(a - b)$$
$$\cos \tfrac{1}{2}c \cos \tfrac{1}{2}(A + B) = \sin \tfrac{1}{2}C \cos \tfrac{1}{2}(a + b)$$
$$\sin \tfrac{1}{2}c \sin \tfrac{1}{2}(A - B) = \cos \tfrac{1}{2}C \sin \tfrac{1}{2}(a - b)$$
$$\sin \tfrac{1}{2}c \cos \tfrac{1}{2}(A - B) = \sin \tfrac{1}{2}C \sin \tfrac{1}{2}(a + b)$$

Napier's Rules for a Right-angled Triangle

With C as the right angle, arrange a, b, $90° - A$, $90° - c$, $90° - B$ in order round the circumference of a circle. Then each of the above "parts" may be regarded as a middle part having two adjacent parts and two opposite parts. The rules are as follows:

sine of a middle part = product of the tangents of the adjacent parts
= product of the cosines of the opposite parts

In the case of a quadrantal triangle, if $c = 90°$, the same rules may be applied to the following parts in order: A, $90° - b$, $C - 90°$, $90° - a$, B.

It may be observed that in each case the two parts adjacent to the right angle or quadrant remain unmodified.

II. Powers, Roots, and Reciprocals

n	n^2	$\sqrt{n}$	$\sqrt{10n}$	n^3	$\sqrt[3]{n}$	$\sqrt[3]{10n}$	$\sqrt[3]{100n}$	$1/n$
1.00	1.0000	1.00000	3.16228	1.00000	1.00000	2.15443	4.64159	1.00000
1.01	1.0201	1.00499	3.17805	1.03030	1.00332	2.16159	4.65701	.990099
1.02	1.0404	1.00995	3.19374	1.06121	1.00662	2.16870	4.67233	.980392
1.03	1.0609	1.01489	3.20936	1.09273	1.00990	2.17577	4.68755	.970874
1.04	1.0816	1.01980	3.22490	1.12486	1.01316	2.18279	4.70267	.961538
1.05	1.1025	1.02470	3.24037	1.15762	1.01640	2.18976	4.71769	.952381
1.06	1.1236	1.02956	3.25576	1.19102	1.01961	2.19669	4.73262	.943396
1.07	1.1449	1.03441	3.27109	1.22504	1.02281	2.20358	4.74746	.934579
1.08	1.1664	1.03923	3.28634	1.25971	1.02599	2.21042	4.76220	.925926
1.09	1.1881	1.04403	3.30151	1.29503	1.02914	2.21722	4.77686	.917431
1.10	1.2100	1.04881	3.31662	1.33100	1.03228	2.22398	4.79142	.909091
1.11	1.2321	1.05357	3.33167	1.36763	1.03540	2.23070	4.80590	.900901
1.12	1.2544	1.05830	3.34664	1.40493	1.03850	2.23738	4.82028	.892857
1.13	1.2769	1.06301	3.36155	1.44290	1.04158	2.24402	4.83459	.884956
1.14	1.2996	1.06771	3.37639	1.48154	1.04464	2.25062	4.84881	.877193
1.15	1.3225	1.07238	3.39116	1.52088	1.04769	2.25718	4.86294	.869565
1.16	1.3456	1.07703	3.40588	1.56090	1.05072	2.26370	4.87700	.862069
1.17	1.3689	1.08167	3.42053	1.60161	1.05373	2.27019	4.89097	.854701
1.18	1.3924	1.08628	3.43511	1.64303	1.05672	2.27664	4.90487	.847458
1.19	1.4161	1.09087	3.44964	1.68516	1.05970	2.28305	4.91868	.840336
1.20	1.4400	1.09545	3.46410	1.72800	1.06266	2.28943	4.93242	.833333
1.21	1.4641	1.10000	3.47851	1.77156	1.06560	2.29577	4.94609	.826446
1.22	1.4884	1.10454	3.49285	1.81585	1.06853	2.30208	4.95968	.819672
1.23	1.5129	1.10905	3.50714	1.86087	1.07144	2.30835	4.97319	.813008
1.24	1.5376	1.11355	3.52136	1.90662	1.07434	2.31459	4.98663	.806452
1.25	1.5625	1.11803	3.53553	1.95312	1.07722	2.32079	5.00000	.800000
1.26	1.5876	1.12250	3.54965	2.00038	1.08008	2.32697	5.01330	.793651
1.27	1.6129	1.12694	3.56371	2.04838	1.08293	2.33311	5.02653	.787402
1.28	1.6384	1.13137	3.57771	2.09715	1.08577	2.33921	5.03968	.781250
1.29	1.6641	1.13578	3.59166	2.14669	1.08859	2.34529	5.05277	.775194
1.30	1.6900	1.14018	3.60555	2.19700	1.09139	2.35133	5.06580	.769231
1.31	1.7161	1.14455	3.61939	2.24809	1.09418	2.35735	5.07875	.763359
1.32	1.7424	1.14891	3.63318	2.29997	1.09696	2.36333	5.09164	.757576
1.33	1.7689	1.15326	3.64692	2.35264	1.09972	2.36928	5.10447	.751880
1.34	1.7956	1.15758	3.66060	2.40610	1.10247	2.37521	5.11723	.746269
1.35	1.8225	1.16190	3.67423	2.46038	1.10521	2.38110	5.12993	.740741
1.36	1.8496	1.16619	3.68782	2.51546	1.10793	2.38697	5.14256	.735294
1.37	1.8769	1.17047	3.70135	2.57135	1.11064	2.39280	5.15514	.729927
1.38	1.9044	1.17473	3.71484	2.62807	1.11334	2.39861	5.16765	.724638
1.39	1.9321	1.17898	3.72827	2.68562	1.11602	2.40439	5.18010	.719424
1.40	1.9600	1.18322	3.74166	2.74400	1.11869	2.41014	5.19249	.714286
1.41	1.9881	1.18743	3.75500	2.80322	1.12135	2.41587	5.20483	.709220
1.42	2.0164	1.19164	3.76829	2.86329	1.12399	2.42156	5.21710	.704225
1.43	2.0449	1.19583	3.78153	2.92421	1.12662	2.42724	5.22932	.699301
1.44	2.0736	1.20000	3.79473	2.98598	1.12924	2.43288	5.24148	.694444
1.45	2.1025	1.20416	3.80789	3.04862	1.13185	2.43850	5.25359	.689655
1.46	2.1316	1.20830	3.32099	3.11214	1.13445	2.44409	5.26564	.684932
1.47	2.1609	1.21244	3.83406	3.17652	1.13703	2.44966	5.27763	.680272
1.48	2.1904	1.21655	3.84708	3.24179	1.13960	2.45520	5.28957	.675676
1.49	2.2201	1.22066	3.86005	3.30795	1.14216	2.46072	5.30146	.671141
1.50	2.2500	1.22474	3.87298	3.37500	1.14471	2.46621	5.31329	.666667
n	n^2	$\sqrt{n}$	$\sqrt{10n}$	n^3	$\sqrt[3]{n}$	$\sqrt[3]{10n}$	$\sqrt[3]{100n}$	$1/n$

Powers — Roots — Reciprocals

n	n^2	$\sqrt{n}$	$\sqrt{10n}$	n^3	$\sqrt[3]{n}$	$\sqrt[3]{10n}$	$\sqrt[3]{100n}$	$1/n$
1.50	2.2500	1.22474	3.87298	3.37500	1.14471	2.46621	5.31329	.666667
1.51	2.2801	1.22882	3.88587	3.44295	1.14725	2.47168	5.32507	.662252
1.52	2.3104	1.23288	3.89872	3.51181	1.14978	2.47712	5.33680	.657895
1.53	2.3409	1.23693	3.91152	3.58158	1.15230	2.48255	5.34848	.653595
1.54	2.3716	1.24097	3.92428	3.65226	1.15480	2.48794	5.36011	.649351
1.55	2.4025	1.24499	3.93700	3.72388	1.15729	2.49332	5.37169	.645161
1.56	2.4336	1.24900	3.94968	3.79642	1.15978	2.49867	5.38321	.641026
1.57	2.4649	1.25300	3.96232	3.86989	1.16225	2.50399	5.39469	.636943
1.58	2.4964	1.25698	3.97492	3.94431	1.16471	2.50930	5.40612	.632911
1.59	2.5281	1.26095	3.98748	4.01968	1.16717	2.51458	5.41750	.628931
1.60	2.5600	1.26491	4.00000	4.09600	1.16961	2.51984	5.42884	.625000
1.61	2.5921	1.26886	4.01248	4.17328	1.17204	2.52508	5.44012	.621118
1.62	2.6244	1.27279	4.02492	4.25153	1.17446	2.53030	5.45136	.617284
1.63	2.6569	1.27671	4.03733	4.33075	1.17687	2.53549	5.46256	.613497
1.64	2.6896	1.28062	4.04969	4.41094	1.17927	2.54067	5.47370	.609756
1.65	2.7225	1.28452	4.06202	4.49212	1.18167	2.54582	5.48481	.606061
1.66	2.7556	1.28841	4.07431	4.57430	1.18405	2.55095	5.49586	.602410
1.67	2.7889	1.29228	4.08656	4.65746	1.18642	2.55607	5.50688	.598802
1.68	2.8224	1.29615	4.09878	4.74163	1.18878	2.56116	5.51785	.595238
1.69	2.8561	1.30000	4.11096	4.82681	1.19114	2.56623	5.52877	.591716
1.70	2.8900	1.30384	4.12311	4.91300	1.19348	2.57128	5.53966	.588235
1.71	2.9241	1.30767	4.13521	5.00021	1.19582	2.57631	5.55050	.584795
1.72	2.9584	1.31149	4.14729	5.08845	1.19815	2.58133	5.56130	581395
1.73	2.9929	1.31529	4.15933	5.17772	1.20046	2.58632	5.57205	.578035
1.74	3.0276	1.31909	4.17133	5.26802	1.20277	2.59129	5.58277	.574713
1.75	3.0625	1.32288	4.18330	5.35938	1.20507	2.59625	5.59344	.571429
1.76	3.0976	1.32665	4.19524	5.45178	1.20736	2.60118	5.60408	.568182
1.77	3.1329	1.33041	4.20714	5.54523	1.20964	2.60610	5.61467	.564972
1.78	3.1684	1.33417	4.21900	5.63975	1.21192	2.61100	5.62523	.561798
1.79	3.2041	1.33791	4.23084	5.73534	1.21418	2.61588	5.63574	.558659
1.80	3.2400	1.34164	4.24264	5.83200	1.21644	2.62074	5.64622	.555556
1.81	3.2761	1.34536	4.25441	5.92974	1.21869	2.62559	5.65665	.552486
1.82	3.3124	1.34907	4.26615	6.02857	1.22093	2.63041	5.66705	.549451
1.83	3.3489	1.35277	4.27785	6.12849	1.22316	2.63522	5.67741	.546448
1.84	3.3856	1.35647	4.28952	6.22950	1.22539	2.64001	5.68773	.543478
1.85	3.4225	1.36015	4.30116	6.33162	1.22760	2.64479	5.69802	.540541
1.86	3.4596	1.36382	4.31277	6.43486	1.22981	2.64954	5.70827	.537634
1.87	3.4969	1.36748	4.32435	6.53920	1.23201	2.65428	5.71848	.534759
1.88	3.5344	1.37113	4.33590	6.64467	1.23420	2.65901	5.72865	.531915
1.89	3.5721	1.37477	4.34741	6.75127	1.23639	2.66371	5.73879	.529101
1.90	3.6100	1.37840	4.35890	6.85900	1.23856	2.66840	5.74890	.526316
1.91	3.6481	1.38203	4.37035	6.96787	1.24073	2.67307	5.75897	.523560
1.92	3.6864	1.38564	4.38178	7.07789	1.24289	2.67773	5.76900	.520833
1.93	3.7249	1.38924	4.39318	7.18906	1.24505	2.68237	5.77900	.518135
1.94	3.7636	1.39284	4.40454	7.30138	1.24719	2.68700	5.78896	.515464
1.95	3.8025	1.39642	4.41588	7.41488	1.24933	2.69161	5.79889	.512821
1.96	3.8416	1.40000	4.42719	7.52954	1.25146	2.69620	5.80879	.510204
1.97	3.8809	1.40357	4.43847	7.64537	1.25359	2.70078	5.81865	.507614
1.98	3.9204	1.40712	4.44972	7.76239	1.25571	2.70534	5.82848	.505051
1.99	3.9601	1.41067	4.46094	7.88060	1.25782	2.70989	5.83827	.502513
2.00	4.0000	1.41421	4.47214	8.00000	1.25992	2.71442	5.84804	.500000
n	n^2	$\sqrt{n}$	$\sqrt{10n}$	n^3	$\sqrt[3]{n}$	$\sqrt[3]{10n}$	$\sqrt[3]{100n}$	$1/n$

Powers — Roots — Reciprocals

n	n^2	$\sqrt{n}$	$\sqrt{10n}$	n^3	$\sqrt[3]{n}$	$\sqrt[3]{10n}$	$\sqrt[3]{100n}$	$1/n$
2.00	4.0000	1.41421	4.47214	8.00000	1.25992	2.71442	5.84804	.500000
2.01	4.0401	1.41774	4.48330	8.12060	1.26202	2.71893	5.85777	.497512
2.02	4.0804	1.42127	4.49444	8.24241	1.26411	2.72344	5.86746	.495050
2.03	4.1209	1.42478	4.50555	8.36543	1.26619	2.72792	5.87713	.492611
2.04	4.1616	1.42829	4.51664	8.48966	1.26827	2.73239	5.88677	.490196
2.05	4.2025	1.43178	4.52769	8.61512	1.27033	2.73685	5.89637	.487805
2.06	4.2436	1.43527	4.53872	8.74182	1.27240	2.74129	5.90594	.485437
2.07	4.2849	1.43875	4.54973	8.86974	1.27445	2.74572	5.91548	.483092
2.08	4.3264	1.44222	4.56070	8.99891	1.27650	2.75014	5.92499	.480769
2.09	4.3681	1.44568	4.57165	9.12933	1.27854	2.75454	5.93447	.478469
2.10	4.4100	1.44914	4.58258	9.26100	1.28058	2.75892	5.94392	.476190
2.11	4.4521	1.45258	4.59347	9.39393	1.28261	2.76330	5.95334	.473934
2.12	4.4944	1.45602	4.60435	9.52813	1.28463	2.76766	5.96273	.471698
2.13	4.5369	1.45945	4.61519	9.66360	1.28665	2.77200	5.97209	.469434
2.14	4.5796	1.46287	4.62601	9.80034	1.28866	2.77633	5.98142	.467290
2.15	4.6225	1.46629	4.63681	9.93838	1.29066	2.78065	5.99073	.465116
2.16	4.6656	1.46969	4.64758	10.0777	1.29266	2.78495	6.00000	.462963
2.17	4.7089	1.47309	4.65833	10.2183	1.29465	2.78924	6.00925	.460829
2.18	4.7524	1.47648	4.66905	10.3602	1.29664	2.79352	6.01846	.458716
2.19	4.7961	1.47986	4.67974	10.5035	1.29862	2.79779	6.02765	.456621
2.20	4.8400	1.48324	4.69042	10.6480	1.30059	2.80204	6.03681	.454545
2.21	4.8841	1.48661	4.70106	10.7939	1.30256	2.80628	6.04594	.452489
2.22	4.9284	1.48997	4.71169	10.9410	1.30452	2.81050	6.05505	.450450
2.23	4.9729	1.49332	4.72229	11.0896	1.30648	2.81472	6.06413	.448430
2.24	5.0176	1.49666	4.73286	11.2394	1.30843	2.81892	6.07318	.446429
2.25	5.0625	1.50000	4.74342	11.3906	1.31037	2.82311	6.08220	.444444
2.26	5.1076	1.50333	4.75395	11.5432	1.31231	2.82728	6.09120	.442478
2.27	5.1529	1.50665	4.76445	11.6971	1.31424	2.83145	6.10017	.440529
2.28	5.1984	1.50997	4.77493	11.8524	1.31617	2.83560	6.10911	.438596
2.29	5.2441	1.51327	4.78539	12.0090	1.31809	2.83974	6.11803	.436681
2.30	5.2900	1.51658	4.79583	12.1670	1.32001	2.84387	6.12693	.434783
2.31	5.3361	1.51987	4.80625	12.3264	1.32192	2.84798	6.13579	.432900
2.32	5.3824	1.52315	4.81664	12.4872	1.32382	2.85209	6.14463	.431034
2.33	5.4289	1.52643	4.82701	12.6493	1.32572	2.85618	6.15345	.429185
2.34	5.4756	1.52971	4.83735	12.8129	1.32761	2.86026	6.16224	.427350
2.35	5.5225	1.53297	4.84768	12.9779	1.32950	2.86433	6.17101	.425532
2.36	5.5696	1.53623	4.85798	13.1443	1.33139	2.86838	6.17975	.423729
2.37	5.6169	1.53948	4.86826	13.3121	1.33326	2.87243	6.18846	.421941
2.38	5.6644	1.54272	4.87852	13.4813	1.33514	2.87646	6.19715	.420168
2.39	5.7121	1.54596	4.88876	13.6519	1.33700	2.88049	6.20582	.418410
2.40	5.7600	1.54919	4.89898	13.8240	1.33887	2.88450	6.21447	.416667
2.41	5.8081	1.55242	4.90918	13.9975	1.34072	2.88850	6.22308	.414938
2.42	5.8564	1.55563	4.91935	14.1725	1.34257	2.89249	6.23168	.413223
2.43	5.9049	1.55885	4.92950	14.3489	1.34442	2.89647	6.24025	.411523
2.44	5.9536	1.56205	4.93964	14.5268	1.34626	2.90044	6.24880	.409836
2.45	6.0025	1.56525	4.94975	14.7061	1.34810	2.90439	6.25732	.408163
2.46	6.0516	1.56844	4.95984	14.8869	1.34993	2.90834	6.26583	.406504
2.47	6.1009	1.57162	4.96991	15.0692	1.35176	2.91227	6.27431	.404858
2.48	6.1504	1.57480	4.97996	15.2530	1.35358	2.91620	6.28276	.403226
2.49	6.2001	1.57797	4.98999	15.4382	1.35540	2.92011	6.29119	.401606
2.50	6.2500	1.58114	5.00000	15.6250	1.35721	2.92402	6.29961	.400000
n	n^2	$\sqrt{n}$	$\sqrt{10n}$	n^3	$\sqrt[3]{n}$	$\sqrt[3]{10n}$	$\sqrt[3]{100n}$	$1/n$

Powers — Roots — Reciprocals

n	n^2	$\sqrt{n}$	$\sqrt{10n}$	n^3	$\sqrt[3]{n}$	$\sqrt[3]{10n}$	$\sqrt[3]{100n}$	$1/n$
2.50	6.2500	1.58114	5.00000	15.6250	1.35721	2.92402	6.29961	.400000
2.51	6.3001	1.58430	5.00999	15.8133	1.35902	2.92791	6.30799	.398406
2.52	6.3504	1.58745	5.01996	16.0030	1.36082	2.93179	6.31636	.396825
2.53	6.4009	1.59060	5.02991	16.1943	1.36262	2.93567	6.32470	.395257
2.54	6.4516	1.59374	5.03984	16.3871	1.36441	2.93953	6.33303	.393701
2.55	6.5025	1.59687	5.04975	16.5814	1.36620	2.94338	6.34133	.392157
2.56	6.5536	1.60000	5.05964	16.7772	1.36798	2.94723	6.34960	.390625
2.57	6.6049	1.60312	5.06952	16.9746	1.36976	2.95106	6.35786	.389105
2.58	6.6564	1.60624	5.07937	17.1735	1.37153	2.95488	6.36610	.387597
2.59	6.7081	1.60935	5.08920	17.3740	1.37330	2.95869	6.37431	.386100
2.60	6.7600	1.61245	5.09902	17.5760	1.37507	2.96250	6.38250	.384615
2.61	6.8121	1.61555	5.10882	17.7796	1.37683	2.96629	6.39068	.383142
2.62	6.8644	1.61864	5.11859	17.9847	1.37859	2.97007	6.39883	.381679
2.63	6.9169	1.62173	5.12835	18.1914	1.38034	2.97385	6.40696	.380228
2.64	6.9696	1.62481	5.13809	18.3997	1.38208	2.97761	6.41507	.378788
2.65	7.0225	1.62788	5.14782	18.6096	1.38383	2.98137	6.42316	.377358
2.66	7.0756	1.63095	5.15752	18.8211	1.38557	2.98511	6.43123	.375940
2.67	7.1289	1.63401	5.16720	19.0342	1.38730	2.98885	6.43928	.374532
2.68	7.1824	1.63707	5.17687	19.2488	1.38903	2.99257	6.44731	.373134
2.69	7.2361	1.64012	5.18652	19.4651	1.39076	2.99629	6.45531	.371747
2.70	7.2900	1.64317	5.19615	19.6830	1.39248	3.00000	6.46330	.370370
2.71	7.3441	1.64621	5.20577	19.9025	1.39419	3.00370	6.47127	.369004
2.72	7.3984	1.64924	5.21536	20.1236	1.39591	3.00739	6.47922	.367647
2.73	7.4529	1.65227	5.22494	20.3464	1.39761	3.01107	6.48715	.366300
2.74	7.5076	1.65529	5.23450	20.5708	1.39932	3.01474	6.49507	.364964
2.75	7.5625	1.65831	5.24404	20.7969	1.40102	3.01841	6.50296	.363636
2.76	7.6176	1.66132	5.25357	21.0246	1.40272	3.02206	6.51083	.362319
2.77	7.6729	1.66433	5.26308	21.2539	1.40441	3.02570	6.51868	.361011
2.78	7.7284	1.66733	5.27257	21.4850	1.40610	3.02934	6.52652	.359712
2.79	7.7841	1.67033	5.28205	21.7176	1.40778	3.03297	6.53434	.358423
2.80	7.8400	1.67332	5.29150	21.9520	1.40946	3.03659	6.54213	.357143
2.81	7.8961	1.67631	5.30094	22.1880	1.41114	3.04020	6.54991	.355872
2.82	7.9524	1.67929	5.31037	22.4258	1.41281	3.04380	6.55767	.354610
2.83	8.0089	1.68226	5.31977	22.6652	1.41448	3.04740	6.56541	.353357
2.84	8.0656	1.68523	5.32917	22.9063	1.41614	3.05098	6.57314	.352113
2.85	8.1225	1.68819	5.33854	23.1491	1.41780	3.05456	6.58084	.350877
2.86	8.1796	1.69115	5.34790	23.3937	1.41946	3.05813	6.58853	.349650
2.87	8.2369	1.69411	5.35724	23.6399	1.42111	3.06169	6.59620	.348432
2.88	8.2944	1.69706	5.36656	23.8879	1.42276	3.06524	6.60385	.347222
2.89	8.3521	1.70000	5.37587	24.1376	1.42440	3.06878	6.61149	.346021
2.90	8.4100	1.70294	5.38516	24.3890	1.42604	3.07232	6.61911	.344828
2.91	8.4681	1.70587	5.39444	24.6422	1.42768	3.07584	6.62671	.343643
2.92	8.5264	1.70880	5.40370	24.8971	1.42931	3.07936	6.63429	.342466
2.93	8.5849	1.71172	5.41295	25.1538	1.43094	3.08287	6.64185	.341297
2.94	8.6436	1.71464	5.42218	25.4122	1.43257	3.08638	6.64940	.340136
2.95	8.7025	1.71756	5.43139	25.6724	1.43419	3.08987	6.65693	.338983
2.96	8.7616	1.72047	5.44059	25.9343	1.43581	3.09336	6.66444	.337838
2.97	8.8209	1.72337	5.44977	26.1981	1.43743	3.09684	6.67194	.336700
2.98	8.8804	1.72627	5.45894	26.4636	1.43904	3.10031	6.67942	.335570
2.99	8.9401	1.72916	5.46809	26.7309	1.44065	3.10378	6.68688	.334448
3.00	9.0000	1.73205	5.47723	27.0000	1.44225	3.10723	6.69433	.333333
n	n^2	$\sqrt{n}$	$\sqrt{10n}$	n^3	$\sqrt[3]{n}$	$\sqrt[3]{10n}$	$\sqrt[3]{100n}$	$1/n$

Powers — Roots — Reciprocals

n	n^2	$\sqrt{n}$	$\sqrt{10\,n}$	n^3	$\sqrt[3]{n}$	$\sqrt[3]{10\,n}$	$\sqrt[3]{100\,n}$	$1/n$
3.00	9.0000	1.73205	5.47723	27.0000	1.44225	3.10723	6.69433	.333333
3.01	9.0601	1.73494	5.48635	27.2709	1.44385	3.11068	6.70176	.332226
3.02	9.1204	1.73781	5.49545	27.5436	1.44545	3.11412	6.70917	.331126
3.03	9.1809	1.74069	5.50454	27.8181	1.44704	3.11756	6.71657	.330033
3.04	9.2416	1.74356	5.51362	28.0945	1.44863	3.12098	6.72395	.328947
3.05	9.3025	1.74642	5.52268	28.3726	1.45022	3.12440	6.73132	.327869
3.06	9.3636	1.74929	5.53173	28.6526	1.45180	3.12781	6.73866	.326797
3.07	9.4249	1.75214	5.54076	28.9344	1.45338	3.13121	6.74600	.325733
3.08	9.4864	1.75499	5.54977	29.2181	1.45496	3.13461	6.75331	.324675
3.09	9.5481	1.75784	5.55878	29.5036	1.45653	3.13800	6.76061	.323625
3.10	9.6100	1.76068	5.56776	29.7910	1.45810	3.14138	6.76790	.322581
3.11	9.6721	1.76352	5.57674	30.0802	1.45967	3.14475	6.77517	.321543
3.12	9.7344	1.76635	5.58570	30.3713	1.46123	3.14812	6.78242	.320513
3.13	9.7969	1.76918	5.59464	30.6643	1.46279	3.15148	6.78966	.319489
3.14	9.8596	1.77200	5.60357	30.9591	1.46434	3.15483	6.79688	.318471
3.15	9.9225	1.77482	5.61249	31.2559	1.46590	3.15818	6.80409	.317460
3.16	9.9856	1.77764	5.62139	31.5545	1.46745	3.16152	6.81128	.316456
3.17	10.0489	1.78045	5.63028	31.8550	1.46899	3.16485	6.81846	.315457
3.18	10.1124	1.78326	5.63915	32.1574	1.47054	3.16817	6.82562	.314465
3.19	10.1761	1.78606	5.64801	32.4618	1.47208	3.17149	6.83277	.313480
3.20	10.2400	1.78885	5.65685	32.7680	1.47361	3.17480	6.83990	.312500
3.21	10.3041	1.79165	5.66569	33.0762	1.47515	3.17811	6.84702	.311526
3.22	10.3684	1.79444	5.67450	33.3862	1.47668	3.18140	6.85412	.310559
3.23	10.4329	1.79722	5.68331	33.6983	1.47820	3.18469	6.86121	.309598
3.24	10.4976	1.80000	5.69210	34.0122	1.47973	3.18798	6.86829	.308642
3.25	10.5625	1.80278	5.70088	34.3281	1.48125	3.19125	6.87534	.307692
3.26	10.6276	1.80555	5.70964	34.6460	1.48277	3.19452	6.88239	.306748
3.27	10.6929	1.80831	5.71839	34.9658	1.48428	3.19778	6.88942	.305810
3.28	10.7584	1.81108	5.72713	35.2876	1.48579	3.20104	6.89643	.304878
3.29	10.8241	1.81384	5.73585	35.6113	1.48730	3.20429	6.90344	.303951
3.30	10.8900	1.81659	5.74456	35.9370	1.48881	3.20753	6.91042	.303030
3.31	10.9561	1.81934	5.75326	36.2647	1.49031	3.21077	6.91740	.302115
3.32	11.0224	1.82209	5.76194	36.5944	1.49181	3.21400	6.92436	.301205
3.33	11.0889	1.82483	5.77062	36.9260	1.49330	3.21722	6.93130	.300300
3.34	11.1556	1.82757	5.77927	37.2597	1.49480	3.22044	6.93823	.299401
3.35	11.2225	1.83030	5.78792	37.5954	1.49629	3.22365	6.94515	.298507
3.36	11.2896	1.83303	5.79655	37.9331	1.49777	3.22686	6.95205	.297619
3.37	11.3569	1.83576	5.80517	38.2728	1.49926	3.23006	6.95894	.296736
3.38	11.4244	1.83848	5.81378	38.6145	1.50074	3.23325	6.96582	.295858
3.39	11.4921	1.84120	5.82237	38.9582	1.50222	3.23643	6.97268	.294985
3.40	11.5600	1.84391	5.83095	39.3040	1.50369	3.23961	6.97953	.294118
3.41	11.6281	1.84662	5.83952	39.6518	1.50517	3.24278	6.98637	.293255
3.42	11.6964	1.84932	5.84808	40.0017	1.50664	3.24595	6.99319	.292398
3.43	11.7649	1.85203	5.85662	40.3536	1.50810	3.24911	7.00000	.291545
3.44	11.8336	1.85472	5.86515	40.7076	1.50957	3.25227	7.00680	.290698
3.45	11.9025	1.85742	5.87367	41.0636	1.51103	3.25542	7.01358	.289855
3.46	11.9716	1.86011	5.88218	41.4217	1.51249	3.25856	7.02035	.289017
3.47	12.0409	1.86279	5.89067	41.7819	1.51394	3.26169	7.02711	.288184
3.48	12.1104	1.86548	5.89915	42.1442	1.51540	3.26482	7.03385	.287356
3.49	12.1801	1.86815	5.90762	42.5085	1.51685	3.26795	7.04058	.286533
3.50	12.2500	1.87083	5.91608	42.8750	1.51829	3.27107	7.04730	.285714
n	n^2	$\sqrt{n}$	$\sqrt{10\,n}$	n^3	$\sqrt[3]{n}$	$\sqrt[3]{10\,n}$	$\sqrt[3]{100\,n}$	$1/n$

Powers — Roots — Reciprocals

n	n^2	$\sqrt{n}$	$\sqrt{10n}$	n^3	$\sqrt[3]{n}$	$\sqrt[3]{10n}$	$\sqrt[3]{100n}$	$1/n$
3.50	12.2500	1.87083	5.91608	42.8750	1.51829	3.27107	7.04730	.285714
3.51	12.3201	1.87350	5.92453	43.2436	1.51974	3.27418	7.05400	.284900
3.52	12.3904	1.87617	5.93296	43.6142	1.52118	3.27729	7.06070	.284091
3.53	12.4609	1.87883	5.94138	43.9870	1.52262	3.28039	7.06738	.283286
3.54	12.5316	1.88149	5.94979	44.3619	1.52406	3.28348	7.07404	.282486
3.55	12.6025	1.88414	5.95819	44.7389	1.52549	3.28657	7.08070	.281690
3.56	12.6736	1.88680	5.96657	45.1180	1.52692	3.28965	7.08734	.280899
3.57	12.7449	1.88944	5.97495	45.4993	1.52835	3.29273	7.09397	.280112
3.58	12.8164	1.89209	5.98331	45.8827	1.52978	3.29580	7.10059	.279330
3.59	12.8881	1.89473	5.99166	46.2683	1.53120	3.29887	7.10719	.278552
3.60	12.9600	1.89737	6.00000	46.6560	1.53262	3.30193	7.11379	.277778
3.61	13.0321	1.90000	6.00833	47.0459	1.53404	3.30498	7.12037	.277008
3.62	13.1044	1.90263	6.01664	47.4379	1.53545	3.30803	7.12694	.276243
3.63	13.1769	1.90526	6.02495	47.8321	1.53686	3.31107	7.13349	.275482
3.64	13.2496	1.90788	6.03324	48.2285	1.53827	3.31411	7.14004	.274725
3.65	13.3225	1.91050	6.04152	48.6271	1.53968	3.31714	7.14657	.273973
3.66	13.3956	1.91311	6.04979	49.0279	1.54109	3.32017	7.15309	.273224
3.67	13.4689	1.91572	6.05805	49.4309	1.54249	3.32319	7.15960	.272480
3.68	13.5424	1.91833	6.06630	49.8360	1.54389	3.32621	7.16610	.271739
3.69	13.6161	1.92094	6.07454	50.2434	1.54529	3.32922	7.17258	.271003
3.70	13.6900	1.92354	6.08276	50.6530	1.54668	3.33222	7.17905	.270270
3.71	13.7641	1.92614	6.09098	51.0648	1.54807	3.33522	7.18552	.269542
3.72	13.8384	1.92873	6.09918	51.4788	1.54946	3.33822	7.19197	.268817
3.73	13.9129	1.93132	6.10737	51.8951	1.55085	3.34120	7.19840	.268097
3.74	13.9876	1.93391	6.11555	52.3136	1.55223	3.34419	7.20483	.267380
3.75	14.0625	1.93649	6.12372	52.7344	1.55362	3.34716	7.21125	.266667
3.76	14.1376	1.93907	6.13188	53.1574	1.55500	3.35014	7.21765	.265957
3.77	14.2129	1.94165	6.14003	53.5826	1.55637	3.35310	7.22405	.265252
3.78	14.2884	1.94422	6.14817	54.0102	1.55775	3.35607	7.23043	.264550
3.79	14.3641	1.94679	6.15630	54.4399	1.55912	3.35902	7.23680	.263852
3.80	14.4400	1.94936	6.16441	54.8720	1.56049	3.36198	7.24316	.263158
3.81	14.5161	1.95192	6.17252	55.3063	1.56186	3.36492	7.24950	.262467
3.82	14.5924	1.95448	6.18061	55.7430	1.56322	3.36786	7.25584	.261780
3.83	14.6689	1.95704	6.18870	56.1819	1.56459	3.37080	7.26217	.261097
3.84	14.7456	1.95959	6.19677	56.6231	1.56595	3.37373	7.26848	.260417
3.85	14.8225	1.96214	6.20484	57.0666	1.56731	3.37666	7.27479	.259740
3.86	14.8996	1.96469	6.21289	57.5125	1.56866	3.37958	7.28108	.259067
3.87	14.9769	1.96723	6.22093	57.9606	1.57001	3.38249	7.28736	.258398
3.88	15.0544	1.96977	6.22896	58.4111	1.57137	3.38540	7.29363	.257732
3.89	15.1321	1.97231	6.23699	58.8639	1.57271	3.38831	7.29989	.257069
3.90	15.2100	1.97484	6.24500	59.3190	1.57406	3.39121	7.30614	.256410
3.91	15.2881	1.97737	6.25300	59.7765	1.57541	3.39411	7.31238	.255754
3.92	15.3664	1.97990	6.26099	60.2363	1.57675	3.39700	7.31861	.255102
3.93	15.4449	1.98242	6.26897	60.6985	1.57809	3.39988	7.32483	.254453
3.94	15.5236	1.98494	6.27694	61.1630	1.57942	3.40277	7.33104	.253807
3.95	15.6025	1.98746	6.28490	61.6299	1.58076	3.40564	7.33723	.253165
3.96	15.6816	1.98997	6.29285	62.0991	1.58209	3.40851	7.34342	.252525
3.97	15.7609	1.99249	6.30079	62.5708	1.58342	3.41138	7.34960	.251889
3.98	15.8404	1.99499	6.30872	63.0448	1.58475	3.41424	7.35576	.251256
3.99	15.9201	1.99750	6.31664	63.5212	1.58608	3.41710	7.36192	.250627
4.00	16.0000	2.00000	6.32456	64.0000	1.58740	3.41995	7.36806	.250000
n	n^2	$\sqrt{n}$	$\sqrt{10n}$	n^3	$\sqrt[3]{n}$	$\sqrt[3]{10n}$	$\sqrt[3]{100n}$	$1/n$

Powers — Roots — Reciprocals

n	n^2	$\sqrt{n}$	$\sqrt{10n}$	n^3	$\sqrt[3]{n}$	$\sqrt[3]{10n}$	$\sqrt[3]{100n}$	$1/n$
4.00	16.0000	2.00000	6.32456	64.0000	1.58740	3.41995	7.36806	.250000
4.01	16.0801	2.00250	6.33246	64.4812	1.58872	3.42280	7.37420	.249377
4.02	16.1604	2.00499	6.34035	64.9648	1.59004	3.42564	7.38032	.248756
4.03	16.2409	2.00749	6.34823	65.4508	1.59136	3.42848	7.38644	.248139
4.04	16.3216	2.00998	6.35610	65.9393	1.59267	3.43131	7.39254	.247525
4.05	16.4025	2.01246	6.36396	66.4301	1.59399	3.43414	7.39864	.246914
4.06	16.4836	2.01494	6.37181	66.9234	1.59530	3.43697	7.40472	.246305
4.07	16.5649	2.01742	6.37966	67.4191	1.59661	3.43979	7.41080	.245700
4.08	16.6464	2.01990	6.38749	67.9173	1.59791	3.44260	7.41686	.245098
4.09	16.7281	2.02237	6.39531	68.4179	1.59922	3.44541	7.42291	.244499
4.10	16.8100	2.02485	6.40312	68.9210	1.60052	3.44822	7.42896	.243902
4.11	16.8921	2.02731	6.41093	69.4265	1.60182	3.45102	7.43499	.243309
4.12	16.9744	2.02978	6.41872	69.9345	1.60312	3.45382	7.44102	.242718
4.13	17.0569	2.03224	6.42651	70.4450	1.60441	3.45661	7.44703	.242131
4.14	17.1396	2.03470	6.43428	70.9579	1.60571	3.45939	7.45304	.241546
4.15	17.2225	2.03715	6.44205	71.4734	1.60700	3.46218	7.45904	.240964
4.16	17.3056	2.03961	6.44981	71.9913	1.60829	3.46496	7.46502	.240385
4.17	17.3889	2.04206	6.45755	72.5117	1.60958	3.46773	7.47100	.239808
4.18	17.4724	2.04450	6.46529	73.0346	1.61086	3.47050	7.47697	.239234
4.19	17.5561	2.04695	6.47302	73.5601	1.61215	3.47327	7.48292	.238663
4.20	17.6400	2.04939	6.48074	74.0880	1.61343	3.47603	7.48887	.238095
4.21	17.7241	2.05183	6.48845	74.6185	1.61471	3.47878	7.49481	.237530
4.22	17.8084	2.05426	6.49615	75.1514	1.61599	3.48154	7.50074	.236967
4.23	17.8929	2.05670	6.50384	75.6870	1.61726	3.48428	7.50666	.236407
4.24	17.9776	2.05913	6.51153	76.2250	1.61853	3.48703	7.51257	.235849
4.25	18.0625	2.06155	6.51920	76.7656	1.61981	3.48977	7.51847	.235294
4.26	18.1476	2.06398	6.52687	77.3088	1.62108	3.49250	7.52437	.234742
4.27	18.2329	2.06640	6.53452	77.8545	1.62234	3.49523	7.53025	.234192
4.28	18.3184	2.06882	6.54217	78.4028	1.62361	3.49796	7.53612	.233645
4.29	18.4041	2.07123	6.54981	78.9536	1.62487	3.50068	7.54199	.233100
4.30	18.4900	2.07364	6.55744	79.5070	1.62613	3.50340	7.54784	.232558
4.31	18.5761	2.07605	6.56506	80.0630	1.62739	3.50611	7.55369	.232019
4.32	18.6624	2.07846	6.57267	80.6216	1.62865	3.50882	7.55953	.231481
4.33	18.7489	2.08087	6.58027	81.1827	1.62991	3.51153	7.56535	.230947
4.34	18.8356	2.08327	6.58787	81.7465	1.63116	3.51423	7.57117	.230415
4.35	18.9225	2.08567	6.59545	82.3129	1.63241	3.51692	7.57698	.229885
4.36	19.0096	2.08806	6.60303	82.8819	1.63366	3.51962	7.58279	.229358
4.37	19.0969	2.09045	6.61060	83.4535	1.63491	3.52231	7.58858	.228833
4.38	19.1844	2.09284	6.61816	84.0277	1.63619	3.52499	7.59436	.228311
4.39	19.2721	2.09523	6.62571	84.6045	1.63740	3.52767	7.60014	.227790
4.40	19.3600	2.09762	6.63325	85.1840	1.63864	3.53035	7.60590	.227273
4.41	19.4481	2.10000	6.64078	85.7661	1.63988	3.53302	7.61166	.226757
4.42	19.5364	2.10238	6.64831	86.3509	1.64112	3.53569	7.61741	.226244
4.43	19.6249	2.10476	6.65582	86.9383	1.64236	3.53835	7.62315	.225734
4.44	19.7136	2.10713	6.66333	87.5284	1.64359	3.54101	7.62888	.225225
4.45	19.8025	2.10950	6.67083	88.1211	1.64483	3.54367	7.63461	.224719
4.46	19.8916	2.11187	6.67832	88.7165	1.64606	3.54632	7.64032	.224215
4.47	19.9809	2.11424	6.68581	89.3146	1.64729	3.54897	7.64603	.223714
4.48	20.0704	2.11660	6.69328	89.9154	1.64851	3.55162	7.65172	.223214
4.49	20.1601	2.11896	6.70075	90.5188	1.64974	3.55426	7.65741	.222717
4.50	20.2500	2.12132	6.70820	91.1250	1.65096	3.55689	7.66309	.222222
n	n^2	$\sqrt{n}$	$\sqrt{10n}$	n^3	$\sqrt[3]{n}$	$\sqrt[3]{10n}$	$\sqrt[3]{100n}$	$1/n$

Powers — Roots — Reciprocals

n	n^2	$\sqrt{n}$	$\sqrt{10n}$	n^3	$\sqrt[3]{n}$	$\sqrt[3]{10n}$	$\sqrt[3]{100n}$	$1/n$
4.50	20.2500	2.12132	6.70820	91.1250	1.65096	3.55689	7.66309	.222222
4.51	20.3401	2.12368	6.71565	91.7339	1.65219	3.55953	7.66877	.221729
4.52	20.4304	2.12603	6.72309	92.3454	1.65341	3.56215	7.67443	.221239
4.53	20.5209	2.12838	6.73053	92.9597	1.65462	3.56478	7.68009	.220751
4.54	20.6116	2.13073	6.73795	93.5767	1.65584	3.56740	7.68573	.220264
4.55	20.7025	2.13307	6.74537	94.1964	1.65706	3.57002	7.69137	.219780
4.56	20.7936	2.13542	6.75278	94.8188	1.65827	3.57263	7.69700	.219298
4.57	20.8849	2.13776	6.76018	95.4440	1.65948	3.57524	7.70262	.218818
4.58	20.9764	2.14009	6.76757	96.0719	1.66069	3.57785	7.70824	.218341
4.59	21.0681	2.14243	6.77495	96.7026	1.66190	3.58045	7.71384	.217865
4.60	21.1600	2.14476	6.78233	97.3360	1.66310	3.58305	7.71944	.217391
4.61	21.2521	2.14709	6.78970	97.9722	1.66431	3.58564	7.72503	.216920
4.62	21.3444	2.14942	6.79706	98.6111	1.66551	3.58823	7.73061	.216450
4.63	21.4369	2.15174	6.80441	99.2528	1.66671	3.59082	7.73619	.215983
4.64	21.5296	2.15407	6.81175	99.8973	1.66791	3.59340	7.74175	.215517
4.65	21.6225	2.15639	6.81909	100.545	1.66911	3.59598	7.74731	.215054
4.66	21.7156	2.15870	6.82642	101.195	1.67030	3.59856	7.75286	.214592
4.67	21.8089	2.16102	6.83374	101.848	1.67150	3.60113	7.75840	.214133
4.68	21.9024	2.16333	6.84105	102.503	1.67269	3.60370	7.76394	.213675
4.69	21.9961	2.16564	6.84836	103.162	1.67388	3.60626	7.76946	.213220
4.70	22.0900	2.16795	6.85565	103.823	1.67507	3.60883	7.77498	.212766
4.71	22.1841	2.17025	6.86294	104.487	1.67626	3.61138	7.78049	.212314
4.72	22.2784	2.17256	6.87023	105.154	1.67744	3.61394	7.78599	.211864
4.73	22.3729	2.17486	6.87750	105.824	1.67863	3.61649	7.79149	.211416
4.74	22.4676	2.17715	6.88477	106.496	1.67981	3.61903	7.79697	.210970
4.75	22.5625	2.17945	6.89202	107.172	1.68099	3.62158	7.80245	.210526
4.76	22.6576	2.18174	6.89928	107.850	1.68217	3.62412	7.80793	.210084
4.77	22.7529	2.18403	6.90652	108.531	1.68334	3.62665	7.81339	.209644
4.78	22.8484	2.18632	6.91375	109.215	1.68452	3.62919	7.81885	.209205
4.79	22.9441	2.18861	6.92098	109.902	1.68569	3.63172	7.82429	.208768
4.80	23.0400	2.19089	6.92820	110.592	1.68687	3.63424	7.82974	.208333
4.81	23.1361	2.19317	6.93542	111.285	1.68804	3.63676	7.83517	.207900
4.82	23.2324	2.19545	6.94262	111.980	1.68920	3.63928	7.84059	.207469
4.83	23.3289	2.19773	6.94982	112.679	1.69037	3.64180	7.84601	.207039
4.84	23.4256	2.20000	6.95701	113.380	1.69154	3.64431	7.85142	.206612
4.85	23.5225	2.20227	6.96419	114.084	1.69270	3.64682	7.85683	.206186
4.86	23.6196	2.20454	6.97137	114.791	1.69386	3.64932	7.86222	.205761
4.87	23.7169	2.20681	6.97854	115.501	1.69503	3.65182	7.86761	.205339
4.88	23.8144	2.20907	6.98570	116.214	1.69619	3.65432	7.87299	.204918
4.89	23.9121	2.21133	6.99285	116.930	1.69734	3.65681	7.87837	.204499
4.90	24.0100	2.21359	7.00000	117.649	1.69850	3.65931	7.88374	.204082
4.91	24.1081	2.21585	7.00714	118.371	1.69965	3.66179	7.88909	.203666
4.92	24.2064	2.21811	7.01427	119.095	1.70081	3.66428	7.89445	.203252
4.93	24.3049	2.22036	7.02140	119.823	1.70196	3.66676	7.89979	.202840
4.94	24.4036	2.22261	7.02851	120.554	1.70311	3.66924	7.90513	.202429
4.95	24.5025	2.22486	7.03562	121.287	1.70426	3.67171	7.91046	.202020
4.96	24.6016	2.22711	7.04273	122.024	1.70540	3.67418	7.91578	.201613
4.97	24.7009	2.22935	7.04982	122.763	1.70655	3.67665	7.92110	.201207
4.98	24.8004	2.23159	7.05691	123.506	1.70769	3.67911	7.92641	.200803
4.99	24.9001	2.23383	7.06399	124.251	1.70884	3.68157	7.93171	.200401
5.00	25.0000	2.23607	7.07107	125.000	1.70998	3.68403	7.93701	.200000
n	n^2	$\sqrt{n}$	$\sqrt{10n}$	n^3	$\sqrt[3]{n}$	$\sqrt[3]{10n}$	$\sqrt[3]{100n}$	$1/n$

Powers — Roots — Reciprocals

n	n^2	$\sqrt{n}$	$\sqrt{10n}$	n^3	$\sqrt[3]{n}$	$\sqrt[3]{10n}$	$\sqrt[3]{100n}$	$1/n$
5.00	25.0000	2.23607	7.07107	125.000	1.70998	3.68403	7.93701	.200000
5.01	25.1001	2.23830	7.07814	125.752	1.71112	3.68649	7.94229	.199601
5.02	25.2004	2.24054	7.08520	126.506	1.71225	3.68894	7.94757	.199203
5.03	25.3009	2.24277	7.09225	127.264	1.71339	3.69138	7.95285	.198807
5.04	25.4016	2.24499	7.09930	128.024	1.71452	3.69383	7.95811	.198413
5.05	25.5025	2.24722	7.10634	128.788	1.71566	3.69627	7.96337	.198020
5.06	25.6036	2.24944	7.11337	129.554	1.71679	3.69871	7.96863	.197628
5.07	25.7049	2.25167	7.12039	130.324	1.71792	3.70114	7.97387	.197239
5.08	25.8064	2.25389	7.12741	131.097	1.71905	3.70357	7.97911	.196850
5.09	25.9081	2.25610	7.13442	131.872	1.72017	3.70600	7.98434	.196464
5.10	26.0100	2.25832	7.14143	132.651	1.72130	3.70843	7.98957	.196078
5.11	26.1121	2.26053	7.14843	133.433	1.72242	3.71085	7.99479	.195695
5.12	26.2144	2.26274	7.15542	134.218	1.72355	3.71327	8.00000	.195312
5.13	26.3169	2.26495	7.16240	135.006	1.72467	3.71569	8.00520	.194932
5.14	26.4196	2.26716	7.16938	135.797	1.72579	3.71810	8.01040	.194553
5.15	26.5225	2.26936	7.17635	136.591	1.72691	3.72051	8.01559	.194175
5.16	26.6256	2.27156	7.18331	137.388	1.72802	3.72292	8.02078	.193798
5.17	26.7289	2.27376	7.19027	138.188	1.72914	3.72532	8.02596	.193424
5.18	26.8324	2.27596	7.19722	138.992	1.73025	3.72772	8.03113	.193050
5.19	26.9361	2.27816	7.20417	139.798	1.73137	3.73012	8.03629	.192678
5.20	27.0400	2.28035	7.21110	140.608	1.73248	3.73251	8.04145	.192308
5.21	27.1441	2.28254	7.21803	141.421	1.73359	3.73490	8.04660	.191939
5.22	27.2484	2.28473	7.22496	142.237	1.73470	3.73729	8.05175	.191571
5.23	27.3529	2.28692	7.23187	143.056	1.73580	3.73968	8.05689	.191205
5.24	27.4576	2.28910	7.23878	143.878	1.73691	3.74206	8.06202	.190840
5.25	27.5625	2.29129	7.24569	144.703	1.73801	3.74443	8.06714	.190476
5.26	27.6676	2.29347	7.25259	145.532	1.73912	3.74681	8.07226	.190114
5.27	27.7729	2.29565	7.25948	146.363	1.74022	3.74918	8.07737	.189753
5.28	27.8784	2.29783	7.26636	147.198	1.74132	3.75155	8.08248	.189394
5.29	27.9841	2.30000	7.27324	148.036	1.74242	3.75392	8.08758	.189036
5.30	28.0900	2.30217	7.28011	148.877	1.74351	3.75629	8.09267	.188679
5.31	28.1961	2.30434	7.28697	149.721	1.74461	3.75865	8.09776	.188324
5.32	28.3024	2.30651	7.29383	150.569	1.74570	3.76101	8.10284	.187970
5.33	28.4089	2.30868	7.30068	151.419	1.74680	3.76336	8.10791	.187617
5.34	28.5156	2.31084	7.30753	152.273	1.74789	3.76571	8.11298	.187266
5.35	28.6225	2.31301	7.31437	153.130	1.74898	3.76806	8.11804	.186916
5.36	28.7296	2.31517	7.32120	153.991	1.75007	3.77041	8.12310	.186567
5.37	28.8369	2.31733	7.32803	154.854	1.75116	3.77275	8.12814	.186220
5.38	28.9444	2.31948	7.33485	155.721	1.75224	3.77509	8.13319	.185874
5.39	29.0521	2.32164	7.34166	156.591	1.75333	3.77743	8.13822	.185529
5.40	29.1600	2.32379	7.34847	157.464	1.75441	3.77976	8.14325	.185185
5.41	29.2681	2.32594	7.35527	158.340	1.75549	3.78209	8.14828	.184843
5.42	29.3764	2.32809	7.36206	159.220	1.75657	3.78442	8.15329	.184502
5.43	29.4849	2.33024	7.36885	160.103	1.75765	3.78675	8.15831	.184162
5.44	29.5936	2.33238	7.37564	160.989	1.75873	3.78907	8.16331	.183824
5.45	29.7025	2.33452	7.38241	161.879	1.75981	3.79139	8.16831	.183486
5.46	29.8116	2.33666	7.38918	162.771	1.76088	3.79371	8.17330	.183150
5.47	29.9209	2.33880	7.39594	163.667	1.76196	3.79603	8.17829	.182815
5.48	30.0304	2.34094	7.40270	164.567	1.76303	3.79834	8.18327	.182482
5.49	30.1401	2.34307	7.40945	165.469	1.76410	3.80065	8.18824	.182149
5.50	30.2500	2.34521	7.41620	166.375	1.76517	3.80295	8.19321	.181818
n	n^2	$\sqrt{n}$	$\sqrt{10n}$	n^3	$\sqrt[3]{n}$	$\sqrt[3]{10n}$	$\sqrt[3]{100n}$	$1/n$

Powers — Roots — Reciprocals

n	n^2	$\sqrt{n}$	$\sqrt{10n}$	n^3	$\sqrt[3]{n}$	$\sqrt[3]{10n}$	$\sqrt[3]{100n}$	$1/n$
5.50	30.2500	2.34521	7.41620	166.375	1.76517	3.80295	8.19321	.181818
5.51	30.3601	2.34734	7.42294	167.284	1.76624	3.80526	8.19818	.181488
5.52	30.4704	2.34947	7.42967	168.197	1.76731	3.80756	8.20313	.181159
5.53	30.5809	2.35160	7.43640	169.112	1.76838	3.80985	8.20808	.180832
5.54	30.6916	2.35372	7.44312	170.031	1.76944	3.81215	8.21303	.180505
5.55	30.8025	2.35584	7.44983	170.954	1.77051	3.81444	8.21797	.180180
5.56	30.9136	2.35797	7.45654	171.880	1.77157	3.81673	8.22290	.179856
5.57	31.0249	2.36008	7.46324	172.809	1.77263	3.81902	8.22783	.179533
5.58	31.1364	2.36220	7.46994	173.741	1.77369	3.82130	8.23275	.179211
5.59	31.2481	2.36432	7.47663	174.677	1.77475	3.82358	8.23766	.178891
5.60	31.3600	2.36643	7.48331	175.616	1.77581	3.82586	8.24257	.178571
5.61	31.4721	2.36854	7.48999	176.558	1.77686	3.82814	8.24747	.178253
5.62	31.5844	2.37065	7.49667	177.504	1.77792	3.83041	8.25237	.177936
5.63	31.6969	2.37276	7.50333	178.454	1.77897	3.83268	8.25726	.177620
5.64	31.8096	2.37487	7.50999	179.406	1.78003	3.83495	8.26215	.177305
5.65	31.9225	2.37697	7.51665	180.362	1.78108	3.83722	8.26703	.176991
5.66	32.0356	2.37908	7.52330	181.321	1.78213	3.83948	8.27190	.176678
5.67	32.1489	2.38118	7.52994	182.284	1.78318	3.84174	8.27677	.176367
5.68	32.2624	2.38328	7.53658	183.250	1.78422	3.84399	8.28164	.176056
5.69	32.3761	2.38537	7.54321	184.220	1.78527	3.84625	8.28649	.175747
5.70	32.4900	2.38747	7.54983	185.193	1.78632	3.84850	8.29134	.175439
5.71	32.6041	2.38956	7.55645	186.169	1.78736	3.85075	8.29619	.175131
5.72	32.7184	2.39165	7.56307	187.149	1.78840	3.85300	8.30103	.174825
5.73	32.8329	2.39374	7.56968	188.133	1.78944	3.85524	8.30587	.174520
5.74	32.9476	2.39583	7.57628	189.119	1.79048	3.85748	8.31069	.174216
5.75	33.0625	2.39792	7.58288	190.109	1.79152	3.85972	8.31552	.173913
5.76	33.1776	2.40000	7.58947	191.103	1.79256	3.86196	8.32034	.173611
5.77	33.2929	2.40208	7.59605	192.100	1.79360	3.86419	8.32515	.173310
5.78	33.4084	2.40416	7.60263	193.101	1.79463	3.86642	8.32995	.173010
5.79	33.5241	2.40624	7.60920	194.105	1.79567	3.86865	8.33476	.172712
5.80	33.6400	2.40832	7.61577	195.112	1.79670	3.87088	8.33955	.172414
5.81	33.7561	2.41039	7.62234	196.123	1.79773	3.87310	8.34434	.172117
5.82	33.8724	2.41247	7.62889	197.137	1.79876	3.87532	8.34913	.171821
5.83	33.9889	2.41454	7.63544	198.155	1.79979	3.87754	8.35390	.171527
5.84	34.1056	2.41661	7.64199	199.177	1.80082	3.87975	8.35868	.171233
5.85	34.2225	2.41868	7.64853	200.202	1.80185	3.88197	8.36345	.170940
5.86	34.3396	2.42074	7.65506	201.230	1.80288	3.88418	8.36821	.170649
5.87	34.4569	2.42281	7.66159	202.262	1.80390	3.88639	8.37297	.170358
5.88	34.5744	2.42487	7.66812	203.297	1.80492	3.88859	8.37772	.170068
5.89	34.6921	2.42693	7.67463	204.336	1.80595	3.89080	8.38247	.169779
5.90	34.8100	2.42899	7.68115	205.379	1.80697	3.89300	8.38721	.169492
5.91	34.9281	2.43105	7.68765	206.425	1.80799	3.89519	8.39194	.169205
5.92	35.0464	2.43311	7.69415	207.475	1.80901	3.89739	8.39667	.168919
5.93	35.1649	2.43516	7.70065	208.528	1.81003	3.89958	8.40140	.168634
5.94	35.2836	2.43721	7.70714	209.585	1.81104	3.90177	8.40612	.168350
5.95	35.4025	2.43926	7.71362	210.645	1.81206	3.90396	8.41083	.168067
5.96	35.5216	2.44131	7.72010	211.709	1.81307	3.90615	8.41554	.167785
5.97	35.6409	2.44336	7.72658	212.776	1.81409	3.90833	8.42025	.167504
5.98	35.7604	2.44540	7.73305	213.847	1.81510	3.91051	8.42494	.167224
5.99	35.8801	2.44745	7.73951	214.922	1.81611	3.91269	8.42964	.166945
6.00	36.0000	2.44949	7.74597	216.000	1.81712	3.91487	8.43433	.166667
n	n^2	$\sqrt{n}$	$\sqrt{10n}$	n^3	$\sqrt[3]{n}$	$\sqrt[3]{10n}$	$\sqrt[3]{100n}$	$1/n$

Powers — Roots — Reciprocals

n	n^2	$\sqrt{n}$	$\sqrt{10n}$	n^3	$\sqrt[3]{n}$	$\sqrt[3]{10n}$	$\sqrt[3]{100n}$	$1/n$
6.00	36.0000	2.44949	7.74597	216.000	1.81712	3.91487	8.43433	.166667
6.01	36.1201	2.45153	7.75242	217.082	1.81813	3.91704	8.43901	.166389
6.02	36.2404	2.45357	7.75887	218.167	1.81914	3.91921	8.44369	.166113
6.03	36.3609	2.45561	7.76531	219.256	1.82014	3.92138	8.44836	.165837
6.04	36.4816	2.45764	7.77174	220.349	1.82115	3.92355	8.45303	.165563
6.05	36.6025	2.45967	7.77817	221.445	1.82215	3.92571	8.45769	.165289
6.06	36.7236	2.46171	7.78460	222.545	1.82316	3.92787	8.46235	.165017
6.07	36.8449	2.46374	7.79102	223.649	1.82416	3.93003	8.46700	.164745
6.08	36.9664	2.46577	7.79744	224.756	1.82516	3.93219	8.47165	.164474
6.09	37.0881	2.46779	7.80385	225.867	1.82616	3.93434	8.47629	.164204
6.10	37.2100	2.46982	7.81025	226.981	1.82716	3.93650	8.48093	.163934
6.11	37.3321	2.47184	7.81665	228.099	1.82816	3.93865	8.48556	.163666
6.12	37.4544	2.47386	7.82304	229.221	1.82915	3.94079	8.49018	.163399
6.13	37.5769	2.47588	7.82943	230.346	1.83015	3.94294	8.49481	.163132
6.14	37.6996	2.47790	7.83582	231.476	1.83115	3.94508	8.49942	.162866
6.15	37.8225	2.47992	7.84219	232.608	1.83214	3.94722	8.50403	.162602
6.16	37.9456	2.48193	7.84857	233.745	1.83313	3.94936	8.50864	.162338
6.17	38.0689	2.48395	7.85493	234.885	1.83412	3.95150	8.51324	.162075
6.18	38.1924	2.48596	7.86130	236.029	1.83511	3.95363	8.51784	.161812
6.19	38.3161	2.48797	7.86766	237.177	1.83610	3.95576	8.52243	.161551
6.20	38.4400	2.48998	7.87401	238.328	1.83709	3.95789	8.52702	.161290
6.21	38.5641	2.49199	7.88036	239.483	1.83808	3.96002	8.53160	.161031
6.22	38.6884	2.49399	7.88670	240.642	1.83906	3.96214	8.53618	.160772
6.23	38.8129	2.49600	7.89303	241.804	1.84005	3.96427	8.54075	.160514
6.24	38.9376	2.49800	7.89937	242.971	1.84103	3.96638	8.54532	.160256
6.25	39.0625	2.50000	7.90569	244.141	1.84202	3.96850	8.54988	.160000
6.26	39.1876	2.50200	7.91202	245.314	1.84300	3.97062	8.55444	.159744
6.27	39.3129	2.50400	7.91833	246.492	1.84398	3.97273	8.55899	.159490
6.28	39.4384	2.50599	7.92465	247.673	1.84496	3.97484	8.56354	.159236
6.29	39.5641	2.50799	7.93095	248.858	1.84594	3.97695	8.56808	.158983
6.30	39.6900	2.50998	7.93725	250.047	1.84691	3.97906	8.57262	.158730
6.31	39.8161	2.51197	7.94355	251.240	1.84789	3.98116	8.57715	.158479
6.32	39.9424	2.51396	7.94984	252.436	1.84887	3.98326	8.58168	.158228
6.33	40.0689	2.51595	7.95613	253.636	1.84984	3.98536	8.58620	.157978
6.34	40.1956	2.51794	7.96241	254.840	1.85082	3.98746	8.59072	.157729
6.35	40.3225	2.51992	7.96869	256.048	1.85179	3.98956	8.59524	.157480
6.36	40.4496	2.52190	7.97496	257.259	1.85276	3.99165	8.59975	.157233
6.37	40.5769	2.52389	7.98123	258.475	1.85373	3.99374	8.60425	.156986
6.38	40.7044	2.52587	7.98749	259.694	1.85470	3.99583	8.60875	.156740
6.39	40.8321	2.52784	7.99375	260.917	1.85567	3.99792	8.61325	.156495
6.40	40.9600	2.52982	8.00000	262.144	1.85664	4.00000	8.61774	.156250
6.41	41.0881	2.53180	8.00625	263.375	1.85760	4.00208	8.62222	.156006
6.42	41.2164	2.53377	8.01249	264.609	1.85857	4.00416	8.62671	.155763
6.43	41.3449	2.53574	8.01873	265.848	1.85953	4.00624	8.63118	.155521
6.44	41.4736	2.53772	8.02496	267.090	1.86050	4.00832	8.63566	.155280
6.45	41.6025	2.53969	8.03119	268.336	1.86146	4.01039	8.64012	.155039
6.46	41.7316	2.54165	8.03741	269.586	1.86242	4.01246	8.64459	.154799
6.47	41.8609	2.54362	8.04363	270.840	1.86338	4.01453	8.64904	.154560
6.48	41.9904	2.54558	8.04984	272.098	1.86434	4.01660	8.65350	.154321
6.49	42.1201	2.54755	8.05605	273.359	1.86530	4.01866	8.65795	.154083
6.50	42.2500	2.54951	8.06226	274.625	1.86626	4.02073	8.66239	.153846
n	n^2	$\sqrt{n}$	$\sqrt{10n}$	n^3	$\sqrt[3]{n}$	$\sqrt[3]{10n}$	$\sqrt[3]{100n}$	$1/n$

Powers — Roots — Reciprocals

n	n^2	$\sqrt{n}$	$\sqrt{10n}$	n^3	$\sqrt[3]{n}$	$\sqrt[3]{10n}$	$\sqrt[3]{100n}$	$1/n$
6.50	42.2500	2.54951	8.06226	274.625	1.86626	4.02073	8.66239	.153846
6.51	42.3801	2.55147	8.06846	275.894	1.86721	4.02279	8.66683	.153610
6.52	42.5104	2.55343	8.07465	277.168	1.86817	4.02485	8.67127	.153374
6.53	42.6409	2.55539	8.08084	278.445	1.86912	4.02690	8.67570	.153139
6.54	42.7716	2.55734	8.08703	279.726	1.87008	4.02896	8.68012	.152905
6.55	42.9025	2.55930	8.09321	281.011	1.87103	4.03101	8.68455	.152672
6.56	43.0336	2.56125	8.09938	282.300	1.87198	4.03306	8.68896	.152439
6.57	43.1649	2.56320	8.10555	283.593	1.87293	4.03511	8.69338	.152207
6.58	43.2964	2.56515	8.11172	284.890	1.87388	4.03715	8.69778	.151976
6.59	43.4281	2.56710	8.11788	286.191	1.87483	4.03920	8.70219	.151745
6.60	43.5600	2.56905	8.12404	287.496	1.87578	4.04124	8.70659	.151515
6.61	43.6921	2.57099	8.13019	288.805	1.87672	4.04328	8.71098	.151286
6.62	43.8244	2.57294	8.13634	290.118	1.87767	4.04532	8.71537	.151057
6.63	43.9569	2.57488	8.14248	291.434	1.87862	4.04735	8.71976	.150830
6.64	44.0896	2.57682	8.14862	292.755	1.87956	4.04939	8.72414	.150602
6.65	44.2225	2.57876	8.15475	294.080	1.88050	4.05142	8.72852	.150376
6.66	44.3556	2.58070	8.16088	295.408	1.88144	4.05345	8.73289	.150150
6.67	44.4889	2.58263	8.16701	296.741	1.88239	4.05548	8.73726	.149925
6.68	44.6224	2.58457	8.17313	298.078	1.88333	4.05750	8.74162	.149701
6.69	44.7561	2.58650	8.17924	299.418	1.88427	4.05953	8.74598	.149477
6.70	44.8900	2.58844	8.18535	300.763	1.88520	4.06155	8.75034	.149254
6.71	45.0241	2.59037	8.19146	302.112	1.88614	4.06357	8.75469	.149031
6.72	45.1584	2.59230	8.19756	303.464	1.88708	4.06559	8.75904	.148810
6.73	45.2929	2.59422	8.20366	304.821	1.88801	4.06760	8.76338	.148588
6.74	45.4276	2.59615	8.20975	306.182	1.88895	4.06961	8.76772	.148368
6.75	45.5625	2.59808	8.21584	307.547	1.88988	4.07163	8.77205	.148148
6.76	45.6976	2.60000	8.22192	308.916	1.89081	4.07364	8.77638	.147929
6.77	45.8329	2.60192	8.22800	310.289	1.89175	4.07564	8.78071	.147710
6.78	45.9684	2.60384	8.23408	311.666	1.89268	4.07765	8.78503	.147493
6.79	46.1041	2.60576	8.24015	313.047	1.89361	4.07965	8.78935	.147275
6.80	46.2400	2.60768	8.24621	314.432	1.89454	4.08166	8.79366	.147059
6.81	46.3761	2.60960	8.25227	315.821	1.89546	4.08365	8.79797	.146843
6.82	46.5124	2.61151	8.25833	317.215	1.89639	4.08565	8.80227	.146628
6.83	46.6489	2.61343	8.26438	318.612	1.89732	4.08765	8.80657	.146413
6.84	46.7856	2.61534	8.27043	320.014	1.89824	4.08964	8.81087	.146199
6.85	46.9225	2.61725	8.27647	321.419	1.89917	4.09163	8.81516	.145985
6.86	47.0596	2.61916	8.28251	322.829	1.90009	4.09362	8.81945	.145773
6.87	47.1969	2.62107	8.28855	324.243	1.90102	4.09561	8.82373	.145560
6.88	47.3344	2.62298	8.29458	325.661	1.90194	4.09760	8.82801	.145349
6.89	47.4721	2.62488	8.30060	327.083	1.90286	4.09958	8.83228	.145138
6.90	47.6100	2.62679	8.30662	328.509	1.90378	4.10157	8.83656	.144928
6.91	47.7481	2.62869	8.31264	329.939	1.90470	4.10355	8.84082	.144718
6.92	47.8864	2.63059	8.31865	331.374	1.90562	4.10552	8.84509	.144509
6.93	48.0249	2.63249	8.32466	332.813	1.90653	4.10750	8.84934	.144300
6.94	48.1636	2.63439	8.33067	334.255	1.90745	4.10948	8.85360	.144092
6.95	48.3025	2.63629	8.33667	335.702	1.90837	4.11145	8.85785	.143885
6.96	48.4416	2.63818	8.34266	337.154	1.90928	4.11342	8.86210	.143678
6.97	48.5809	2.64008	8.34865	338.609	1.91019	4.11539	8.86634	.143472
6.98	48.7204	2.64197	8.35464	340.068	1.91111	4.11736	8.87058	.143266
6.99	48.8601	2.64386	8.36062	341.532	1.91202	4.11932	8.87481	.143062
7.00	49.0000	2.64575	8.36660	343.000	1.91293	4.12129	8.87904	.142857
n	n^2	$\sqrt{n}$	$\sqrt{10n}$	n^3	$\sqrt[3]{n}$	$\sqrt[3]{10n}$	$\sqrt[3]{100n}$	$1/n$

Powers — Roots — Reciprocals

n	n^2	$\sqrt{n}$	$\sqrt{10n}$	n^3	$\sqrt[3]{n}$	$\sqrt[3]{10n}$	$\sqrt[3]{100n}$	$1/n$
7.00	49.0000	2.64575	8.36660	343.000	1.91293	4.12129	8.87904	.142857
7.01	49.1401	2.64764	8.37257	344.472	1.91384	4.12325	8.88327	.142653
7.02	49.2804	2.64953	8.37854	345.948	1.91475	4.12521	8.88749	.142450
7.03	49.4209	2.65141	8.38451	347.429	1.91566	4.12716	8.89171	.142248
7.04	49.5616	2.65330	8.39047	348.914	1.91657	4.12912	8.89592	.142045
7.05	49.7025	2.65518	8.39643	350.403	1.91747	4.13107	8.90013	.141844
7.06	49.8436	2.65707	8.40238	351.896	1.91838	4.13303	8.90434	.141643
7.07	49.9849	2.65895	8.40833	353.393	1.91929	4.13498	8.90854	.141443
7.08	50.1264	2.66083	8.41427	354.895	1.92019	4.13693	8.91274	.141243
7.09	50.2681	2.66271	8.42021	356.401	1.92109	4.13887	8.91693	.141044
7.10	50.4100	2.66458	8.42615	357.911	1.92200	4.14082	8.92112	.140845
7.11	50.5521	2.66646	8.43208	359.425	1.92290	4.14276	8.92531	.140647
7.12	50.6944	2.66833	8.43801	360.944	1.92380	4.14470	8.92949	.140449
7.13	50.8369	2.67021	8.44393	362.467	1.92470	4.14664	8.93367	.140252
7.14	50.9796	2.67208	8.44985	363.994	1.92560	4.14858	8.93784	.140056
7.15	51.1225	2.67395	8.45577	365.526	1.92650	4.15052	8.94201	.139860
7.16	51.2656	2.67582	8.46168	367.062	1.92740	4.15245	8.94618	.139665
7.17	51.4089	2.67769	8.46759	368.602	1.92829	4.15438	8.95034	.139470
7.18	51.5524	2.67955	8.47349	370.146	1.92919	4.15631	8.95450	.139276
7.19	51.6961	2.68142	8.47939	371.695	1.93008	4.15824	8.95866	.139082
7.20	51.8400	2.68328	8.48528	373.248	1.93098	4.16017	8.96281	.138889
7.21	51.9841	2.68514	8.49117	374.805	1.93187	4.16209	8.96696	.138696
7.22	52.1284	2.68701	8.49706	376.367	1.93277	4.16402	8.97110	.138504
7.23	52.2729	2.68887	8.50294	377.933	1.93366	4.16594	8.97524	.138313
7.24	52.4176	2.69072	8.50882	379.503	1.93455	4.16786	8.97938	.138122
7.25	52.5625	2.69258	8.51469	381.078	1.93544	4.16978	8.98351	.137931
7.26	52.7076	2.69444	8.52056	382.657	1.93633	4.17169	8.98764	.137741
7.27	52.8529	2.69629	8.52643	384.241	1.93722	4.17361	8.99176	.137552
7.28	52.9984	2.69815	8.53229	385.828	1.93810	4.17552	8.99588	.137363
7.29	53.1441	2.70000	8.53815	387.420	1.93899	4.17743	9.00000	.137174
7.30	53.2900	2.70185	8.54400	389.017	1.93988	4.17934	9.00411	.136986
7.31	53.4361	2.70370	8.54985	390.618	1.94076	4.18125	9.00822	.136799
7.32	53.5824	2.70555	8.55570	392.223	1.94165	4.18315	9.01233	.136612
7.33	53.7289	2.70740	8.56154	393.833	1.94253	4.18506	9.01643	.136426
7.34	53.8756	2.70924	8.56738	395.447	1.94341	4.18696	9.02053	.136240
7.35	54.0225	2.71109	8.57321	397.065	1.94430	4.18886	9.02462	.136054
7.36	54.1696	2.71293	8.57904	398.688	1.94518	4.19076	9.02871	.135870
7.37	54.3169	2.71477	8.58487	400.316	1.94606	4.19266	9.03280	.135685
7.38	54.4644	2.71662	8.59069	401.947	1.94694	4.19455	9.03689	.135501
7.39	54.6121	2.71846	8.59651	403.583	1.94782	4.19644	9.04097	.135318
7.40	54.7600	2.72029	8.60233	405.224	1.94870	4.19834	9.04504	.135135
7.41	54.9081	2.72213	8.60814	406.869	1.94957	4.20023	9.04911	.134953
7.42	55.0564	2.72397	8.61394	408.518	1.95045	4.20212	9.05318	.134771
7.43	55.2049	2.72580	8.61974	410.172	1.95132	4.20400	9.05725	.134590
7.44	55.3536	2.72764	8.62554	411.831	1.95220	4.20589	9.06131	.134409
7.45	55.5025	2.72947	8.63134	413.494	1.95307	4.20777	9.06537	.134228
7.46	55.6516	2.73130	8.63713	415.161	1.95395	4.20965	9.06942	.134048
7.47	55.8009	2.73313	8.64292	416.833	1.95482	4.21153	9.07347	.133869
7.48	55.9504	2.73496	8.64870	418.509	1.95569	4.21341	9.07752	.133690
7.49	56.1001	2.73679	8.65448	420.190	1.95656	4.21529	9.08156	.133511
7.50	56.2500	2.73861	8.66025	421.875	1.95743	4.21716	9.08560	.133333
n	n^2	$\sqrt{n}$	$\sqrt{10n}$	n^3	$\sqrt[3]{n}$	$\sqrt[3]{10n}$	$\sqrt[3]{100n}$	$1/n$

Powers — Roots — Reciprocals

n	n^2	$\sqrt{n}$	$\sqrt{10n}$	n^3	$\sqrt[3]{n}$	$\sqrt[3]{10n}$	$\sqrt[3]{100n}$	$1/n$
7.50	56.2500	2.73861	8.66025	421.875	1.95743	4.21716	9.08560	.133333
7.51	56.4001	2.74044	8.66603	423.565	1.95830	4.21904	9.08964	.133156
7.52	56.5504	2.74226	8.67179	425.259	1.95917	4.22091	9.09367	.132979
7.53	56.7009	2.74408	8.67756	426.958	1.96004	4.22278	9.09770	.132802
7.54	56.8516	2.74591	8.68332	428.661	1.96091	4.22465	9.10173	.132626
7.55	57.0025	2.74773	8.68907	430.369	1.96177	4.22651	9.10575	.132450
7.56	57.1536	2.74955	8.69483	432.081	1.96264	4.22838	9.10977	.132275
7.57	57.3049	2.75136	8.70057	433.798	1.96350	4.23024	9.11378	.132100
7.58	57.4564	2.75318	8.70632	435.520	1.96437	4.23210	9.11779	.131926
7.59	57.6081	2.75500	8.71206	437.245	1.96523	4.23396	9.12180	.131752
7.60	57.7600	2.75681	8.71780	438.976	1.96610	4.23582	9.12581	.131579
7.61	57.9121	2.75862	8.72353	440.711	1.96696	4.23768	9.12981	.131406
7.62	58.0644	2.76043	8.72926	442.451	1.96782	4.23954	9.13380	.131234
7.63	58.2169	2.76225	8.73499	444.195	1.96868	4.24139	9.13780	.131062
7.64	58.3696	2.76405	8.74071	445.944	1.96954	4.24324	9.14179	.130890
7.65	58.5225	2.76586	8.74643	447.697	1.97040	4.24509	9.14577	.130719
7.66	58.6756	2.76767	8.75214	449.455	1.97126	4.24694	9.14976	.130548
7.67	58.8289	2.76948	8.75785	451.218	1.97211	4.24879	9.15374	.130378
7.68	58.9824	2.77128	8.76356	452.985	1.97297	4.25063	9.15771	.130208
7.69	59.1361	2.77308	8.76926	454.757	1.97383	4.25248	9.16169	.130039
7.70	59.2900	2.77489	8.77496	456.533	1.97468	4.25432	9.16566	.129870
7.71	59.4441	2.77669	8.78066	458.314	1.97554	4.25616	9.16962	.129702
7.72	59.5984	2.77849	8.78635	460.100	1.97639	4.25800	9.17359	.129534
7.73	59.7529	2.78029	8.79204	461.890	1.97724	4.25984	9.17754	.129366
7.74	59.9076	2.78209	8.79773	463.685	1.97809	4.26167	9.18150	.129199
7.75	60.0625	2.78388	8.80341	465.484	1.97895	4.26351	9.18545	.129032
7.76	60.2176	2.78568	8.80909	467.289	1.97980	4.26534	9.18940	.128866
7.77	60.3729	2.78747	8.81476	469.097	1.98065	4.26717	9.19335	.128700
7.78	60.5284	2.78927	8.82043	470.911	1.98150	4.26900	9.19729	.128535
7.79	60.6841	2.79106	8.82610	472.729	1.98234	4.27083	9.20123	.128370
7.80	60.8400	2.79285	8.83176	474.552	1.98319	4.27266	9.20516	.128205
7.81	60.9961	2.79464	8.83742	476.380	1.98404	4.27448	9.20910	.128041
7.82	61.1524	2.79643	8.84308	478.212	1.98489	4.27631	9.21302	.127877
7.83	61.3089	2.79821	8.84873	480.049	1.98573	4.27813	9.21695	.127714
7.84	61.4656	2.80000	8.85438	481.890	1.98658	4.27995	9.22087	.127551
7.85	61.6225	2.80179	8.86002	483.737	1.98742	4.28177	9.22479	.127389
7.86	61.7796	2.80357	8.86566	485.588	1.98826	4.28359	9.22871	.127226
7.87	61.9369	2.80535	8.87130	487.443	1.98911	4.28540	9.23262	.127065
7.88	62.0944	2.80713	8.87694	489.304	1.98995	4.28722	9.23653	.126904
7.89	62.2521	2.80891	8.88257	491.169	1.99079	4.28903	9.24043	.126743
7.90	62.4100	2.81069	8.88819	493.039	1.99163	4.29084	9.24434	.126582
7.91	62.5681	2.81247	8.89382	494.914	1.99247	4.29265	9.24823	.126422
7.92	62.7264	2.81425	8.89944	496.793	1.99331	4.29446	9.25213	.126263
7.93	62.8849	2.81603	8.90505	498.677	1.99415	4.29627	9.25602	.126103
7.94	63.0436	2.81780	8.91067	500.566	1.99499	4.29807	9.25991	.125945
7.95	63.2025	2.81957	8.91628	502.460	1.99582	4.29987	9.26380	.125786
7.96	63.3616	2.82135	8.92188	504.358	1.99666	4.30168	9.26768	.125628
7.97	63.5209	2.82312	8.92749	506.262	1.99750	4.30348	9.27156	.125471
7.98	63.6804	2.82489	8.93308	508.170	1.99833	4.30528	9.27544	.125313
7.99	63.8401	2.82666	8.93868	510.082	1.99917	4.30707	9.27931	.125156
8.00	64.0000	2.82843	8.94427	512.000	2.00000	4.30887	9.28318	.125000
n	n^2	$\sqrt{n}$	$\sqrt{10n}$	n^3	$\sqrt[3]{n}$	$\sqrt[3]{10n}$	$\sqrt[3]{100n}$	$1/n$

Powers — Roots — Reciprocals

n	n^2	$\sqrt{n}$	$\sqrt{10n}$	n^3	$\sqrt[3]{n}$	$\sqrt[3]{10n}$	$\sqrt[3]{100n}$	$1/n$
8.00	64.0000	2.82843	8.94427	512.000	2.00000	4.30887	9.28318	.125000
8.01	64.1601	2.83019	8.94986	513.922	2.00083	4.31066	9.28704	.124844
8.02	64.3204	2.83196	8.95545	515.850	2.00167	4.31246	9.29091	.124688
8.03	64.4809	2.83373	8.96103	517.782	2.00250	4.31425	9.29477	.124533
8.04	64.6416	2.83549	8.96660	519.718	2.00333	4.31604	9.29862	.124378
8.05	64.8025	2.83725	8.97218	521.660	2.00416	4.31783	9.30248	.124224
8.06	64.9636	2.83901	8.97775	523.607	2.00499	4.31961	9.30633	.124069
8.07	65.1249	2.84077	8.98332	525.558	2.00582	4.32140	9.31018	.123916
8.08	65.2864	2.84253	8.98888	527.514	2.00664	4.32318	9.31402	.123762
8.09	65.4481	2.84429	8.99444	529.475	2.00747	4.32497	9.31786	.123609
8.10	65.6100	2.84605	9.00000	531.441	2.00830	4.32675	9.32170	.123457
8.11	65.7721	2.84781	9.00555	533.412	2.00912	4.32853	9.32553	.123305
8.12	65.9344	2.84956	9.01110	535.387	2.00995	4.33031	9.32936	.123153
8.13	66.0969	2.85132	9.01665	537.368	2.01078	4.33208	9.33319	.123001
8.14	66.2596	2.85307	9.02219	539.353	2.01160	4.33386	9.33702	.122850
8.15	66.4225	2.85482	9.02774	541.343	2.01242	4.33563	9.34084	.122699
8.16	66.5856	2.85657	9.03327	543.338	2.01325	4.33741	9.34466	.122549
8.17	66.7489	2.85832	9.03881	545.339	2.01407	4.33918	9.34847	.122399
8.18	66.9124	2.86007	9.04434	547.343	2.01489	4.34095	9.35229	.122249
8.19	67.0761	2.86182	9.04986	549.353	2.01571	4.34271	9.35610	.122100
8.20	67.2400	2.86356	9.05539	551.368	2.01653	4.34448	9.35990	.121951
8.21	67.4041	2.86531	9.06091	553.388	2.01735	4.34625	9.36370	.121803
8.22	67.5684	2.86705	9.06642	555.412	2.01817	4.34801	9.36751	.121655
8.23	67.7329	2.86880	9.07193	557.442	2.01899	4.34977	9.37130	.121507
8.24	67.8976	2.87054	9.07744	559.476	2.01980	4.35153	9.37510	.121359
8.25	68.0625	2.87228	9.08295	561.516	2.02062	4.35329	9.37889	.121212
8.26	68.2276	2.87402	9.08845	563.560	2.02144	4.35505	9.38268	.121065
8.27	68.3929	2.87576	9.09395	565.609	2.02225	4.35681	9.38646	.120919
8.28	68.5584	2.87750	9.09945	567.664	2.02307	4.35856	9.39024	.120773
8.29	68.7241	2.87924	9.10494	569.723	2.02388	4.36032	9.39402	.120627
8.30	68.8900	2.88097	9.11043	571.787	2.02469	4.36207	9.39780	.120482
8.31	69.0561	2.88271	9.11592	573.856	2.02551	4.36382	9.40157	.120337
8.32	69.2224	2.88444	9.12140	575.930	2.02632	4.36557	9.40534	.120192
8.33	69.3889	2.88617	9.12688	578.010	2.02713	4.36732	9.40911	.120048
8.34	69.5556	2.88791	9.13236	580.094	2.02794	4.36907	9.41287	.119904
8.35	69.7225	2.88964	9.13783	582.183	2.02875	4.37081	9.41663	.119760
8.36	69.8896	2.89137	9.14330	584.277	2.02956	4.37256	9.42039	.119617
8.37	70.0569	2.89310	9.14877	586.376	2.03037	4.37430	9.42414	.119474
8.38	70.2244	2.89482	9.15423	588.480	2.03118	4.37604	9.42789	.119332
8.39	70.3921	2.89655	9.15969	590.590	2.03199	4.37778	9.43164	.119190
8.40	70.5600	2.89828	9.16515	592.704	2.03279	4.37952	9.43539	.119048
8.41	70.7281	2.90000	9.17061	594.823	2.03360	4.38126	9.43913	.118906
8.42	70.8964	2.90172	9.17606	596.948	2.03440	4.38299	9.44287	.118765
8.43	71.0649	2.90345	9.18150	599.077	2.03521	4.38473	9.44661	.118624
8.44	71.2336	2.90517	9.18695	601.212	2.03601	4.38646	9.45034	.118483
8.45	71.4025	2.90689	9.19239	603.351	2.03682	4.38819	9.45407	.118343
8.46	71.5716	2.90861	9.19783	605.496	2.03762	4.38992	9.45780	.118203
8.47	71.7409	2.91033	9.20326	607.645	2.03842	4.39165	9.46152	.118064
8.48	71.9104	2.91204	9.20869	609.800	2.03923	4.39338	9.46525	.117925
8.49	72.0801	2.91376	9.21412	611.960	2.04003	4.39510	9.46897	.117786
8.50	72.2500	2.91548	9.21954	614.125	2.04083	4.39683	9.47268	.117647
n	n^2	$\sqrt{n}$	$\sqrt{10n}$	n^3	$\sqrt[3]{n}$	$\sqrt[3]{10n}$	$\sqrt[3]{100n}$	$1/n$

Powers — Roots — Reciprocals

n	n^2	$\sqrt{n}$	$\sqrt{10n}$	n^3	$\sqrt[3]{n}$	$\sqrt[3]{10n}$	$\sqrt[3]{100n}$	$1/n$
8.50	72.2500	2.91548	9.21954	614.125	2.04083	4.39683	9.47268	.117647
8.51	72.4201	2.91719	9.22497	616.295	2.04163	4.39855	9.47640	.117509
8.52	72.5904	2.91890	9.23038	618.470	2.04243	4.40028	9.48011	.117371
8.53	72.7609	2.92062	9.23580	620.650	2.04323	4.40200	9.48381	.117233
8.54	72.9316	2.92233	9.24121	622.836	2.04402	4.40372	9.48752	.117096
8.55	73.1025	2.92404	9.24662	625.026	2.04482	4.40543	9.49122	.116959
8.56	73.2736	2.92575	9.25203	627.222	2.04562	4.40715	9.49492	.116822
8.57	73.4449	2.92746	9.25743	629.423	2.04641	4.40887	9.49861	.116686
8.58	73.6164	2.92916	9.26283	631.629	2.04721	4.41058	9.50231	.116550
8.59	73.7881	2.93087	9.26823	633.840	2.04801	4.41229	9.50600	.116414
8.60	73.9600	2.93258	9.27362	636.056	2.04880	4.41400	9.50969	.116279
8.61	74.1321	2.93428	9.27901	638.277	2.04959	4.41571	9.51337	.116144
8.62	74.3044	2.93598	9.28440	640.504	2.05039	4.41742	9.51705	.116009
8.63	74.4769	2.93769	9.28978	642.736	2.05118	4.41913	9.52073	.115875
8.64	74.6496	2.93939	9.29516	644.973	2.05197	4.42084	9.52441	.115741
8.65	74.8225	2.94109	9.30054	647.215	2.05276	4.42254	9.52808	.115607
8.66	74.9956	2.94279	9.30591	649.462	2.05355	4.42425	9.53175	.115473
8.67	75.1689	2.94449	9.31128	651.714	2.05434	4.42595	9.53542	.115340
8.68	75.3424	2.94618	9.31665	653.972	2.05513	4.42765	9.53908	.115207
8.69	75.5161	2.94788	9.32202	656.235	2.05592	4.42935	9.54274	.115075
8.70	75.6900	2.94958	9.32738	658.503	2.05671	4.43105	9.54640	.114943
8.71	75.8641	2.95127	9.33274	660.776	2.05750	4.43274	9.55006	.114811
8.72	76.0384	2.95296	9.33809	663.055	2.05828	4.43444	9.55371	.114679
8.73	76.2129	2.95466	9.34345	665.339	2.05907	4.43613	9.55736	.114548
8.74	76.3876	2.95635	9.34880	667.628	2.05986	4.43783	9.56101	.114416
8.75	76.5625	2.95804	9.35414	669.922	2.06064	4.43952	9.56466	.114286
8.76	76.7376	2.95973	9.35949	672.221	2.06143	4.44121	9.56830	.114155
8.77	76.9129	2.96142	9.36483	674.526	2.06221	4.44290	9.57194	.114025
8.78	77.0884	2.96311	9.37017	676.836	2.06299	4.44459	9.57557	.113895
8.79	77.2641	2.96479	9.37550	679.151	2.06378	4.44627	9.57921	.113766
8.80	77.4400	2.96648	9.38083	681.472	2.06456	4.44796	9.58284	.113636
8.81	77.6161	2.96816	9.38616	683.798	2.06534	4.44964	9.58647	.113507
8.82	77.7924	2.96985	9.39149	686.129	2.06612	4.45133	9.59009	.113379
8.83	77.9689	2.97153	9.39681	688.465	2.06690	4.45301	9.59372	.113250
8.84	78.1456	2.97321	9.40213	690.807	2.06768	4.45469	9.59734	.113122
8.85	78.3225	2.97489	9.40744	693.154	2.06846	4.45637	9.60095	.112994
8.86	78.4996	2.97658	9.41276	695.506	2.06924	4.45805	9.60457	.112867
8.87	78.6769	2.97825	9.41807	697.864	2.07002	4.45972	9.60818	.112740
8.88	78.8544	2.97993	9.42338	700.227	2.07080	4.46140	9.61179	.112613
8.89	79.0321	2.98161	9.42868	702.595	2.07157	4.46307	9.61540	.112486
8.90	79.2100	2.98329	9.43398	704.969	2.07235	4.46475	9.61900	.112360
8.91	79.3881	2.98496	9.43928	707.348	2.07313	4.46642	9.62260	.112233
8.92	79.5664	2.98664	9.44458	709.732	2.07390	4.46809	9.62620	.112108
8.93	79.7449	2.98831	9.44987	712.122	2.07468	4.46976	9.62980	.111982
8.94	79.9236	2.98998	9.45516	714.517	2.07545	4.47142	9.63339	.111857
8.95	80.1025	2.99166	9.46044	716.917	2.07622	4.47309	9.63698	.111732
8.96	80.2816	2.99333	9.46573	719.323	2.07700	4.47476	9.64057	.111607
8.97	80.4609	2.99500	9.47101	721.734	2.07777	4.47642	9.64415	.111483
8.98	80.6404	2.99666	9.47629	724.151	2.07854	4.47808	9.64774	.111359
8.99	80.8201	2.99833	9.48156	726.573	2.07931	4.47974	9.65132	.111235
9.00	81.0000	3.00000	9.48683	729.000	2.08008	4.48140	9.65489	.111111
n	n^2	$\sqrt{n}$	$\sqrt{10n}$	n^3	$\sqrt[3]{n}$	$\sqrt[3]{10n}$	$\sqrt[3]{100n}$	$1/n$

Powers — Roots — Reciprocals

n	n^2	$\sqrt{n}$	$\sqrt{10n}$	n^3	$\sqrt[3]{n}$	$\sqrt[3]{10n}$	$\sqrt[3]{100n}$	$1/n$
9.00	81.0000	3.00000	9.48683	729.000	2.08008	4.48140	9.65489	.111111
9.01	81.1801	3.00167	9.49210	731.433	2.08085	4.48306	9.65847	.110988
9.02	81.3604	3.00333	9.49737	733.871	2.08162	4.48472	9.66204	.110865
9.03	81.5409	3.00500	9.50263	736.314	2.08239	4.48638	9.66561	.110742
9.04	81.7216	3.00666	9.50789	738.763	2.08316	4.48803	9.66918	.110619
9.05	81.9025	3.00832	9.51315	741.218	2.08393	4.48969	9.67274	.110497
9.06	82.0836	3.00998	9.51840	743.677	2.08470	4.49134	9.67630	.110375
9.07	82.2649	3.01164	9.52365	746.143	2.08546	4.49299	9.67986	.110254
9.08	82.4464	3.01330	9.52890	748.613	2.08623	4.49464	9.68342	.110132
9.09	82.6281	3.01496	9.53415	751.089	2.08699	4.49629	9.68697	.110011
9.10	82.8100	3.01662	9.53939	753.571	2.08776	4.49794	9.69052	.109890
9.11	82.9921	3.01828	9.54463	756.058	2.08852	4.49959	9.69407	.109769
9.12	83.1744	3.01993	9.54987	758.551	2.08929	4.50123	9.69762	.109649
9.13	83.3569	3.02159	9.55510	761.048	2.09005	4.50288	9.70116	.109529
9.14	83.5396	3.02324	9.56033	763.552	2.09081	4.50452	9.70470	.109409
9.15	83.7225	3.02490	9.56556	766.061	2.09158	4.50616	9.70824	.109290
9.16	83.9056	3.02655	9.57079	768.575	2.09234	4.50781	9.71177	.109170
9.17	84.0889	3.02820	9.57601	771.095	2.09310	4.50945	9.71531	.109051
9.18	84.2724	3.02985	9.58123	773.621	2.09386	4.51108	9.71884	.108932
9.19	84.4561	3.03150	9.58645	776.152	2.09462	4.51272	9.72236	.108814
9.20	84.6400	3.03315	9.59166	778.688	2.09538	4.51436	9.72589	.108696
9.21	84.8241	3.03480	9.59687	781.230	2.09614	4.51599	9.72941	.108578
9.22	85.0084	3.03645	9.60208	783.777	2.09690	4.51763	9.73293	.108460
9.23	85.1929	3.03809	9.60729	786.330	2.09765	4.51926	9.73645	.108342
9.24	85.3776	3.03974	9.61249	788.889	2.09841	4.52089	9.73996	.108225
9.25	85.5625	3.04138	9.61769	791.453	2.09917	4.52252	9.74348	.108108
9.26	85.7476	3.04302	9.62289	794.023	2.09992	4.52415	9.74699	.107991
9.27	85.9329	3.04467	9.62808	796.598	2.10068	4.52578	9.75049	.107875
9.28	86.1184	3.04631	9.63328	799.179	2.10144	4.52740	9.75400	.107759
9.29	86.3041	3.04795	9.63846	801.765	2.10219	4.52903	9.75750	.107643
9.30	86.4900	3.04959	9.64365	804.357	2.10294	4.53065	9.76100	.107527
9.31	86.6761	3.05123	9.64883	806.954	2.10370	4.53228	9.76450	.107411
9.32	86.8624	3.05287	9.65401	809.558	2.10445	4.53390	9.76799	.107296
9.33	87.0489	3.05450	9.65919	812.166	2.10520	4.53552	9.77148	.107181
9.34	87.2356	3.05614	9.66437	814.781	2.10595	4.53714	9.77497	.107066
9.35	87.4225	3.05778	9.66954	817.400	2.10671	4.53876	9.77846	.106952
9.36	87.6096	3.05941	9.67471	820.026	2.10746	4.54038	9.78195	.106838
9.37	87.7969	3.06105	9.67988	822.657	2.10821	4.54199	9.78543	.106724
9.38	87.9844	3.06268	9.68504	825.294	2.10896	4.54361	9.78891	.106610
9.39	88.1721	3.06431	9.69020	827.936	2.10971	4.54522	9.79239	.106496
9.40	88.3600	3.06594	9.69536	830.584	2.11045	4.54684	9.79586	.106383
9.41	88.5481	3.06757	9.70052	833.238	2.11120	4.54845	9.79933	.106270
9.42	88.7364	3.06920	9.70567	835.897	2.11195	4.55006	9.80280	.106157
9.43	88.9249	3.07083	9.71082	838.562	2.11270	4.55167	9.80627	.106045
9.44	89.1136	3.07246	9.71597	841.232	2.11344	4.55328	9.80974	.105932
9.45	89.3025	3.07409	9.72111	843.909	2.11419	4.55488	9.81320	.105820
9.46	89.4916	3.07571	9.72625	846.591	2.11494	4.55649	9.81666	.105708
9.47	89.6809	3.07734	9.73139	849.278	2.11568	4.55809	9.82012	.105597
9.48	89.8704	3.07896	9.73653	851.971	2.11642	4.55970	9.82357	.105485
9.49	90.0601	3.08058	9.74166	854.670	2.11717	4.56130	9.82703	.105374
9.50	90.2500	3.08221	9.74679	857.375	2.11791	4.56290	9.83048	.105263
n	n^2	$\sqrt{n}$	$\sqrt{10n}$	n^3	$\sqrt[3]{n}$	$\sqrt[3]{10n}$	$\sqrt[3]{100n}$	$1/n$

n	n^2	$\sqrt{n}$	$\sqrt{10n}$	n^3	$\sqrt[3]{n}$	$\sqrt[3]{10n}$	$\sqrt[3]{100n}$	$1/n$
9.50	90.2500	3.08221	9.74679	857.375	2.11791	4.56290	9.83048	.105263
9.51	90.4401	3.08383	9.75192	860.085	2.11865	4.56450	9.83392	.105152
9.52	90.6304	3.08545	9.75705	862.801	2.11940	4.56610	9.83737	.105042
9.53	90.8209	3.08707	9.76217	865.523	2.12014	4.56770	9.84081	.104932
9.54	91.0116	3.08869	9.76729	868.251	2.12088	4.56930	9.84425	.104822
9.55	91.2025	3.09031	9.77241	870.984	2.12162	4.57089	9.84769	.104712
9.56	91.3936	3.09192	9.77753	873.723	2.12236	4.57249	9.85113	.104603
9.57	91.5849	3.09354	9.78264	876.467	2.12310	4.57408	9.85456	.104493
9.58	91.7764	3.09516	9.78775	879.218	2.12384	4.57567	9.85799	.104384
9.59	91.9681	3.09677	9.79285	881.974	2.12458	4.57727	9.86142	.104275
9.60	92.1600	3.09839	9.79796	884.736	2.12532	4.57886	9.86485	.104167
9.61	92.3521	3.10000	9.80306	887.504	2.12605	4.58045	9.86827	.104058
9.62	92.5444	3.10161	9.80816	890.277	2.12679	4.58204	9.87169	.103950
9.63	92.7369	3.10322	9.81326	893.056	2.12753	4.58362	9.87511	.103842
9.64	92.9296	3.10483	9.81835	895.841	2.12826	4.58521	9.87853	.103734
9.65	93.1225	3.10644	9.82344	898.632	2.12900	4.58679	9.88195	.103627
9.66	93.3156	3.10805	9.82853	901.429	2.12974	4.58838	9.88536	.103520
9.67	93.5089	3.10966	9.83362	904.231	2.13047	4.58996	9.88877	.103413
9.68	93.7024	3.11127	9.83870	907.039	2.13120	4.59154	9.89217	.103306
9.69	93.8961	3.11288	9.84378	909.853	2.13194	4.59312	9.89558	.103199
9.70	94.0900	3.11448	9.84886	912.673	2.13267	4.59470	9.89898	.103093
9.71	94.2841	3.11609	9.85393	915.499	2.13340	4.59628	9.90238	.102987
9.72	94.4784	3.11769	9.85901	918.330	2.13414	4.59786	9.90578	.102881
9.73	94.6729	3.11929	9.86408	921.167	2.13487	4.59943	9.90918	.102775
9.74	94.8676	3.12090	9.86914	924.010	2.13560	4.60101	9.91257	.102669
9.75	95.0625	3.12250	9.87421	926.859	2.13633	4.60258	9.91596	.102564
9.76	95.2576	3.12410	9.87927	929.714	2.13706	4.60416	9.91935	.102459
9.77	95.4529	3.12570	9.88433	932.575	2.13779	4.60573	9.92274	.102354
9.78	95.6484	3.12730	9.88939	935.441	2.13852	4.60730	9.92612	.102249
9.79	95.8441	3.12890	9.89444	938.314	2.13925	4.60887	9.92950	.102145
9.80	96.0400	3.13050	9.89949	941.192	2.13997	4.61044	9.93288	.102041
9.81	96.2361	3.13209	9.90454	944.076	2.14070	4.61200	9.93626	.101937
9.82	96.4324	3.13369	9.90959	946.966	2.14143	4.61357	9.93964	.101833
9.83	96.6289	3.13528	9.91464	949.862	2.14216	4.61514	9.94301	.101729
9.84	96.8256	3.13688	9.91968	952.764	2.14288	4.61670	9.94638	.101626
9.85	97.0225	3.13847	9.92472	955.672	2.14361	4.61826	9.94975	.101523
9.86	97.2196	3.14006	9.92975	958.585	2.14433	4.61983	9.95311	.101420
9.87	97.4169	3.14166	9.93479	961.505	2.14506	4.62139	9.95648	.101317
9.88	97.6144	3.14325	9.93982	964.430	2.14578	4.62295	9.95984	.101215
9.89	97.8121	3.14484	9.94485	967.362	2.14651	4.62451	9.96320	.101112
9.90	98.0100	3.14643	9.94987	970.299	2.14723	4.62607	9.96655	.101010
9.91	98.2081	3.14802	9.95490	973.242	2.14795	4.62762	9.96991	.100908
9.92	98.4064	3.14960	9.95992	976.191	2.14867	4.62918	9.97326	.100806
9.93	98.6049	3.15119	9.96494	979.147	2.14940	4.63073	9.97661	.100705
9.94	98.8036	3.15278	9.96995	982.108	2.15012	4.63229	9.97996	.100604
9.95	99.0025	3.15436	9.97497	985.075	2.15084	4.63384	9.98331	.100503
9.96	99.2016	3.15595	9.97998	988.048	2.15156	4.63539	9.98665	.100402
9.97	99.4009	3.15753	9.98499	991.027	2.15228	4.63694	9.98999	.100301
9.98	99.6004	3.15911	9.98999	994.012	2.15300	4.63849	9.99333	.100200
9.99	99.8001	3.16070	9.99500	997.003	2.15372	4.64004	9.99667	.100100
10.00	100.000	3.16228	10.0000	1000.00	2.15443	4.64159	10.0000	.100000
n	n^2	$\sqrt{n}$	$\sqrt{10n}$	n^3	$\sqrt[3]{n}$	$\sqrt[3]{10n}$	$\sqrt[3]{100n}$	$1/n$

III. Common Logarithms of Numbers

FROM

1 TO 10 000

TO

FIVE DECIMAL PLACES

1 — 100

N	Log	N	Log	N	Log	N	Log	N	Log
0	———	**20**	1.30 103	**40**	1.60 206	**60**	1.77 815	**80**	1.90 309
1	0.00 000	21	1.32 222	41	1.61 278	61	1.78 533	81	1.90 849
2	0.30 103	22	1.34 242	42	1.62 325	62	1.79 239	82	1.91 381
3	0.47 712	23	1.36 173	43	1.63 347	63	1.79 934	83	1.91 908
4	0.60 206	24	1.38 021	44	1.64 345	64	1.80 618	84	1.92 428
5	0.69 897	25	1.39 794	45	1.65 321	65	1.81 291	85	1.92 942
6	0.77 815	26	1.41 497	46	1.66 276	66	1.81 954	86	1.93 450
7	0.84 510	27	1.43 136	47	1.67 210	67	1.82 607	87	1.93 952
8	0.90 309	28	1.44 716	48	1.68 124	68	1.83 251	88	1.94 448
9	0.95 424	29	1.46 240	49	1.69 020	69	1.83 885	89	1.94 939
10	1.00 000	**30**	1.47 712	**50**	1.69 897	**70**	1.84 510	**90**	1.95 424
11	1.04 139	31	1.49 136	51	1.70 757	71	1.85 126	91	1.95 904
12	1.07 918	32	1.50 515	52	1.71 600	72	1.85 733	92	1.96 379
13	1.11 394	33	1.51 851	53	1.72 428	73	1.86 332	93	1.96 848
14	1.14 613	34	1.53 148	54	1.73 239	74	1.86 923	94	1.97 313
15	1.17 609	35	1.54 407	55	1.74 036	75	1.87 506	95	1.97 772
16	1.20 412	36	1.55 630	56	1.74 819	76	1.88 081	96	1.98 227
17	1.23 045	37	1.56 820	57	1.75 587	77	1.88 649	97	1.98 677
18	1.25 527	38	1.57 978	58	1.76 343	78	1.89 209	98	1.99 123
19	1.27 875	39	1.59 106	59	1.77 085	79	1.89 763	99	1.99 564
N	Log	N	Log	N	Log	N	Log	N	Log

N.	0	1	2	3	4	5	6	7	8	9
100	00 000	043	087	130	173	217	260	303	346	389
101	432	475	518	561	604	647	689	732	775	817
102	860	903	945	988	*030	*072	*115	*157	*199	*242
103	01 284	326	368	410	452	494	536	578	620	662
104	703	745	787	828	870	912	953	995	*036	*078
105	02 119	160	202	243	284	325	366	407	449	490
106	531	572	612	653	694	735	776	816	857	898
107	938	979	*019	*060	*100	*141	*181	*222	*262	*302
108	03 342	383	423	463	503	543	583	623	663	703
109	743	782	822	862	902	941	981	*021	*060	*100
110	04 139	179	218	258	297	336	376	415	454	493
111	532	571	610	650	689	727	766	805	844	883
112	922	961	999	*038	*077	*115	*154	*192	*231	*269
113	05 308	346	385	423	461	500	538	576	614	652
114	690	729	767	805	843	881	918	956	994	*032
115	06 070	108	145	183	221	258	296	333	371	408
116	446	483	521	558	595	633	670	707	744	781
117	819	856	893	930	967	*004	*041	*078	*115	*151
118	07 188	225	262	298	335	372	408	445	482	518
119	555	591	628	664	700	737	773	809	846	882
120	918	954	990	*027	*063	*099	*135	*171	*207	*243
121	08 279	314	350	386	422	458	493	529	565	600
122	636	672	707	743	778	814	849	884	920	955
123	991	*026	*061	*096	*132	*167	*202	*237	*272	*307
124	09 342	377	412	447	482	517	552	587	621	656
125	691	726	760	795	830	864	899	934	968	*003
126	10 037	072	106	140	175	209	243	278	312	346
127	380	415	449	483	517	551	585	619	653	687
128	721	755	789	823	857	890	924	958	992	*025
129	11 059	093	126	160	193	227	261	294	327	361
130	394	428	461	494	528	561	594	628	661	694
131	727	760	793	826	860	893	926	959	992	*024
132	12 057	090	123	156	189	222	254	287	320	352
133	385	418	450	483	516	548	581	613	646	678
134	710	743	775	808	840	872	905	937	969	*001
135	13 033	066	098	130	162	194	226	258	290	322
136	354	386	418	450	481	513	545	577	609	640
137	672	704	735	767	799	830	862	893	925	956
138	988	*019	*051	*082	*114	*145	*176	*208	*239	*270
139	14 301	333	364	395	426	457	489	520	551	582
140	613	644	675	706	737	768	799	829	860	891
141	922	953	983	*014	*045	*076	*106	*137	*168	*198
142	15 229	259	290	320	351	381	412	442	473	503
143	534	564	594	625	655	685	715	746	776	806
144	836	866	897	927	957	987	*017	*047	*077	*107
145	16 137	167	197	227	256	286	316	346	376	406
146	435	465	495	524	554	584	613	643	673	702
147	732	761	791	820	850	879	909	938	967	997
148	17 026	056	085	114	143	173	202	231	260	289
149	319	348	377	406	435	464	493	522	551	580
150	609	638	667	696	725	754	782	811	840	869
N.	0	1	2	3	4	5	6	7	8	9

Prop. Pts.

	44	43	42
1	4.4	4.3	4.2
2	8.8	8.6	8.4
3	13.2	12.9	12.6
4	17.6	17.2	16.8
5	22.0	21.5	21.0
6	26.4	25.8	25.2
7	30.8	30.1	29.4
8	35.2	34.4	33.6
9	39.6	38.7	37.8

	41	40	39
1	4.1	4.0	3.9
2	8.2	8.0	7.8
3	12.3	12.0	11.7
4	16.4	16.0	15.6
5	20.5	20.0	19.5
6	24.6	24.0	23.4
7	28.7	28.0	27.3
8	32.8	32.0	31.2
9	36.9	36.0	35.1

	38	37	36
1	3.8	3.7	3.6
2	7.6	7.4	7.2
3	11.4	11.1	10.8
4	15.2	14.8	14.4
5	19.0	18.5	18.0
6	22.8	22.2	21.6
7	26.6	25.9	25.2
8	30.4	29.6	28.8
9	34.2	33.3	32.4

	35	34	33
1	3.5	3.4	3.3
2	7.0	6.8	6.6
3	10.5	10.2	9.9
4	14.0	13.6	13.2
5	17.5	17.0	16.5
6	21.0	20.4	19.8
7	24.5	23.8	23.1
8	28.0	27.2	26.4
9	31.5	30.6	29.7

	32	31	30
1	3.2	3.1	3.0
2	6.4	6.2	6.0
3	9.6	9.3	9.0
4	12.8	12.4	12.0
5	16.0	15.5	15.0
6	19.2	18.6	18.0
7	22.4	21.7	21.0
8	25.6	24.8	24.0
9	28.8	27.9	27.0

Prop. Pts.

N.	0	1	2	3	4	5	6	7	8	9
150	17 609	638	667	696	725	754	782	811	840	869
151	898	926	955	984	*013	*041	*070	*099	*127	*156
152	18 184	213	241	270	298	327	355	384	412	441
153	469	498	526	554	583	611	639	667	696	724
154	752	780	808	837	865	893	921	949	977	*005
155	19 033	061	089	117	145	173	201	229	257	285
156	312	340	368	396	424	451	479	507	535	562
157	590	618	645	673	700	728	756	783	811	838
158	866	893	921	948	976	*003	*030	*058	*085	*112
159	20 140	167	194	222	249	276	303	330	358	385
160	412	439	466	493	520	548	575	602	629	656
161	683	710	737	763	790	817	844	871	898	925
162	952	978	*005	*032	*059	*085	*112	*139	*165	*192
163	21 219	245	272	299	325	352	378	405	431	458
164	484	511	537	564	590	617	643	669	696	722
165	748	775	801	827	854	880	906	932	958	985
166	22 011	037	063	089	115	141	167	194	220	246
167	272	298	324	350	376	401	427	453	479	505
168	531	557	583	608	634	660	686	712	737	763
169	789	814	840	866	891	917	943	968	994	*019
170	23 045	070	096	121	147	172	198	223	249	274
171	300	325	350	376	401	426	452	477	502	528
172	553	578	603	629	654	679	704	729	754	779
173	805	830	855	880	905	930	955	980	*005	*030
174	24 055	080	105	130	155	180	204	229	254	279
175	304	329	353	378	403	428	452	477	502	527
176	551	576	601	625	650	674	699	724	748	773
177	797	822	846	871	895	920	944	969	993	*018
178	25 042	066	091	115	139	164	188	212	237	261
179	285	310	334	358	382	406	431	455	479	503
180	527	551	575	600	624	648	672	696	720	744
181	768	792	816	840	864	888	912	935	959	983
182	26 007	031	055	079	102	126	150	174	198	221
183	245	269	293	316	340	364	387	411	435	458
184	482	505	529	553	576	600	623	647	670	694
185	717	741	764	788	811	834	858	881	905	928
186	951	975	998	*021	*045	*068	*091	*114	*138	*161
187	27 184	207	231	254	277	300	323	346	370	393
188	416	439	462	485	508	531	554	577	600	623
189	646	669	692	715	738	761	784	807	830	852
190	875	898	921	944	967	989	*012	*035	*058	*081
191	28 103	126	149	171	194	217	240	262	285	307
192	330	353	375	398	421	443	466	488	511	533
193	556	578	601	623	646	668	691	713	735	758
194	780	803	825	847	870	892	914	937	959	981
195	29 003	026	048	070	092	115	137	159	181	203
196	226	248	270	292	314	336	358	380	403	425
197	447	469	491	513	535	557	579	601	623	645
198	667	688	710	732	754	776	798	820	842	863
199	885	907	929	951	973	994	*016	*038	*060	*081
200	30 103	125	146	168	190	211	233	255	276	298
N.	0	1	2	3	4	5	6	7	8	9

Prop. Pts.

	29	**28**	**27**	**26**	**25**	**24**	**23**	**22**	**21**
1	2.9	2.8	2.7	2.6	2.5	2.4	2.3	2.2	2.1
2	5.8	5.6	5.4	5.2	5.0	4.8	4.6	4.4	4.2
3	8.7	8.4	8.1	7.8	7.5	7.2	6.9	6.6	6.3
4	11.6	11.2	10.8	10.4	10.0	9.6	9.2	8.8	8.4
5	14.5	14.0	13.5	13.0	12.5	12.0	11.5	11.0	10.5
6	17.4	16.8	16.2	15.6	15.0	14.4	13.8	13.2	12.6
7	20.3	19.6	18.9	18.2	17.5	16.8	16.1	15.4	14.7
8	23.2	22.4	21.6	20.8	20.0	19.2	18.4	17.6	16.8
9	26.1	25.2	24.3	23.4	22.5	21.6	20.7	19.8	18.9

Prop. Pts.

N.	0	1	2	3	4	5	6	7	8	9
200	30 103	125	146	168	190	211	233	255	276	298
201	320	341	363	384	406	428	449	471	492	514
202	535	557	578	600	621	643	664	685	707	728
203	750	771	792	814	835	856	878	899	920	942
204	963	984	*006	*027	*048	*069	*091	*112	*133	*154
205	31 175	197	218	239	260	281	302	323	345	366
206	387	408	429	450	471	492	513	534	555	576
207	597	618	639	660	681	702	723	744	765	785
208	806	827	848	869	890	911	931	952	973	994
209	32 015	035	056	077	098	118	139	160	181	201
210	222	243	263	284	305	325	346	366	387	408
211	428	449	469	490	510	531	552	572	593	613
212	634	654	675	695	715	736	756	777	797	818
213	838	858	879	899	919	940	960	980	*001	*021
214	33 041	062	082	102	122	143	163	183	203	224
215	244	264	284	304	325	345	365	385	405	425
216	445	465	486	506	526	546	566	586	606	626
217	646	666	686	706	726	746	766	786	806	826
218	846	866	885	905	925	945	965	985	*005	*025
219	34 044	064	084	104	124	143	163	183	203	223
220	242	262	282	301	321	341	361	380	400	420
221	439	459	479	498	518	537	557	577	596	616
222	635	655	674	694	713	733	753	772	792	811
223	830	850	869	889	908	928	947	967	986	*005
224	35 025	044	064	083	102	122	141	160	180	199
225	218	238	257	276	295	315	334	353	372	392
226	411	430	449	468	488	507	526	545	564	583
227	603	622	641	660	679	698	717	736	755	774
228	793	813	832	851	870	889	908	927	946	965
229	984	*003	*021	*040	*059	*078	*097	*116	*135	*154
230	36 173	192	211	229	248	267	286	305	324	342
231	361	380	399	418	436	455	474	493	511	530
232	549	568	586	605	624	642	661	680	698	717
233	736	754	773	791	810	829	847	866	884	903
234	922	940	959	977	996	*014	*033	*051	*070	*088
235	37 107	125	144	162	181	199	218	236	254	273
236	291	310	328	346	365	383	401	420	438	457
237	475	493	511	530	548	566	585	603	621	639
238	658	676	694	712	731	749	767	785	803	822
239	840	858	876	894	912	931	949	967	985	*003
240	38 021	039	057	075	093	112	130	148	166	184
241	202	220	238	256	274	292	310	328	346	364
242	382	399	417	435	453	471	489	507	525	543
243	561	578	596	614	632	650	668	686	703	721
244	739	757	775	792	810	828	846	863	881	899
245	917	934	952	970	987	*005	*023	*041	*058	*076
246	39 094	111	129	146	164	182	199	217	235	252
247	270	287	305	322	340	358	375	393	410	428
248	445	463	480	498	515	533	550	568	585	602
249	620	637	655	672	690	707	724	742	759	777
250	794	811	829	846	863	881	898	915	933	950
N.	0	1	2	3	4	5	6	7	8	9

Prop. Pts.

log 2
=.30102 99957

	22	21
1	2.2	2.1
2	4.4	4.2
3	6.6	6.3
4	8.8	8.4
5	11.0	10.5
6	13.2	12.6
7	15.4	14.7
8	17.6	16.8
9	19.8	18.9

	20	19
1	2.0	1.9
2	4.0	3.8
3	6.0	5.7
4	8.0	7.6
5	10.0	9.5
6	12.0	11.4
7	14.0	13.3
8	16.0	15.2
9	18.0	17.1

	18	17
1	1.8	1.7
2	3.6	3.4
3	5.4	5.1
4	7.2	6.8
5	9.0	8.5
6	10.8	10.2
7	12.6	11.9
8	14.4	13.6
9	16.2	15.3

Prop. Pts.

N.	0	1	2	3	4	5	6	7	8	9
250	39 794	811	829	846	863	881	898	915	933	950
251	967	985	*002	*019	*037	*054	*071	*088	*106	*123
252	40 140	157	175	192	209	226	243	261	278	295
253	312	329	346	364	381	398	415	432	449	466
254	483	500	518	535	552	569	586	603	620	637
255	654	671	688	705	722	739	756	773	790	807
256	824	841	858	875	892	909	926	943	960	976
257	993	*010	*027	*044	*061	*078	*095	*111	*128	*145
258	41 162	179	196	212	229	246	263	280	296	313
259	330	347	363	380	397	414	430	447	464	481
260	497	514	531	547	564	581	597	614	631	647
261	664	681	697	714	731	747	764	780	797	814
262	830	847	863	880	896	913	929	946	963	979
263	996	*012	*029	*045	*062	*078	*095	*111	*127	*144
264	42 160	177	193	210	226	243	259	275	292	308
265	325	341	357	374	390	406	423	439	455	472
266	488	504	521	537	553	570	586	602	619	635
267	651	667	684	700	716	732	749	765	781	797
268	813	830	846	862	878	894	911	927	943	959
269	975	991	*008	*024	*040	*056	*072	*088	*104	*120
270	43 136	152	169	185	201	217	233	249	265	281
271	297	313	329	345	361	377	393	409	425	441
272	457	473	489	505	521	537	553	569	584	600
273	616	632	648	664	680	696	712	727	743	759
274	775	791	807	823	838	854	870	886	902	917
275	933	949	965	981	996	*012	*028	*044	*059	*075
276	44 091	107	122	138	154	170	185	201	217	232
277	248	264	279	295	311	326	342	358	373	389
278	404	420	436	451	467	483	498	514	529	545
279	560	576	592	607	623	638	654	669	685	700
280	716	731	747	762	778	793	809	824	840	855
281	871	886	902	917	932	948	963	979	994	*010
282	45 025	040	056	071	086	102	117	133	148	163
283	179	194	209	225	240	255	271	286	301	317
284	332	347	362	378	393	408	423	439	454	469
285	484	500	515	530	545	561	576	591	606	621
286	637	652	667	682	697	712	728	743	758	773
287	788	803	818	834	849	864	879	894	909	924
288	939	954	969	984	*000	*015	*030	*045	*060	*075
289	46 090	105	120	135	150	165	180	195	210	225
290	240	255	270	285	300	315	330	345	359	374
291	389	404	419	434	449	464	479	494	509	523
292	538	553	568	583	598	613	627	642	657	672
293	687	702	716	731	746	761	776	790	805	820
294	835	850	864	879	894	909	923	938	953	967
295	982	997	*012	*026	*041	*056	*070	*085	*100	*114
296	47 129	144	159	173	188	202	217	232	246	261
297	276	290	305	319	334	349	363	378	392	407
298	422	436	451	465	480	494	509	524	538	553
299	567	582	596	611	625	640	654	669	683	698
300	712	727	741	756	770	784	799	813	828	842
N.	0	1	2	3	4	5	6	7	8	9

Prop. Pts.

	18	**17**
1	1.8	1.7
2	3.6	3.4
3	5.4	5.1
4	7.2	6.8
5	9.0	8.5
6	10.8	10.2
7	12.6	11.9
8	14.4	13.6
9	16.2	15.3

M
$= \log_{10} e$
$= \log_{10} 2.718\cdots$
$= .43429\ 44819$

	16	**15**
1	1.6	1.5
2	3.2	3.0
3	4.8	4.5
4	6.4	6.0
5	8.0	7.5
3	9.6	9.0
7	11.2	10.5
8	12.8	12.0
9	14.4	13.5

	14
1	1.4
2	2.8
3	4.2
4	5 6
5	7.0
6	8.4
7	9.8
8	11.2
9	12.6

Prop. Pts.

N.	0	1	2	3	4	5	6	7	8	9
300	47 712	727	741	756	770	784	799	813	828	842
301	857	871	885	900	914	929	943	958	972	986
302	48 001	015	029	044	058	073	087	101	116	130
303	144	159	173	187	202	216	230	244	259	273
304	287	302	316	330	344	359	373	387	401	416
305	430	444	458	473	487	501	515	530	544	558
306	572	586	601	615	629	643	657	671	686	700
307	714	728	742	756	770	785	799	813	827	841
308	855	869	883	897	911	926	940	954	968	982
309	996	*010	*024	*038	*052	*066	*080	*094	*108	*122
310	49 136	150	164	178	192	206	220	234	248	262
311	276	290	304	318	332	346	360	374	388	402
312	415	429	443	457	471	485	499	513	527	541
313	554	568	582	596	610	624	638	651	665	679
314	693	707	721	734	748	762	776	790	803	817
315	831	845	859	872	886	900	914	927	941	955
316	969	982	996	*010	*024	*037	*051	*065	*079	*092
317	50 106	120	133	147	161	174	188	202	215	229
318	243	256	270	284	297	311	325	338	352	365
319	379	393	406	420	433	447	461	474	488	501
320	515	529	542	556	569	583	596	610	623	637
321	651	664	678	691	705	718	732	745	759	772
322	786	799	813	826	840	853	866	880	893	907
323	920	934	947	961	974	987	*001	*014	*028	*041
324	51 055	068	081	095	108	121	135	148	162	175
325	188	202	215	228	242	255	268	282	295	308
326	322	335	348	362	375	388	402	415	428	441
327	455	468	481	495	508	521	534	548	561	574
328	587	601	614	627	640	654	667	680	693	706
329	720	733	746	759	772	786	799	812	825	838
330	851	865	878	891	904	917	930	943	957	970
331	983	996	*009	*022	*035	*048	*061	*075	*088	*101
332	52 114	127	140	153	166	179	192	205	218	231
333	244	257	270	284	297	310	323	336	349	362
334	375	388	401	414	427	440	453	466	479	492
335	504	517	530	543	556	569	582	595	608	621
336	634	647	660	673	686	699	711	724	737	750
337	763	776	789	802	815	827	840	853	866	879
338	892	905	917	930	943	956	969	982	994	*007
339	53 020	033	046	058	071	084	097	110	122	135
340	148	161	173	186	199	212	224	237	250	263
341	275	288	301	314	326	339	352	364	377	390
342	403	415	428	441	453	466	479	491	504	517
343	529	542	555	567	580	593	605	618	631	643
344	656	668	681	694	706	719	732	744	757	769
345	782	794	807	820	832	845	857	870	882	895
346	908	920	933	945	958	970	983	995	*008	*020
347	54 033	045	058	070	083	095	108	120	133	145
348	158	170	183	195	208	220	233	245	258	270
349	283	295	307	320	332	345	357	370	382	394
350	407	419	432	444	456	469	481	494	506	518
N.	0	1	2	3	4	5	6	7	8	9

Prop. Pts.

log 3
=.47712 12547

log π
=.49714 98727

	15	14
1	1.5	1.4
2	3.0	2.8
3	4.5	4.2
4	6.0	5.6
5	7.5	7.0
6	9.0	8.4
7	10.5	9.8
8	12.0	11.2
9	13.5	12.6

	13	12
1	1.3	1.2
2	2.6	2.4
3	3.9	3.6
4	5.2	4.8
5	6.5	6.0
6	7.8	7.2
7	9.1	8.4
8	10.4	9.6
9	11.7	10.8

Prop. Pts.

N.	0	1	2	3	4	5	6	7	8	9
350	54 407	419	432	444	456	469	481	494	506	518
351	531	543	555	568	580	593	605	617	630	642
352	654	667	679	691	704	716	728	741	753	765
353	777	790	802	814	827	839	851	864	876	888
354	900	913	925	937	949	962	974	986	998	*011
355	55 023	035	047	060	072	084	096	108	121	133
356	145	157	169	182	194	206	218	230	242	255
357	267	279	291	303	315	328	340	352	364	376
358	388	400	413	425	437	449	461	473	485	497
359	509	522	534	546	558	570	582	594	606	618
360	630	642	654	666	678	691	703	715	727	739
361	751	763	775	787	799	811	823	835	847	859
362	871	883	895	907	919	931	943	955	967	979
363	991	*003	*015	*027	*038	*050	*062	*074	*086	*098
364	56 110	122	134	146	158	170	182	194	205	217
365	229	241	253	265	277	289	301	312	324	336
366	348	360	372	384	396	407	419	431	443	455
367	467	478	490	502	514	526	538	549	561	573
368	585	597	608	620	632	644	656	667	679	691
369	703	714	726	738	750	761	773	785	797	808
370	820	832	844	855	867	879	891	902	914	926
371	937	949	961	972	984	996	*008	*019	*031	*043
372	57 054	066	078	089	101	113	124	136	148	159
373	171	183	194	206	217	229	241	252	264	276
374	287	299	310	322	334	345	357	368	380	392
375	403	415	426	438	449	461	473	484	496	507
376	519	530	542	553	565	576	588	600	611	623
377	634	646	657	669	680	692	703	715	726	738
378	749	761	772	784	795	807	818	830	841	852
379	864	875	887	898	910	921	933	944	955	967
380	978	990	*001	*013	*024	*035	*047	*058	*070	*081
381	58 092	104	115	127	138	149	161	172	184	195
382	206	218	229	240	252	263	274	286	297	309
383	320	331	343	354	365	377	388	399	410	422
384	433	444	456	467	478	490	501	512	524	535
385	546	557	569	580	591	602	614	625	636	647
386	659	670	681	692	704	715	726	737	749	760
387	771	782	794	805	816	827	838	850	861	872
388	883	894	906	917	928	939	950	961	973	984
389	995	*006	*017	*028	*040	*051	*062	*073	*084	*095
390	59 106	118	129	140	151	162	173	184	195	207
391	218	229	240	251	262	273	284	295	306	318
392	329	340	351	362	373	384	395	406	417	428
393	439	450	461	472	483	494	506	517	528	539
394	550	561	572	583	594	605	616	627	638	649
395	660	671	682	693	704	715	726	737	748	759
396	770	780	791	802	813	824	835	846	857	868
397	879	890	901	912	923	934	945	956	966	977
398	988	999	*010	*021	*032	*043	*054	*065	*076	*086
399	60 097	108	119	130	141	152	163	173	184	195
400	206	217	228	239	249	260	271	282	293	304
N.	**0**	**1**	**2**	**3**	**4**	**5**	**6**	**7**	**8**	**9**

Prop. Pts.

	13	12
1	1.3	1.2
2	2.6	2.4
3	3.9	3.6
4	5.2	4.8
5	6.5	6.0
6	7.8	7.2
7	9.1	8.4
8	10.4	9.6
9	11.7	10.8

	11	10
1	1.1	1.0
2	2.2	2.0
3	3.3	3.0
4	4.4	4.0
5	5.5	5.0
6	6.6	6.0
7	7.7	7.0
8	8.8	8.0
9	9.9	9.0

Prop. Pts.

N.	0	1	2	3	4	5	6	7	8	9
400	60 206	217	228	239	249	260	271	282	293	304
401	314	325	336	347	358	369	379	390	401	412
402	423	433	444	455	466	477	487	498	509	520
403	531	541	552	563	574	584	595	606	617	627
404	638	649	660	670	681	692	703	713	724	735
405	746	756	767	778	788	799	810	821	831	842
406	853	863	874	885	895	906	917	927	938	949
407	959	970	981	991	*002	*013	*023	*034	*045	*055
408	61 066	077	087	098	109	119	130	140	151	162
409	172	183	194	204	215	225	236	247	257	268
410	278	289	300	310	321	331	342	352	363	374
411	384	395	405	416	426	437	448	458	469	479
412	490	500	511	521	532	542	553	563	574	584
413	595	606	616	627	637	648	658	669	679	690
414	700	711	721	731	742	752	763	773	784	794
415	805	815	826	836	847	857	868	878	888	899
416	909	920	930	941	951	962	972	982	993	*003
417	62 014	024	034	045	055	066	076	086	097	107
418	118	128	138	149	159	170	180	190	201	211
419	221	232	242	252	263	273	284	294	304	315
420	325	335	346	356	366	377	387	397	408	418
421	428	439	449	459	469	480	490	500	511	521
422	531	542	552	562	572	583	593	603	613	624
423	634	644	655	665	675	685	696	706	716	726
424	737	747	757	767	778	788	798	808	818	829
425	839	849	859	870	880	890	900	910	921	931
426	941	951	961	972	982	992	*002	*012	*022	*033
427	63 043	053	063	073	083	094	104	114	124	134
428	144	155	165	175	185	195	205	215	225	236
429	246	256	266	276	286	296	306	317	327	337
430	347	357	367	377	387	397	407	417	428	438
431	448	458	468	478	488	498	508	518	528	538
432	548	558	568	579	589	599	609	619	629	639
433	649	659	669	679	689	699	709	719	729	739
434	749	759	769	779	789	799	809	819	829	839
435	849	859	869	879	889	899	909	919	929	939
436	949	959	969	979	988	998	*008	*018	*028	*038
437	64 048	058	068	078	088	098	108	118	128	137
438	147	157	167	177	187	197	207	217	227	237
439	246	256	266	276	286	296	306	316	326	335
440	345	355	365	375	385	395	404	414	424	434
441	444	454	464	473	483	493	503	513	523	532
442	542	552	562	572	582	591	601	611	621	631
443	640	650	660	670	680	689	699	709	719	729
444	738	748	758	768	777	787	797	807	816	826
445	836	846	856	865	875	885	895	904	914	924
446	933	943	953	963	972	982	992	*002	*011	*021
447	65 031	040	050	060	070	079	089	099	108	118
448	128	137	147	157	167	176	186	196	205	215
449	225	234	244	254	263	273	283	292	302	312
450	321	331	341	350	360	369	379	389	398	408
N.	0	1	2	3	4	5	6	7	8	9

Prop. Pts.

	11	10
1	1.1	1.0
2	2.2	2.0
3	3.3	3.0
4	4.4	4.0
5	5.5	5.0
6	6.6	6.0
7	7.7	7.0
8	8.8	8.0
9	9.9	9.0

$\log M$
$= \log [\log e]$
$= 9.63778\ 431$
-10

	9
1	0.9
2	1.8
3	2.7
4	3.6
5	4.5
6	5.4
7	6.3
8	7.2
9	8.1

Prop. Pts.

N.	0	1	2	3	4	5	6	7	8	9
450	65 321	331	341	350	360	369	379	389	398	408
451	418	427	437	447	456	466	475	485	495	504
452	514	523	533	543	552	562	571	581	591	600
453	610	619	629	639	648	658	667	677	686	696
454	706	715	725	734	744	753	763	772	782	792
455	801	811	820	830	839	849	858	868	877	887
456	896	906	916	925	935	944	954	963	973	982
457	992	*001	*011	*020	*030	*039	*049	*058	*068	*077
458	66 087	096	106	115	124	134	143	153	162	172
459	181	191	200	210	219	229	238	247	257	266
460	276	285	295	304	314	323	332	342	351	361
461	370	380	389	398	408	417	427	436	445	455
462	464	474	483	492	502	511	521	530	539	549
463	558	567	577	586	596	605	614	624	633	642
464	652	661	671	680	689	699	708	717	727	736
465	745	755	764	773	783	792	801	811	820	829
466	839	848	857	867	876	885	894	904	913	922
467	932	941	950	960	969	978	987	997	*006	*015
468	67 025	034	043	052	062	071	080	089	099	108
469	117	127	136	145	154	164	173	182	191	201
470	210	219	228	237	247	256	265	274	284	293
471	302	311	321	330	339	348	357	367	376	385
472	394	403	413	422	431	440	449	459	468	477
473	486	495	504	514	523	532	541	550	560	569
474	578	587	596	605	614	624	633	642	651	660
475	669	679	688	697	706	715	724	733	742	752
476	761	770	779	788	797	806	815	825	834	843
477	852	861	870	879	888	897	906	916	925	934
478	943	952	961	970	979	988	997	*006	*015	*024
479	68 034	043	052	061	070	079	088	097	106	115
480	124	133	142	151	160	169	178	187	196	205
481	215	224	233	242	251	260	269	278	287	296
482	305	314	323	332	341	350	359	368	377	386
483	395	404	413	422	431	440	449	458	467	476
484	485	494	502	511	520	529	538	547	556	565
485	574	583	592	601	610	619	628	637	646	655
486	664	673	681	690	699	708	717	726	735	744
487	753	762	771	780	789	797	806	815	824	833
488	842	851	860	869	878	886	895	904	913	922
489	931	940	949	958	966	975	984	993	*002	*011
490	69 020	028	037	046	055	064	073	082	090	099
491	108	117	126	135	144	152	161	170	179	188
492	197	205	214	223	232	241	249	258	267	276
493	285	294	302	311	320	329	338	346	355	364
494	373	381	390	399	408	417	425	434	443	452
495	461	469	478	487	496	504	513	522	531	539
496	548	557	566	574	583	592	601	609	618	627
497	636	644	653	662	671	679	688	697	705	714
498	723	732	740	749	758	767	775	784	793	801
499	810	819	827	836	845	854	862	871	880	888
500	897	906	914	923	932	940	949	958	966	975
N.	0	1	2	3	4	5	6	7	8	9

Prop. Pts.

	10	9
1	1.0	0.9
2	2.0	1.8
3	3.0	2.7
4	4.0	3.6
5	5.0	4.5
6	6.0	5.4
7	7.0	6.3
8	8.0	7.2
9	9.0	8.1

	8
1	0.8
2	1.6
3	2.4
4	3.2
5	4.0
6	4.8
7	5.6
8	6.4
9	7.2

Prop. Pts.

N.	0	1	2	3	4	5	6	7	8	9
500	69 897	906	914	923	932	940	949	958	966	975
501	984	992	*001	*010	*018	*027	*036	*044	*053	*062
502	70 070	079	088	096	105	114	122	131	140	148
503	157	165	174	183	191	200	209	217	226	234
504	243	252	260	269	278	286	295	303	312	321
505	329	338	346	355	364	372	381	389	398	406
506	415	424	432	441	449	458	467	475	484	492
507	501	509	518	526	535	544	552	561	569	578
508	586	595	603	612	621	629	638	646	655	663
509	672	680	689	697	706	714	723	731	740	749
510	757	766	774	783	791	800	808	817	825	834
511	842	851	859	868	876	885	893	902	910	919
512	927	935	944	952	961	969	978	986	995	*003
513	71 012	020	029	037	046	054	063	071	079	088
514	096	105	113	122	130	139	147	155	164	172
515	181	189	198	206	214	223	231	240	248	257
516	265	273	282	290	299	307	315	324	332	341
517	349	357	366	374	383	391	399	408	416	425
518	433	441	450	458	466	475	483	492	500	508
519	517	525	533	542	550	559	567	575	584	592
520	600	609	617	625	634	642	650	659	667	675
521	684	692	700	709	717	725	734	742	750	759
522	767	775	784	792	800	809	817	825	834	842
523	850	858	867	875	883	892	900	908	917	925
524	933	941	950	958	966	975	983	991	999	*008
525	72 016	024	032	041	049	057	066	074	082	090
526	099	107	115	123	132	140	148	156	165	173
527	181	189	198	206	214	222	230	239	247	255
528	263	272	280	288	296	304	313	321	329	337
529	346	354	362	370	378	387	395	403	411	419
530	428	436	444	452	460	469	477	485	493	501
531	509	518	526	534	542	550	558	567	575	583
532	591	599	607	616	624	632	640	648	656	665
533	673	681	689	697	705	713	722	730	738	746
534	754	762	770	779	787	795	803	811	819	827
535	835	843	852	860	868	876	884	892	900	908
536	916	925	933	941	949	957	965	973	981	989
537	997	*006	*014	*022	*030	*038	*046	*054	*062	*070
538	73 078	086	094	102	111	119	127	135	143	151
539	159	167	175	183	191	199	207	215	223	231
540	239	247	255	263	272	280	288	296	304	312
541	320	328	336	344	352	360	368	376	384	392
542	400	408	416	424	432	440	448	456	464	472
543	480	488	496	504	512	520	528	536	544	552
544	560	568	576	584	592	600	608	616	624	632
545	640	648	656	664	672	679	687	695	703	711
546	719	727	735	743	751	759	767	775	783	791
547	799	807	815	823	830	838	846	854	862	870
548	878	886	894	902	910	918	926	933	941	949
549	957	965	973	981	989	997	*005	*013	*020	*028
550	74 036	044	052	060	068	076	084	092	099	107
N.	0	1	2	3	4	5	6	7	8	9

Prop. Pts.

log 5
=.69897 00043

	9	8
1	0.9	0.8
2	1.8	1.6
3	2.7	2.4
4	3.6	3.2
5	4.5	4.0
6	5.4	4.8
7	6.3	5.6
8	7.2	6.4
9	8.1	7.2

	7
1	0.7
2	1.4
3	2.1
4	2.8
5	3.5
6	4.2
7	4.9
8	5.6
9	6.3

Prop. Pts.

N.	0	1	2	3	4	5	6	7	8	9
550	74 036	044	052	060	068	076	084	092	099	107
551	115	123	131	139	147	155	162	170	178	186
552	194	202	210	218	225	233	241	249	257	265
553	273	280	288	296	304	312	320	327	335	343
554	351	359	367	374	382	390	398	406	414	421
555	429	437	445	453	461	468	476	484	492	500
556	507	515	523	531	539	547	554	562	570	578
557	586	593	601	609	617	624	632	640	648	656
558	663	671	679	687	695	702	710	718	726	733
559	741	749	757	764	772	780	788	796	803	811
560	819	827	834	842	850	858	865	873	881	889
561	896	904	912	920	927	935	943	950	958	966
562	974	981	989	997	*005	*012	*020	*028	*035	*043
563	75 051	059	066	074	082	089	097	105	113	120
564	128	136	143	151	159	166	174	182	189	197
565	205	213	220	228	236	243	251	259	266	274
566	282	289	297	305	312	320	328	335	343	351
567	358	366	374	381	389	397	404	412	420	427
568	435	442	450	458	465	473	481	488	496	504
569	511	519	526	534	542	549	557	565	572	580
570	587	595	603	610	618	626	633	641	648	656
571	664	671	679	686	694	702	709	717	724	732
572	740	747	755	762	770	778	785	793	800	808
573	815	823	831	838	846	853	861	868	876	884
574	891	899	906	914	921	929	937	944	952	959
575	967	974	982	989	997	*005	*012	*020	*027	*035
576	76 042	050	057	065	072	080	087	095	103	110
577	118	125	133	140	148	155	163	170	178	185
578	193	200	208	215	223	230	238	245	253	260
579	268	275	283	290	298	305	313	320	328	335
580	343	350	358	365	373	380	388	395	403	410
581	418	425	433	440	448	455	462	470	477	485
582	492	500	507	515	522	530	537	545	552	559
583	567	574	582	589	597	604	612	619	626	634
584	641	649	656	664	671	678	686	693	701	708
585	716	723	730	738	745	753	760	768	775	782
586	790	797	805	812	819	827	834	842	849	856
587	864	871	879	886	893	901	908	916	923	930
588	938	945	953	960	967	975	982	989	997	*004
589	77 012	019	026	034	041	048	056	063	070	078
590	085	093	100	107	115	122	129	137	144	151
591	159	166	173	181	188	195	203	210	217	225
592	232	240	247	254	262	269	276	283	291	298
593	305	313	320	327	335	342	349	357	364	371
594	379	386	393	401	408	415	422	430	437	444
595	452	459	466	474	481	488	495	503	510	517
596	525	532	539	546	554	561	568	576	583	590
597	597	605	612	619	627	634	641	648	656	663
598	670	677	685	692	699	706	714	721	728	735
599	743	750	757	764	772	779	786	793	801	808
600	815	822	830	837	844	851	859	866	873	880
N.	0	1	2	3	4	5	6	7	8	9

Prop. Pts.

	8	7
1	0.8	0.7
2	1.6	1.4
3	2.4	2.1
4	3.2	2.8
5	4.0	3.5
6	4.8	4.2
7	5.6	4.9
8	6.4	5.6
9	7.2	6.3

N.	0	1	2	3	4	5	6	7	8	9
600	77 815	822	830	837	844	851	859	866	873	880
601	887	895	902	909	916	924	931	938	945	952
602	960	967	974	981	988	996	*003	*010	*017	*025
603	78 032	039	046	053	061	068	075	082	089	097
604	104	111	118	125	132	140	147	154	161	168
605	176	183	190	197	204	211	219	226	233	240
606	247	254	262	269	276	283	290	297	305	312
607	319	326	333	340	347	355	362	369	376	383
608	390	398	405	412	419	426	433	440	447	455
609	462	469	476	483	490	497	504	512	519	526
610	533	540	547	554	561	569	576	583	590	597
611	604	611	618	625	633	640	647	654	661	668
612	675	682	689	696	704	711	718	725	732	739
613	746	753	760	767	774	781	789	796	803	810
614	817	824	831	838	845	852	859	866	873	880
615	888	895	902	909	916	923	930	937	944	951
616	958	965	972	979	986	993	*000	*007	*014	*021
617	79 029	036	043	050	057	064	071	078	085	092
618	099	106	113	120	127	134	141	148	155	162
619	169	176	183	190	197	204	211	218	225	232
620	239	246	253	260	267	274	281	288	295	302
621	309	316	323	330	337	344	351	358	365	372
622	379	386	393	400	407	414	421	428	435	442
623	449	456	463	470	477	484	491	498	505	511
624	518	525	532	539	546	553	560	567	574	581
625	588	595	602	609	616	623	630	637	644	650
626	657	664	671	678	685	692	699	706	713	720
627	727	734	741	748	754	761	768	775	782	789
628	796	803	810	817	824	831	837	844	851	858
629	865	872	879	886	893	900	906	913	920	927
630	934	941	948	955	962	969	975	982	989	996
631	80 003	010	017	024	030	037	044	051	058	065
632	072	079	085	092	099	106	113	120	127	134
633	140	147	154	161	168	175	182	188	195	202
634	209	216	223	229	236	243	250	257	264	271
635	277	284	291	298	305	312	318	325	332	339
636	346	353	359	366	373	380	387	393	400	407
637	414	421	428	434	441	448	455	462	468	475
638	482	489	496	502	509	516	523	530	536	543
639	550	557	564	570	577	584	591	598	604	611
640	618	625	632	638	645	652	659	665	672	679
641	686	693	699	706	713	720	726	733	740	747
642	754	760	767	774	781	787	794	801	808	814
643	821	828	835	841	848	855	862	868	875	882
644	889	895	902	909	916	922	929	936	943	949
645	956	963	969	976	983	990	996	*003	*010	*017
646	81 023	030	037	043	050	057	064	070	077	084
647	090	097	104	111	117	124	131	137	144	151
648	158	164	171	178	184	191	198	204	211	218
649	224	231	238	245	251	258	265	271	278	285
650	291	298	305	311	318	325	331	338	345	351
N.	0	1	2	3	4	5	6	7	8	9

Prop. Pts.

	8	7
1	0.8	0.7
2	1.6	1.4
3	2.4	2.1
4	3.2	2.8
5	4.0	3.5
6	4.8	4.2
7	5.6	4.9
8	6.4	5.6
9	7.2	6.3

	6
1	0.6
2	1.2
3	1.8
4	2.4
5	3.0
6	3.6
7	4.2
8	4.8
9	5.4

Prop. Pts.

N.	0	1	2	3	4	5	6	7	8	9
650	81 291	298	305	311	318	325	331	338	345	351
651	358	365	371	378	385	391	398	405	411	418
652	425	431	438	445	451	458	465	471	478	485
653	491	498	505	511	518	525	531	538	544	551
654	558	564	571	578	584	591	598	604	611	617
655	624	631	637	644	651	657	664	671	677	684
656	690	697	704	710	717	723	730	737	743	750
657	757	763	770	776	783	790	796	803	809	816
658	823	829	836	842	849	856	862	869	875	882
659	889	895	902	908	915	921	928	935	941	948
660	954	961	968	974	981	987	994	*000	*007	*014
661	82 020	027	033	040	046	053	060	066	073	079
662	086	092	099	105	112	119	125	132	138	145
663	151	158	164	171	178	184	191	197	204	210
664	217	223	230	236	243	249	256	263	269	276
665	282	289	295	302	308	315	321	328	334	341
666	347	354	360	367	373	380	387	393	400	406
667	413	419	426	432	439	445	452	458	465	471
668	478	484	491	497	504	510	517	523	530	536
669	543	549	556	562	569	575	582	588	595	601
670	607	614	620	627	633	640	646	653	659	666
671	672	679	685	692	698	705	711	718	724	730
672	737	743	750	756	763	769	776	782	789	795
673	802	808	814	821	827	834	840	847	853	860
674	866	872	879	885	892	898	905	911	918	924
675	930	937	943	950	956	963	969	975	982	988
676	995	*001	*008	*014	*020	*027	*033	*040	*046	*052
677	83 059	065	072	078	085	091	097	104	110	117
678	123	129	136	142	149	155	161	168	174	181
679	187	193	200	206	213	219	225	232	238	245
680	251	257	264	270	276	283	289	296	302	308
681	315	321	327	334	340	347	353	359	366	372
682	378	385	391	398	404	410	417	423	429	436
683	442	448	455	461	467	474	480	487	493	499
684	506	512	518	525	531	537	544	550	556	563
685	569	575	582	588	594	601	607	613	620	626
686	632	639	645	651	658	664	670	677	683	689
687	696	702	708	715	721	727	734	740	746	753
688	759	765	771	778	784	790	797	803	809	816
689	822	828	835	841	847	853	860	866	872	879
690	885	891	897	904	910	916	923	929	935	942
691	948	954	960	967	973	979	985	992	998	*004
692	84 011	017	023	029	036	042	048	055	061	067
693	073	080	086	092	098	105	111	117	123	130
694	136	142	148	155	161	167	173	180	186	192
695	198	205	211	217	223	230	236	242	248	255
696	261	267	273	280	286	292	298	305	311	317
697	323	330	336	342	348	354	361	367	373	379
698	386	392	398	404	410	417	423	429	435	442
699	448	454	460	466	473	479	485	491	497	504
700	510	516	522	528	535	541	547	553	559	566
N.	0	1	2	3	4	5	6	7	8	9

Prop. Pts.

	7	6
1	0.7	0.6
2	1.4	1.2
3	2.1	1.8
4	2.8	2.4
5	3.5	3.0
6	4.2	3.6
7	4.9	4.2
8	5.6	4.8
9	6.3	5.4

N.	0	1	2	3	4	5	6	7	8	9
700	84 510	516	522	528	535	541	547	553	559	566
701	572	578	584	590	597	603	609	615	621	628
702	634	640	646	652	658	665	671	677	683	689
703	696	702	708	714	720	726	733	739	745	751
704	757	763	770	776	782	788	794	800	807	813
705	819	825	831	837	844	850	856	862	868	874
706	880	887	893	899	905	911	917	924	930	936
707	942	948	954	960	967	973	979	985	991	997
708	85 003	009	016	022	028	034	040	046	052	058
709	065	071	077	083	089	095	101	107	114	120
710	126	132	138	144	150	156	163	169	175	181
711	187	193	199	205	211	217	224	230	236	242
712	248	254	260	266	272	278	285	291	297	303
713	309	315	321	327	333	339	345	352	358	364
714	370	376	382	388	394	400	406	412	418	425
715	431	437	443	449	455	461	467	473	479	485
716	491	497	503	509	516	522	528	534	540	546
717	552	558	564	570	576	582	588	594	600	606
718	612	618	625	631	637	643	649	655	661	667
719	673	679	685	691	697	703	709	715	721	727
720	733	739	745	751	757	763	769	775	781	788
721	794	800	806	812	818	824	830	836	842	848
722	854	860	866	872	878	884	890	896	902	908
723	914	920	926	932	938	944	950	956	962	968
724	974	980	986	992	998	*004	*010	*016	*022	*028
725	86 034	040	046	052	058	064	070	076	082	088
726	094	100	106	112	118	124	130	136	141	147
727	153	159	165	171	177	183	189	195	201	207
728	213	219	225	231	237	243	249	255	261	267
729	273	279	285	291	297	303	308	314	320	326
730	332	338	344	350	356	362	368	374	380	386
731	392	398	404	410	415	421	427	433	439	445
732	451	457	463	469	475	481	487	493	499	504
733	510	516	522	528	534	540	546	552	558	564
734	570	576	581	587	593	599	605	611	617	623
735	629	635	641	646	652	658	664	670	676	682
736	688	694	700	705	711	717	723	729	735	741
737	747	753	759	764	770	776	782	788	794	800
738	806	812	817	823	829	835	841	847	853	859
739	864	870	876	882	888	894	900	906	911	917
740	923	929	935	941	947	953	958	964	970	976
741	982	988	994	999	*005	*011	*017	*023	*029	*035
742	87 040	046	052	058	064	070	075	081	087	093
743	099	105	111	116	122	128	134	140	146	151
744	157	163	169	175	181	186	192	198	204	210
745	216	221	227	233	239	245	251	256	262	268
746	274	280	286	291	297	303	309	315	320	326
747	332	338	344	349	355	361	367	373	379	384
748	390	396	402	408	413	419	425	431	437	442
749	448	454	460	466	471	477	483	489	495	500
750	506	512	518	523	529	535	541	547	552	558
N.	0	1	2	3	4	5	6	7	8	9

Prop. Pts.

log 7 =.84509 80400

	7	6
1	0.7	0.6
2	1.4	1.2
3	2.1	1.8
4	2.8	2.4
5	3.5	3.0
6	4.2	3.6
7	4.9	4.2
8	5.6	4.8
9	6.3	5.4

	5
1	0.5
2	1.0
3	1.5
4	2.0
5	2.5
6	3.0
7	3.5
8	4.0
9	4.5

Prop. Pts.

N.	0	1	2	3	4	5	6	7	8	9
750	87 506	512	518	523	529	535	541	547	552	558
751	564	570	576	581	587	593	599	604	610	616
752	622	628	633	639	645	651	656	662	668	674
753	679	685	691	697	703	708	714	720	726	731
754	737	743	749	754	760	766	772	777	783	789
755	795	800	806	812	818	823	829	835	841	846
756	852	858	864	869	875	881	887	892	898	904
757	910	915	921	927	933	938	944	950	955	961
758	967	973	978	984	990	996	*001	*007	*013	*018
759	88 024	030	036	041	047	053	058	064	070	076
760	081	087	093	098	104	110	116	121	127	133
761	138	144	150	156	161	167	173	178	184	190
762	195	201	207	213	218	224	230	235	241	247
763	252	258	264	270	275	281	287	292	298	304
764	309	315	321	326	332	338	343	349	355	360
765	366	372	377	383	389	395	400	406	412	417
766	423	429	434	440	446	451	457	463	468	474
767	480	485	491	497	502	508	513	519	525	530
768	536	542	547	553	559	564	570	576	581	587
769	593	598	604	610	615	621	627	632	638	643
770	649	655	660	666	672	677	683	689	694	700
771	705	711	717	722	728	734	739	745	750	756
772	762	767	773	779	784	790	795	801	807	812
773	818	824	829	835	840	846	852	857	863	868
774	874	880	885	891	897	902	908	913	919	925
775	930	936	941	947	953	958	964	969	975	981
776	986	992	997	*003	*009	*014	*020	*025	*031	*037
777	89 042	048	053	059	064	070	076	081	087	092
778	098	104	109	115	120	126	131	137	143	148
779	154	159	165	170	176	182	187	193	198	204
780	209	215	221	226	232	237	243	248	254	260
781	265	271	276	282	287	293	298	304	310	315
782	321	326	332	337	343	348	354	360	365	371
783	376	382	387	393	398	404	409	415	421	426
784	432	437	443	448	454	459	465	470	476	481
785	487	492	498	504	509	515	520	526	531	537
786	542	548	553	559	564	570	575	581	586	592
787	597	603	609	614	620	625	631	636	642	647
788	653	658	664	669	675	680	686	691	697	702
789	708	713	719	724	730	735	741	746	752	757
790	763	768	774	779	785	790	796	801	807	812
791	818	823	829	834	840	845	851	856	862	867
792	873	878	883	889	894	900	905	911	916	922
793	927	933	938	944	949	955	960	966	971	977
794	982	988	993	998	*004	*009	*015	*020	*026	*031
795	90 037	042	048	053	059	064	069	075	080	086
796	091	097	102	108	113	119	124	129	135	140
797	146	151	157	162	168	173	179	184	189	195
798	200	206	211	217	222	227	233	238	244	249
799	255	260	266	271	276	282	287	293	298	304
800	309	314	320	325	331	336	342	347	352	358
N.	0	1	2	3	4	5	6	7	8	9

Prop. Pts.

	6	5
1	0.6	0.5
2	1.2	1.0
3	1.8	1.5
4	2.4	2.0
5	3.0	2.5
6	3.6	3.0
7	4.2	3.5
8	4.8	4.0
9	5.4	4.5

Prop. Pts.

N.	0	1	2	3	4	5	6	7	8	9
800	90 309	314	320	325	331	336	342	347	352	358
801	363	369	374	380	385	390	396	401	407	412
802	417	423	428	434	439	445	450	455	461	466
803	472	477	482	488	493	499	504	509	515	520
804	526	531	536	542	547	553	558	563	569	574
805	580	585	590	596	601	607	612	617	623	628
806	634	639	644	650	655	660	666	671	677	682
807	687	693	698	703	709	714	720	725	730	736
808	741	747	752	757	763	768	773	779	784	789
809	795	800	806	811	816	822	827	832	838	843
810	849	854	859	865	870	875	881	886	891	897
811	902	907	913	918	924	929	934	940	945	950
812	956	961	966	972	977	982	988	993	998	*004
813	91 009	014	020	025	030	036	041	046	052	057
814	062	068	073	078	084	089	094	100	105	110
815	116	121	126	132	137	142	148	153	158	164
816	169	174	180	185	190	196	201	206	212	217
817	222	228	233	238	243	249	254	259	265	270
818	275	281	286	291	297	302	307	312	318	323
819	328	334	339	344	350	355	360	365	371	376
820	381	387	392	397	403	408	413	418	424	429
821	434	440	445	450	455	461	466	471	477	482
822	487	492	498	503	508	514	519	524	529	535
823	540	545	551	556	561	566	572	577	582	587
824	593	598	603	609	614	619	624	630	635	640
825	645	651	656	661	666	672	677	682	687	693
826	698	703	709	714	719	724	730	735	740	745
827	751	756	761	766	772	777	782	787	793	798
828	803	808	814	819	824	829	834	840	845	850
829	855	861	866	871	876	882	887	892	897	903
830	908	913	918	924	929	934	939	944	950	955
831	960	965	971	976	981	986	991	997	*002	*007
832	92 012	018	023	028	033	038	044	049	054	059
833	065	070	075	080	085	091	096	101	106	111
834	117	122	127	132	137	143	148	153	158	163
835	169	174	179	184	189	195	200	205	210	215
836	221	226	231	236	241	247	252	257	262	267
837	273	278	283	288	293	298	304	309	314	319
838	324	330	335	340	345	350	355	361	366	371
839	376	381	387	392	397	402	407	412	418	423
840	428	433	438	443	449	454	459	464	469	474
841	480	485	490	495	500	505	511	516	521	526
842	531	536	542	547	552	557	562	567	572	578
843	583	588	593	598	603	609	614	619	624	629
844	634	639	645	650	655	660	665	670	675	681
845	686	691	696	701	706	711	716	722	727	732
846	737	742	747	752	758	763	768	773	778	783
847	788	793	799	804	809	814	819	824	829	834
848	840	845	850	855	860	865	870	875	881	886
849	891	896	901	906	911	916	921	927	932	937
850	942	947	952	957	962	967	973	978	983	988
N.	**0**	**1**	**2**	**3**	**4**	**5**	**6**	**7**	**8**	**9**

Prop. Pts.

	6	5
1	0.6	0.5
2	1.2	1.0
3	1.8	1.5
4	2.4	2.0
5	3.0	2.5
6	3.6	3.0
7	4.2	3.5
8	4.8	4.0
9	5.4	4.5

Prop. Pts.

N.	0	1	2	3	4	5	6	7	8	9
850	92 942	947	952	957	962	967	973	978	983	988
851	993	998	*003	*008	*013	*018	*024	*029	*034	*039
852	93 044	049	054	059	064	069	075	080	085	090
853	095	100	105	110	115	120	125	131	136	141
854	146	151	156	161	166	171	176	181	186	192
855	197	202	207	212	217	222	227	232	237	242
856	247	252	258	263	268	273	278	283	288	293
857	298	303	308	313	318	323	328	334	339	344
858	349	354	359	364	369	374	379	384	389	394
859	399	404	409	414	420	425	430	435	440	445
860	450	455	460	465	470	475	480	485	490	495
861	500	505	510	515	520	526	531	536	541	546
862	551	556	561	566	571	576	581	586	591	596
863	601	606	611	616	621	626	631	636	641	646
864	651	656	661	666	671	676	682	687	692	697
865	702	707	712	717	722	727	732	737	742	747
866	752	757	762	767	772	777	782	787	792	797
867	802	807	812	817	822	827	832	837	842	847
868	852	857	862	867	872	877	882	887	892	897
869	902	907	912	917	922	927	932	937	942	947
870	952	957	962	967	972	977	982	987	992	997
871	94 002	007	012	017	022	027	032	037	042	047
872	052	057	062	067	072	077	082	086	091	096
873	101	106	111	116	121	126	131	136	141	146
874	151	156	161	166	171	176	181	186	191	196
875	201	206	211	216	221	226	231	236	240	245
876	250	255	260	265	270	275	280	285	290	295
877	300	305	310	315	320	325	330	335	340	345
878	349	354	359	364	369	374	379	384	389	394
879	399	404	409	414	419	424	429	433	438	443
880	448	453	458	463	468	473	478	483	488	493
881	498	503	507	512	517	522	527	532	537	542
882	547	552	557	562	567	571	576	581	586	591
883	596	601	606	611	616	621	626	630	635	640
884	645	650	655	660	665	670	675	680	685	689
885	694	699	704	709	714	719	724	729	734	738
886	743	748	753	758	763	768	773	778	783	787
887	792	797	802	807	812	817	822	827	832	836
888	841	846	851	856	861	866	871	876	880	885
889	890	895	900	905	910	915	919	924	929	934
890	939	944	949	954	959	963	968	973	978	983
891	988	993	998	*002	*007	*012	*017	*022	*027	*032
892	95 036	041	046	051	056	061	066	071	075	080
893	085	090	095	100	105	109	114	119	124	129
894	134	139	143	148	153	158	163	168	173	177
895	182	187	192	197	202	207	211	216	221	226
896	231	236	240	245	250	255	260	265	270	274
897	279	284	289	294	299	303	308	313	318	323
898	328	332	337	342	347	352	357	361	366	371
899	376	381	386	390	395	400	405	410	415	419
900	424	429	434	439	444	448	453	458	463	468
N.	0	1	2	3	4	5	6	7	8	9

Prop. Pts.

	6	5
1	0.6	0.5
2	1.2	1.0
3	1.8	1.5
4	2.4	2.0
5	3.0	2.5
6	3.6	3.0
7	4.2	3.5
8	4.8	4.0
9	5.4	4.5

	4
1	0.4
2	0.8
3	1.2
4	1.6
5	2.0
6	2.4
7	2.8
8	3.2
9	3.6

Prop. Pts.

N.	0	1	2	3	4	5	6	7	8	9
900	95 424	429	434	439	444	448	453	458	463	468
901	472	477	482	487	492	497	501	506	511	516
902	521	525	530	535	540	545	550	554	559	564
903	569	574	578	583	588	593	598	602	607	612
904	617	622	626	631	636	641	646	650	655	660
905	665	670	674	679	684	689	694	698	703	708
906	713	718	722	727	732	737	742	746	751	756
907	761	766	770	775	780	785	789	794	799	804
908	809	813	818	823	828	832	837	842	847	852
909	856	861	866	871	875	880	885	890	895	899
910	**904**	909	914	918	923	928	933	938	942	947
911	**952**	957	961	966	971	976	980	985	990	995
912	**999**	*004	*009	*014	*019	*023	*028	*033	*038	*042
913	**96 047**	052	057	061	066	071	076	080	085	090
914	**095**	099	104	109	114	118	123	128	133	137
915	142	147	152	156	161	166	171	175	180	185
916	190	194	199	204	209	213	218	223	227	232
917	237	242	246	251	256	261	265	270	275	280
918	284	289	294	298	303	308	313	317	322	327
919	332	336	341	346	350	355	360	365	369	374
920	379	384	388	393	398	402	407	412	417	421
921	426	431	435	440	445	450	454	459	464	468
922	473	478	483	487	492	497	501	506	511	515
923	520	525	530	534	539	544	548	553	558	562
924	567	572	577	581	586	591	595	600	605	609
925	614	619	624	628	633	638	642	647	652	656
926	661	666	670	675	680	685	689	694	699	703
927	708	713	717	722	727	731	736	741	745	750
928	755	759	764	769	774	778	783	788	792	797
929	802	806	811	816	820	825	830	834	839	844
930	848	853	858	862	867	872	876	881	886	890
931	895	900	904	909	914	918	923	928	932	937
932	942	946	951	956	960	965	970	974	979	984
933	988	993	997	*002	*007	*011	*016	*021	*025	*030
934	97 035	039	044	049	053	058	063	067	072	077
935	081	086	090	095	100	104	109	114	118	123
936	128	132	137	142	146	151	155	160	165	169
937	174	179	183	188	192	197	202	206	211	216
938	220	225	230	234	239	243	248	253	257	262
939	267	271	276	280	285	290	294	299	304	308
940	313	317	322	327	331	336	340	345	350	354
941	359	364	368	373	377	382	387	391	396	400
942	405	410	414	419	424	428	433	437	442	447
943	451	456	460	465	470	474	479	483	488	493
944	497	502	506	511	516	520	525	529	534	539
945	543	548	552	557	562	566	571	575	580	585
946	589	594	598	603	607	612	617	621	626	630
947	635	640	644	649	653	658	663	667	672	676
948	681	685	690	695	699	704	708	713	717	722
949	727	731	736	740	745	749	754	759	763	768
950	772	777	782	786	791	795	800	804	809	813
N.	0	1	2	3	4	5	6	7	8	9

Prop. Pts.

	5	4
1	0.5	0.4
2	1.0	0.8
3	1.5	1.2
4	2.0	1.6
5	2.5	2.0
6	3.0	2.4
7	3.5	2.8
8	4.0	3.2
9	4.5	3.6

Prop. Pts.

950 — Logarithms of Numbers — 1000

N.	0	1	2	3	4	5	6	7	8	9
950	97 772	777	782	786	791	795	800	804	809	813
951	818	823	827	832	836	841	845	850	855	859
952	864	868	873	877	882	886	891	896	900	905
953	909	914	918	923	928	932	937	941	946	950
954	955	959	964	968	973	978	982	987	991	996
955	98 000	005	009	014	019	023	028	032	037	041
956	046	050	055	059	064	068	073	078	082	087
957	091	096	100	105	109	114	118	123	127	132
958	137	141	146	150	155	159	164	168	173	177
959	182	186	191	195	200	204	209	214	218	223
960	227	232	236	241	245	250	254	259	263	268
961	272	277	281	286	290	295	299	304	308	313
962	318	322	327	331	336	340	345	349	354	358
963	363	367	372	376	381	385	390	394	399	403
964	408	412	417	421	426	430	435	439	444	448
965	453	457	462	466	471	475	480	484	489	493
966	498	502	507	511	516	520	525	529	534	538
967	543	547	552	556	561	565	570	574	579	583
968	588	592	597	601	605	610	614	619	623	628
969	632	637	641	646	650	655	659	664	668	673
970	677	682	686	691	695	700	704	709	713	717
971	722	726	731	735	740	744	749	753	758	762
972	767	771	776	780	784	789	793	798	802	807
973	811	816	820	825	829	834	838	843	847	851
974	856	860	865	869	874	878	883	887	892	896
975	900	905	909	914	918	923	927	932	936	941
976	945	949	954	958	963	967	972	976	981	985
977	989	994	998	*003	*007	*012	*016	*021	*025	*029
978	99 034	038	043	047	052	056	061	065	069	074
979	078	083	087	092	096	100	105	109	114	118
980	123	127	131	136	140	145	149	154	158	162
981	167	171	176	180	185	189	193	198	202	207
982	211	216	220	224	229	233	238	242	247	251
983	255	260	264	269	273	277	282	286	291	295
984	300	304	308	313	317	322	326	330	335	339
985	344	348	352	357	361	366	370	374	379	383
986	388	392	396	401	405	410	414	419	423	427
987	432	436	441	445	449	454	458	463	467	471
988	476	480	484	489	493	498	502	506	511	515
989	520	524	528	533	537	542	546	550	555	559
990	564	568	572	577	581	585	590	594	599	603
991	607	612	616	621	625	629	634	638	642	647
992	651	656	660	664	669	673	677	682	686	691
993	695	699	704	708	712	717	721	726	730	734
994	739	743	747	752	756	760	765	769	774	778
995	782	787	791	795	800	804	808	813	817	822
996	826	830	835	839	843	848	852	856	861	865
997	870	874	878	883	887	891	896	900	904	909
998	913	917	922	926	930	935	939	944	948	952
999	957	961	965	970	974	978	983	987	991	996
1000	00 000	004	009	013	017	022	026	030	035	039
N.	0	1	2	3	4	5	6	7	8	9

Prop. Pts.

	5	4
1	0.5	0.4
2	1.0	0.8
3	1.5	1.2
4	2.0	1.6
5	2.5	2.0
6	3.0	2.4
7	3.5	2.8
8	4.0	3.2
9	4.5	3.6

Prop. Pts.

IV. Natural Trigonometric Functions

FROM

0° TO 90° AT INTERVALS OF ONE MINUTE

TO

FIVE DECIMAL PLACES

0°—Natural Trigonometric Functions—1°

′	Sin	Tan	Ctn	Cos	
0	.00000	.00000	——	1.0000	60
1	029	029	3437.7	000	59
2	058	058	1718.9	000	58
3	087	087	1145.9	000	57
4	116	116	859.44	000	56
5	.00145	.00145	687.55	1.0000	55
6	175	175	572.96	000	54
7	204	204	491.11	000	53
8	233	233	429.72	000	52
9	262	262	381.97	000	51
10	.00291	.00291	343.77	1.0000	50
11	320	320	312.52	.99999	49
12	349	349	286.48	999	48
13	378	378	264.44	999	47
14	407	407	245.55	999	46
15	.00436	.00436	229.18	.99999	45
16	465	465	214.86	999	44
17	495	495	202.22	999	43
18	524	524	190.98	999	42
19	553	553	180.93	998	41
20	.00582	.00582	171.89	.99998	40
21	611	611	163.70	998	39
22	640	640	156.26	998	38
23	669	669	149.47	998	37
24	698	698	143.24	998	36
25	.00727	.00727	137.51	.99997	35
26	756	756	132.22	997	34
27	785	785	127.32	997	33
28	814	815	122.77	997	32
29	844	844	118.54	996	31
30	.00873	.00873	114.59	.99996	30
31	902	902	110.89	996	29
32	931	931	107.43	996	28
33	960	960	104.17	995	27
34	.00989	.00989	101.11	995	26
35	.01018	.01018	98.218	.99995	25
36	047	047	95.489	995	24
37	076	076	92.908	994	23
38	105	105	90.463	994	22
39	134	135	88.144	994	21
40	.01164	.01164	85.940	.99993	20
41	193	193	83.844	993	19
42	222	222	81.847	993	18
43	251	251	79.943	992	17
44	280	280	78.126	992	16
45	.01309	.01309	76.390	.99991	15
46	338	338	74.729	991	14
47	367	367	73.139	991	13
48	396	396	71.615	990	12
49	425	425	70.153	990	11
50	.01454	.01455	68.750	.99989	10
51	483	484	67.402	989	9
52	513	513	66.105	989	8
53	542	542	64.858	988	7
54	571	571	63.657	988	6
55	.01600	.01600	62.499	.99987	5
56	629	629	61.383	987	4
57	658	658	60.306	986	3
58	687	687	59.266	986	2
59	716	716	58.261	985	1
60	.01745	.01746	57.290	.99985	0
	Cos	Ctn	Tan	Sin	′

89°

′	Sin	Tan	Ctn	Cos	
0	.01745	.01746	57.290	.99985	60
1	774	775	56.351	984	59
2	803	804	55.442	984	58
3	832	833	54.561	983	57
4	862	862	53.709	983	56
5	.01891	.01891	52.882	.99982	55
6	920	920	52.081	982	54
7	949	949	51.303	981	53
8	.01978	.01978	50.549	980	52
9	.02007	.02007	49.816	980	51
10	.02036	.02036	49.104	.99979	50
11	065	066	48.412	979	49
12	094	095	47.740	978	48
13	123	124	47.085	977	47
14	152	153	46.449	977	46
15	.02181	.02182	45.829	.99976	45
16	211	211	45.226	976	44
17	240	240	44.639	975	43
18	269	269	44.066	974	42
19	298	298	43.508	974	41
20	.02327	.02328	42.964	.99973	40
21	356	357	42.433	972	39
22	385	386	41.916	972	38
23	414	415	41.411	971	37
24	443	444	40.917	970	36
25	.02472	.02473	40.436	.99969	35
26	501	502	39.965	969	34
27	530	531	39.506	968	33
28	560	560	39.057	967	32
29	589	589	38.618	966	31
30	.02618	.02619	38.188	.99966	30
31	647	648	37.769	965	29
32	676	677	37.358	964	28
33	705	706	36.956	963	27
34	734	735	36.563	963	26
35	.02763	.02764	36.178	.99962	25
36	792	793	35.801	961	24
37	821	822	35.431	960	23
38	850	851	35.070	959	22
39	879	881	34.715	959	21
40	.02908	.02910	34.368	.99958	20
41	938	939	34.027	957	19
42	967	968	33.694	956	18
43	.02996	.02997	33.366	955	17
44	.03025	.03026	33.045	954	16
45	.03054	.03055	32.730	.99953	15
46	083	084	32.421	952	14
47	112	114	32.118	952	13
48	141	143	31.821	951	12
49	170	172	31.528	950	11
50	.03199	.03201	31.242	.99949	10
51	228	230	30.960	948	9
52	257	259	30.683	947	8
53	286	288	30.412	946	7
54	316	317	30.145	945	6
55	.03345	.03346	29.882	.99944	5
56	374	376	29.624	943	4
57	403	405	29.371	942	3
58	432	434	29.122	941	2
59	461	463	28.877	940	1
60	.03490	.03492	28.636	.99939	0
	Cos	Ctn	Tan	Sin	′

88°

2°—Natural Trigonometric Functions—3°

′	Sin	Tan	Ctn	Cos	
0	.03490	.03492	28.636	.99939	**60**
1	519	521	.399	938	59
2	548	550	28.166	937	58
3	577	579	27.937	936	57
4	606	609	.712	935	56
5	.03635	.03638	27.490	.99934	**55**
6	664	667	.271	933	54
7	693	696	27.057	932	53
8	723	725	26.845	931	52
9	752	754	.637	930	51
10	.03781	.03783	26.432	.99929	**50**
11	810	812	.230	927	49
12	839	842	26.031	926	48
13	868	871	25.835	925	47
14	897	900	.642	924	46
15	.03926	.03929	25.452	.99923	**45**
16	955	958	.264	922	44
17	.03984	.03987	25.080	921	43
18	.04013	.04016	24.898	919	42
19	042	046	.719	918	41
20	.04071	.04075	24.542	.99917	**40**
21	100	104	.368	916	39
22	129	133	.196	915	38
23	159	162	24.026	913	37
24	188	191	23.859	912	36
25	.04217	.04220	23.695	.99911	**35**
26	246	250	.532	910	34
27	275	279	.372	909	33
28	304	308	.214	907	32
29	333	337	23.058	906	31
30	.04362	.04366	22.904	.99905	**30**
31	391	395	.752	904	29
32	420	424	.602	902	28
33	449	454	.454	901	27
34	478	483	.308	900	26
35	.04507	.04512	22.164	.99898	**25**
36	536	541	22.022	897	24
37	565	570	21.881	896	23
38	594	599	.743	894	22
39	623	628	.606	893	21
40	.04653	.04658	21.470	.99892	**20**
41	682	687	.337	890	19
42	711	716	.205	889	18
43	740	745	21.075	888	17
44	769	774	20.946	886	16
45	.04798	.04803	20.819	.99885	**15**
46	827	833	.693	883	14
47	856	862	.569	882	13
48	885	891	.446	881	12
49	914	920	.325	879	11
50	.04943	.04949	20.206	.99878	**10**
51	.04972	.04978	20.087	876	9
52	.05001	.05007	19.970	875	8
53	030	037	.855	873	7
54	059	066	.740	872	6
55	.05088	.05095	19.627	.99870	**5**
56	117	124	.516	869	4
57	146	153	.405	867	3
58	175	182	.296	866	2
59	205	212	.188	864	1
60	.05234	.05241	19.081	.99863	**0**
	Cos	Ctn	Tan	Sin	′

87°

′	Sin	Tan	Ctn	Cos	
0	.05234	.05241	19.081	.99863	**60**
1	263	270	18.976	861	59
2	292	299	.871	860	58
3	321	328	.768	858	57
4	350	357	.666	857	56
5	.05379	.05387	18.564	.99855	**55**
6	408	416	.464	854	54
7	437	445	.366	852	53
8	466	474	.268	851	52
9	495	503	.171	849	51
10	.05524	.05533	18.075	.99847	**50**
11	553	562	17.980	846	49
12	582	591	.886	844	48
13	611	620	.793	842	47
14	640	649	.702	841	46
15	.05669	.05678	17.611	.99839	**45**
16	698	708	.521	838	44
17	727	737	.431	836	43
18	756	766	.343	834	42
19	785	795	.256	833	41
20	.05814	.05824	17.169	.99831	**40**
21	844	854	17.084	829	39
22	873	883	16.999	827	38
23	902	912	.915	826	37
24	931	941	.832	824	36
25	.05960	.05970	16.750	.99822	**35**
26	.05989	.05999	.668	821	34
27	.06018	.06029	.587	819	33
28	047	058	.507	817	32
29	076	087	.428	815	31
30	.06105	.06116	16.350	.99813	**30**
31	134	145	.272	812	29
32	163	175	.195	810	28
33	192	204	.119	808	27
34	221	233	16.043	806	26
35	.06250	.06262	15.969	.99804	**25**
36	279	291	.895	803	24
37	308	321	.821	801	23
38	337	350	.748	799	22
39	366	379	.676	797	21
40	.06395	.06408	15.605	.99795	**20**
41	424	438	.534	793	19
42	453	467	.464	792	18
43	482	496	.394	790	17
44	511	525	.325	788	16
45	.06540	.06554	15.257	.99786	**15**
46	569	584	.189	784	14
47	598	613	.122	782	13
48	627	642	15.056	780	12
49	656	671	14.990	778	11
50	.06685	.06700	14.924	.99776	**10**
51	714	730	.860	774	9
52	743	759	.795	772	8
53	773	788	.732	770	7
54	802	817	.669	768	6
55	.06831	.06847	14.606	.99766	**5**
56	860	876	.544	764	4
57	889	905	.482	762	3
58	918	934	.421	760	2
59	947	963	.361	758	1
60	.06976	.06993	14.301	.99756	**0**
	Cos	Ctn	Tan	Sin	′

86°

4°—Natural Trigonometric Functions—5°

′	Sin	Tan	Ctn	Cos	
0	.06976	.06993	14.301	.99756	**60**
1	.07005	.07022	.241	754	59
2	034	051	.182	752	58
3	063	080	.124	750	57
4	092	110	.065	748	56
5	.07121	.07139	14.008	.99746	**55**
6	150	168	13.951	744	54
7	179	197	.894	742	53
8	208	227	.838	740	52
9	237	256	.782	738	51
10	.07266	.07285	13.727	.99736	**50**
11	295	314	.672	734	49
12	324	344	.617	731	48
13	353	373	.563	729	47
14	382	402	.510	727	46
15	.07411	.07431	13.457	.99725	**45**
16	440	461	.404	723	44
17	469	490	.352	721	43
18	498	519	.300	719	42
19	527	548	.248	716	41
20	.07556	.07578	13.197	.99714	**40**
21	585	607	.146	712	39
22	614	636	.096	710	38
23	643	665	13.046	708	37
24	672	695	12.996	705	36
25	.07701	.07724	12.947	.99703	**35**
26	730	753	.898	701	34
27	759	782	.850	699	33
28	788	812	.801	696	32
29	817	841	.754	694	31
30	.07846	.07870	12.706	.99692	**30**
31	875	899	.659	689	29
32	904	929	.612	687	28
33	933	958	.566	685	27
34	962	.07987	.520	683	26
35	.07991	.08017	12.474	.99680	**25**
36	.08020	046	.429	678	24
37	049	075	.384	676	23
38	078	104	.339	673	22
39	107	134	.295	671	21
40	.08136	.08163	12.251	.99668	**20**
41	165	192	.207	666	19
42	194	221	.163	664	18
43	223	251	.120	661	17
44	252	280	.077	659	16
45	.08281	.08309	12.035	.99657	**15**
46	310	339	11.992	654	14
47	339	368	.950	652	13
48	368	397	.909	649	12
49	397	427	.867	647	11
50	.08426	.08456	11.826	.99644	**10**
51	455	485	.785	642	9
52	484	514	.745	639	8
53	513	544	.705	637	7
54	542	573	.664	635	6
55	.08571	.08602	11.625	.99632	**5**
56	600	632	.585	630	4
57	629	661	.546	627	3
58	658	690	.507	625	2
59	687	720	.468	622	1
60	.08716	.08749	11.430	.99619	**0**
	Cos	Ctn	Tan	Sin	′

85°

′	Sin	Tan	Ctn	Cos	
0	.08716	.08749	11.430	.99619	**60**
1	745	778	.392	617	59
2	774	807	.354	614	58
3	803	837	.316	612	57
4	831	866	.279	609	56
5	.08860	.08895	11.242	.99607	**55**
6	889	925	.205	604	54
7	918	954	.168	602	53
8	947	.08983	.132	599	52
9	.08976	.09013	.095	596	51
10	.09005	.09042	11.059	.99594	**50**
11	034	071	11.024	591	49
12	063	101	10.988	588	48
13	092	130	.953	586	47
14	121	159	.918	583	46
15	.09150	.09189	10.883	.99580	**45**
16	179	218	.848	578	44
17	208	247	.814	575	43
18	237	277	.780	572	42
19	266	306	.746	570	41
20	.09295	.09335	10.712	.99567	**40**
21	324	365	.678	564	39
22	353	394	.645	562	38
23	382	423	.612	559	37
24	411	453	.579	556	36
25	.09440	.09482	10.546	.99553	**35**
26	469	511	.514	551	34
27	498	541	.481	548	33
28	527	570	.449	545	32
29	556	600	.417	542	31
30	.09585	.09629	10.385	.99540	**30**
31	614	658	.354	537	29
32	642	688	.322	534	28
33	671	717	.291	531	27
34	700	746	.260	528	26
35	.09729	.09776	10.229	.99526	**25**
36	758	805	.199	523	24
37	787	834	.168	520	23
38	816	864	.138	517	22
39	845	893	.108	514	21
40	.09874	.09923	10.078	.99511	**20**
41	903	952	.048	508	19
42	932	.09981	10.019	506	18
43	961	.10011	9.9893	503	17
44	.09990	040	.9601	500	16
45	.10019	.10069	9.9310	.99497	**15**
46	048	099	.9021	494	14
47	077	128	.8734	491	13
48	106	158	.8448	488	12
49	135	187	.8164	485	11
50	.10164	.10216	9.7882	.99482	**10**
51	192	246	.7601	479	9
52	221	275	.7322	476	8
53	250	305	.7044	473	7
54	279	334	.6768	470	6
55	.10308	.10363	9.6493	.99467	**5**
56	337	393	.6220	464	4
57	366	422	.5949	461	3
58	395	452	.5679	458	2
59	424	481	.5411	455	1
60	.10453	.10510	9.5144	.99452	**0**
	Cos	Ctn	Tan	Sin	′

84°

6°—Natural Trigonometric Functions—7°

′	Sin	Tan	Ctn	Cos	
0	.10453	.10510	9.5144	.99452	**60**
1	482	540	.4878	449	59
2	511	569	.4614	446	58
3	540	599	.4352	443	57
4	569	628	.4090	440	56
5	.10597	.10657	9.3831	.99437	**55**
6	626	687	.3572	434	54
7	655	716	.3315	431	53
8	684	746	.3060	428	52
9	713	775	.2806	424	51
10	.10742	.10805	9.2553	.99421	**50**
11	771	834	.2302	418	49
12	800	863	.2052	415	48
13	829	893	.1803	412	47
14	858	922	.1555	409	46
15	.10887	.10952	9.1309	.99406	**45**
16	916	.10981	.1065	402	44
17	945	.11011	.0821	399	43
18	.10973	040	.0579	396	42
19	.11002	070	.0338	393	41
20	.11031	.11099	9.0098	.99390	**40**
21	060	128	8.9860	386	39
22	089	158	.9623	383	38
23	118	187	.9387	380	37
24	147	217	.9152	377	36
25	.11176	.11246	8.8919	.99374	**35**
26	205	276	.8686	370	34
27	234	305	.8455	367	33
28	263	335	.8225	364	32
29	291	364	.7996	360	31
30	.11320	.11394	8.7769	.99357	**30**
31	349	423	.7542	354	29
32	378	452	.7317	351	28
33	407	482	.7093	347	27
34	436	511	.6870	344	26
35	.11465	.11541	8.6648	.99341	**25**
36	494	570	.6427	337	24
37	523	600	.6208	334	23
38	552	629	.5989	331	22
39	580	659	.5772	327	21
40	.11609	.11688	8.5555	.99324	**20**
41	638	718	.5340	320	19
42	667	747	.5126	317	18
43	696	777	.4913	314	17
44	725	806	.4701	310	16
45	.11754	.11836	8.4490	.99307	**15**
46	783	865	.4280	303	14
47	812	895	.4071	300	13
48	840	924	.3863	297	12
49	869	954	.3656	293	11
50	.11898	.11983	8.3450	.99290	**10**
51	927	.12013	.3245	286	9
52	956	042	.3041	283	8
53	.11985	072	.2838	279	7
54	.12014	101	.2636	276	6
55	.12043	.12131	8.2434	.99272	**5**
56	071	160	.2234	269	4
57	100	190	.2035	265	3
58	129	219	.1837	262	2
59	158	249	.1640	258	1
60	.12187	.12278	8.1443	.99255	**0**
	Cos	Ctn	Tan	Sin	′

83°

′	Sin	Tan	Ctn	Cos	
0	.12187	.12278	8.1443	.99255	**60**
1	216	308	.1248	251	59
2	245	338	.1054	248	58
3	274	367	.0860	244	57
4	302	397	.0667	240	56
5	.12331	.12426	8.0476	.99237	**55**
6	360	456	.0285	233	54
7	389	485	8.0095	230	53
8	418	515	7.9906	226	52
9	447	544	.9718	222	51
10	.12476	.12574	7.9530	.99219	**50**
11	504	603	.9344	215	49
12	533	633	.9158	211	48
13	562	662	.8973	208	47
14	591	692	.8789	204	46
15	.12620	.12722	7.8606	.99200	**45**
16	649	751	.8424	197	44
17	678	781	.8243	193	43
18	706	810	.8062	189	42
19	735	840	.7882	186	41
20	.12764	.12869	7.7704	.99182	**40**
21	793	899	.7525	178	39
22	822	929	.7348	175	38
23	851	958	.7171	171	37
24	880	.12988	.6996	167	36
25	.12908	.13017	7.6821	.99163	**35**
26	937	047	.6647	160	34
27	966	076	.6473	156	33
28	.12995	106	.6301	152	32
29	.13024	136	.6129	148	31
30	.13053	.13165	7.5958	.99144	**30**
31	081	195	.5787	141	29
32	110	224	.5618	137	28
33	139	254	.5449	133	27
34	168	284	.5281	129	26
35	.13197	.13313	7.5113	.99125	**25**
36	226	343	.4947	122	24
37	254	372	.4781	118	23
38	283	402	.4615	114	22
39	312	432	.4451	110	21
40	.13341	.13461	7.4287	.99106	**20**
41	370	491	.4124	102	19
42	399	521	.3962	098	18
43	427	550	.3800	094	17
44	456	580	.3639	091	16
45	.13485	.13609	7.3479	.99087	**15**
46	514	639	.3319	083	14
47	543	669	.3160	079	13
48	572	698	.3002	075	12
49	600	728	.2844	071	11
50	.13629	.13758	7.2687	.99067	**10**
51	658	787	.2531	063	9
52	687	817	.2375	059	8
53	716	846	.2220	055	7
54	744	876	.2066	051	6
55	.13773	.13906	7.1912	.99047	**5**
56	802	935	.1759	043	4
57	831	965	.1607	039	3
58	860	.13995	.1455	035	2
59	889	.14024	.1304	031	1
60	.13917	.14054	7.1154	.99027	**0**
	Cos	Ctn	Tan	Sin	′

82°

8°—Natural Trigonometric Functions—9°

′	Sin	Tan	Ctn	Cos	
0	.13917	.14054	7.1154	.99027	60
1	946	084	.1004	023	59
2	.13975	113	.0855	019	58
3	.14004	143	.0706	015	57
4	033	173	.0558	011	56
5	.14061	.14202	7.0410	.99006	55
6	090	232	.0264	.99002	54
7	119	262	7.0117	.98998	53
8	148	291	6.9972	994	52
9	177	321	.9827	990	51
10	.14205	.14351	6.9682	.98986	50
11	234	381	.9538	982	49
12	263	410	.9395	978	48
13	292	440	.9252	973	47
14	320	470	.9110	969	46
15	.14349	.14499	6.8969	.98965	45
16	378	529	.8828	961	44
17	407	559	.8687	957	43
18	436	588	.8548	953	42
19	464	618	.8408	948	41
20	.14493	.14648	6.8269	.98944	40
21	522	678	.8131	940	39
22	551	707	.7994	936	38
23	580	737	.7856	931	37
24	608	767	.7720	927	36
25	.14637	.14796	6.7584	.98923	35
26	666	826	.7448	919	34
27	695	856	.7313	914	33
28	723	886	.7179	910	32
29	752	915	.7045	906	31
30	.14781	.14945	6.6912	.98902	30
31	810	.14975	.6779	897	29
32	838	.15005	.6646	893	28
33	867	034	.6514	889	27
34	896	064	.6383	884	26
35	.14925	.15094	6.6252	.98880	25
36	954	124	.6122	876	24
37	.14982	153	.5992	871	23
38	.15011	183	.5863	867	22
39	040	213	.5734	863	21
40	.15069	.15243	6.5606	.98858	20
41	097	272	.5478	854	19
42	126	302	.5350	849	18
43	155	332	.5223	845	17
44	184	362	.5097	841	16
45	.15212	.15391	6.4971	.98836	15
46	241	421	.4846	832	14
47	270	451	.4721	827	13
48	299	481	.4596	823	12
49	327	511	.4472	818	11
50	.15356	.15540	6.4348	.98814	10
51	385	570	.4225	809	9
52	414	600	.4103	805	8
53	442	630	.3980	800	7
54	471	660	.3859	796	6
55	.15500	.15689	6.3737	.98791	5
56	529	719	.3617	787	4
57	557	749	.3496	782	3
58	586	779	.3376	778	2
59	615	809	.3257	773	1
60	.15643	.15838	6.3138	.98769	0
	Cos	Ctn	Tan	Sin	′

81°

′	Sin	Tan	Ctn	Cos	
0	.15643	.15838	6.3138	.98769	60
1	672	868	.3019	764	59
2	701	898	.2901	760	58
3	730	928	.2783	755	57
4	758	958	.2666	751	56
5	.15787	.15988	6.2549	.98746	55
6	816	.16017	.2432	741	54
7	845	047	.2316	737	53
8	873	077	.2200	732	52
9	902	107	.2085	728	51
10	.15931	.16137	6.1970	.98723	50
11	959	167	.1856	718	49
12	.15988	196	.1742	714	48
13	.16017	226	.1628	709	47
14	046	256	.1515	704	46
15	.16074	.16286	6.1402	.98700	45
16	103	316	.1290	695	44
17	132	346	.1178	690	43
18	160	376	.1066	686	42
19	189	405	.0955	681	41
20	.16218	.16435	6.0844	.98676	40
21	246	465	.0734	671	39
22	275	495	.0624	667	38
23	304	525	.0514	662	37
24	333	555	.0405	657	36
25	.16361	.16585	6.0296	.98652	35
26	390	615	.0188	648	34
27	419	645	6.0080	643	33
28	447	674	5.9972	638	32
29	476	704	.9865	633	31
30	.16505	.16734	5.9758	.98629	30
31	533	764	.9651	624	29
32	562	794	.9545	619	28
33	591	824	.9439	614	27
34	620	854	.9333	609	26
35	.16648	.16884	5.9228	.98604	25
36	677	914	.9124	600	24
37	706	944	.9019	595	23
38	734	.16974	.8915	590	22
39	763	.17004	.8811	585	21
40	.16792	.17033	5.8708	.98580	20
41	820	063	.8605	575	19
42	849	093	.8502	570	18
43	878	123	.8400	565	17
44	906	153	.8298	561	16
45	.16935	.17183	5.8197	.98556	15
46	964	213	.8095	551	14
47	.16992	243	.7994	546	13
48	.17021	273	.7894	541	12
49	050	303	.7794	536	11
50	.17078	.17333	5.7694	.98531	10
51	107	363	.7594	526	9
52	136	393	.7495	521	8
53	164	423	.7396	516	7
54	193	453	.7297	511	6
55	.17222	.17483	5.7199	.98506	5
56	250	513	.7101	501	4
57	279	543	.7004	496	3
58	308	573	.6906	491	2
59	336	603	.6809	486	1
60	.17365	.17633	5.6713	.98481	0
	Cos	Ctn	Tan	Sin	′

80°

10°—Natural Trigonometric Functions—11°

′	Sin	Tan	Ctn	Cos	
0	.17365	.17633	5.6713	.98481	60
1	393	663	.6617	476	59
2	422	693	.6521	471	58
3	451	723	.6425	466	57
4	479	753	.6329	461	56
5	.17508	.17783	5.6234	.98455	55
6	537	813	.6140	450	54
7	565	843	.6045	445	53
8	594	873	.5951	440	52
9	623	903	.5857	435	51
10	.17651	.17933	5.5764	.98430	50
11	680	963	.5671	425	49
12	708	.17993	.5578	420	48
13	737	.18023	.5485	414	47
14	766	053	.5393	409	46
15	.17794	.18083	5.5301	.98404	45
16	823	113	.5209	399	44
17	852	143	.5118	394	43
18	880	173	.5026	389	42
19	909	203	.4936	383	41
20	.17937	.18233	5.4845	.98378	40
21	966	263	.4755	373	39
22	.17995	293	.4665	368	38
23	.18023	323	.4575	362	37
24	052	353	.4486	357	36
25	.18081	.18384	5.4397	.98352	35
26	109	414	.4308	347	34
27	138	444	.4219	341	33
28	166	474	.4131	336	32
29	195	504	.4043	331	31
30	.18224	.18534	5.3955	.98325	30
31	252	564	.3868	320	29
32	281	594	.3781	315	28
33	309	624	.3694	310	27
34	338	654	.3607	304	26
35	.18367	.18684	5.3521	.98299	25
36	395	714	.3435	294	24
37	424	745	.3349	288	23
38	452	775	.3263	283	22
39	481	805	.3178	277	21
40	.18509	.18835	5.3093	.98272	20
41	538	865	.3008	267	19
42	567	895	.2924	261	18
43	595	925	.2839	256	17
44	624	955	.2755	250	16
45	.18652	.18986	5.2672	.98245	15
46	681	.19016	.2588	240	14
47	710	046	.2505	234	13
48	738	076	.2422	229	12
49	767	106	.2339	223	11
50	.18795	.19136	5.2257	.98218	10
51	824	166	.2174	212	9
52	852	197	.2092	207	8
53	881	227	.2011	201	7
54	910	257	.1929	196	6
55	.18938	.19287	5.1848	.98190	5
56	967	317	.1767	185	4
57	.18995	347	.1686	179	3
58	.19024	378	.1606	174	2
59	052	408	.1526	168	1
60	.19081	.19438	5.1446	.98163	0
	Cos	Ctn	Tan	Sin	′

79°

′	Sin	Tan	Ctn	Cos	
0	.19081	.19438	5.1446	.98163	60
1	109	468	.1366	157	59
2	138	498	.1286	152	58
3	167	529	.1207	146	57
4	195	559	.1128	140	56
5	.19224	.19589	5.1049	.98135	55
6	252	619	.0970	129	54
7	281	649	.0892	124	53
8	309	680	.0814	118	52
9	338	710	.0736	112	51
10	.19366	.19740	5.0658	.98107	50
11	395	770	.0581	101	49
12	423	801	.0504	096	48
13	452	831	.0427	090	47
14	481	861	.0350	084	46
15	.19509	.19891	5.0273	.98079	45
16	538	921	.0197	073	44
17	566	952	.0121	067	43
18	595	.19982	5.0045	061	42
19	623	.20012	4.9969	056	41
20	.19652	.20042	4.9894	.98050	40
21	680	073	.9819	044	39
22	709	103	.9744	039	38
23	737	133	.9669	033	37
24	766	164	.9594	027	36
25	.19794	.20194	4.9520	.98021	35
26	823	224	.9446	016	34
27	851	254	.9372	010	33
28	880	285	.9298	.98004	32
29	908	315	.9225	.97998	31
30	.19937	.20345	4.9152	.97992	30
31	965	376	.9078	987	29
32	.19994	406	.9006	981	28
33	.20022	436	.8933	975	27
34	051	466	.8860	969	26
35	.20079	.20497	4.8788	.97963	25
36	108	527	.8716	958	24
37	136	557	.8644	952	23
38	165	588	.8573	946	22
39	193	618	.8501	940	21
40	.20222	.20648	4.8430	.97934	20
41	250	679	.8359	928	19
42	279	709	.8288	922	18
43	307	739	.8218	916	17
44	336	770	.8147	910	16
45	.20364	.20800	4.8077	.97905	15
46	393	830	.8007	899	14
47	421	861	.7937	893	13
48	450	891	.7867	887	12
49	478	921	.7798	881	11
50	.20507	.20952	4.7729	.97875	10
51	535	.20982	.7659	869	9
52	563	.21013	.7591	863	8
53	592	043	.7522	857	7
54	620	073	.7453	851	6
55	.20649	.21104	4.7385	.97845	5
56	677	134	.7317	839	4
57	706	164	.7249	833	3
58	734	195	.7181	827	2
59	763	225	.7114	821	1
60	.20791	.21256	4.7046	.97815	0
	Cos	Ctn	Tan	Sin	′

78°

12°—Natural Trigonometric Functions—13°

′	Sin	Tan	Ctn	Cos	
0	.20791	.21256	4.7046	.97815	60
1	820	286	.6979	809	59
2	848	316	.6912	803	58
3	877	347	.6845	797	57
4	905	377	.6779	791	56
5	.20933	.21408	4.6712	.97784	55
6	962	438	.6646	778	54
7	.20990	469	.6580	772	53
8	.21019	499	.6514	766	52
9	047	529	.6448	760	51
10	.21076	.21560	4.6382	.97754	50
11	104	590	.6317	748	49
12	132	621	.6252	742	48
13	161	651	.6187	735	47
14	189	682	.6122	729	46
15	.21218	.21712	4.6057	.97723	45
16	246	743	.5993	717	44
17	275	773	.5928	711	43
18	303	804	.5864	705	42
19	331	834	.5800	698	41
20	.21360	.21864	4.5736	.97692	40
21	388	895	.5673	686	39
22	417	925	.5609	680	38
23	445	956	.5546	673	37
24	474	.21986	.5483	667	36
25	.21502	.22017	4.5420	.97661	35
26	530	047	.5357	655	34
27	559	078	.5294	648	33
28	587	108	.5232	642	32
29	616	139	.5169	636	31
30	.21644	.22169	4.5107	.97630	30
31	672	200	.5045	623	29
32	701	231	.4983	617	28
33	729	261	.4922	611	27
34	758	292	.4860	604	26
35	.21786	.22322	4.4799	.97598	25
36	814	353	.4737	592	24
37	843	383	.4676	585	23
38	871	414	.4615	579	22
39	899	444	.4555	573	21
40	.21928	.22475	4.4494	.97566	20
41	956	505	.4434	560	19
42	.21985	536	.4373	553	18
43	.22013	567	.4313	547	17
44	041	597	.4253	541	16
45	.22070	.22628	4.4194	.97534	15
46	098	658	.4134	528	14
47	126	689	.4075	521	13
48	155	719	.4015	515	12
49	183	750	.3956	508	11
50	.22212	.22781	4.3897	.97502	10
51	240	811	.3838	496	9
52	268	842	.3779	489	8
53	297	872	.3721	483	7
54	325	903	.3662	476	6
55	.22353	.22934	4.3604	.97470	5
56	382	964	.3546	463	4
57	410	.22995	.3488	457	3
58	438	.23026	.3430	450	2
59	467	056	.3372	444	1
60	.22495	.23087	4.3315	.97437	0
	Cos	Ctn	Tan	Sin	′

77°

′	Sin	Tan	Ctn	Cos	
0	.22495	.23087	4.3315	.97437	60
1	523	117	.3257	430	59
2	552	148	.3200	424	58
3	580	179	.3143	417	57
4	608	209	.3086	411	56
5	.22637	.23240	4.3029	.97404	55
6	665	271	.2972	398	54
7	693	301	.2916	391	53
8	722	332	.2859	384	52
9	750	363	.2803	378	51
10	.22778	.23393	4.2747	.97371	50
11	807	424	.2691	365	49
12	835	455	.2635	358	48
13	863	485	.2580	351	47
14	892	516	.2524	345	46
15	.22920	.23547	4.2468	.97338	45
16	948	578	.2413	331	44
17	.22977	608	.2358	325	43
18	.23005	639	.2303	318	42
19	033	670	.2248	311	41
20	.23062	.23700	4.2193	.97304	40
21	090	731	.2139	298	39
22	118	762	.2084	291	38
23	146	793	.2030	284	37
24	175	823	.1976	278	36
25	.23203	.23854	4.1922	.97271	35
26	231	885	.1868	264	34
27	260	916	.1814	257	33
28	288	946	.1760	251	32
29	316	.23977	.1706	244	31
30	.23345	.24008	4.1653	.97237	30
31	373	039	.1600	230	29
32	401	069	.1547	223	28
33	429	100	.1493	217	27
34	458	131	.1441	210	26
35	.23486	.24162	4.1388	.97203	25
36	514	193	.1335	196	24
37	542	223	.1282	189	23
38	571	254	.1230	182	22
39	599	285	.1178	176	21
40	.23627	.24316	4.1126	.97169	20
41	656	347	.1074	162	19
42	684	377	.1022	155	18
43	712	408	.0970	148	17
44	740	439	.0918	141	16
45	.23769	.24470	4.0867	.97134	15
46	797	501	.0815	127	14
47	825	532	.0764	120	13
48	853	562	.0713	113	12
49	882	593	.0662	106	11
50	.23910	.24624	4.0611	.97100	10
51	938	655	.0560	093	9
52	966	686	.0509	086	8
53	.23995	717	.0459	079	7
54	.24023	747	.0408	072	6
55	.24051	.24778	4.0358	.97065	5
56	079	809	.0308	058	4
57	108	840	.0257	051	3
58	136	871	.0207	044	2
59	164	902	.0158	037	1
60	.24192	.24933	4.0108	.97030	0
	Cos	Ctn	Tan	Sin	′

76°

′	Sin	Tan	Ctn	Cos	
0	.24192	.24933	4.0108	.97030	**60**
1	220	964	.0058	023	59
2	249	.24995	4.0009	015	58
3	277	.25026	3.9959	008	57
4	305	056	.9910	.97001	56
5	.24333	.25087	3.9861	.96994	**55**
6	362	118	.9812	987	54
7	390	149	.9763	980	53
8	418	180	.9714	973	52
9	446	211	.9665	966	51
10	.24474	.25242	3.9617	.96959	**50**
11	503	273	.9568	952	49
12	531	304	.9520	945	48
13	559	335	.9471	937	47
14	587	366	.9423	930	46
15	.24615	.25397	3.9375	.96923	**45**
16	644	428	.9327	916	44
17	672	459	.9279	909	43
18	700	490	.9232	902	42
19	728	521	.9184	894	41
20	.24756	.25552	3.9136	.96887	**40**
21	784	583	.9089	880	39
22	813	614	.9042	873	38
23	841	645	.8995	866	37
24	869	676	.8947	858	36
25	.24897	.25707	3.8900	.96851	**35**
26	925	738	.8854	844	34
27	954	769	.8807	837	33
28	.24982	800	.8760	829	32
29	.25010	831	.8714	822	31
30	.25038	.25862	3.8667	.96815	**30**
31	066	893	.8621	807	29
32	094	924	.8575	800	28
33	122	955	.8528	793	27
34	151	.25986	.8482	786	26
35	.25179	.26017	3.8436	.96778	**25**
36	207	048	.8391	771	24
37	235	079	.8345	764	23
38	263	110	.8299	756	22
39	291	141	.8254	749	21
40	.25320	.26172	3.8208	.96742	**20**
41	348	203	.8163	734	19
42	376	235	.8118	727	18
43	404	266	.8073	719	17
44	432	297	.8028	712	16
45	.25460	.26328	3.7983	.96705	**15**
46	488	359	.7938	697	14
47	516	390	.7893	690	13
48	545	421	.7848	682	12
49	573	452	.7804	675	11
50	.25601	.26483	3.7760	.96667	**10**
51	629	515	.7715	660	9
52	657	546	.7671	653	8
53	685	577	.7627	645	7
54	713	608	.7583	638	6
55	.25741	.26639	3.7539	.96630	**5**
56	769	670	.7495	623	4
57	798	701	.7451	615	3
58	826	733	.7408	608	2
59	854	764	.7364	600	1
60	.25882	.26795	3.7321	.96593	**0**
	Cos	Ctn	Tan	Sin	′

75°

′	Sin	Tan	Ctn	Cos	
0	.25882	.26795	3.7321	.96593	**60**
1	910	826	.7277	585	59
2	938	857	.7234	578	58
3	966	888	.7191	570	57
4	.25994	920	.7148	562	56
5	.26022	.26951	3.7105	.96555	**55**
6	050	.26982	.7062	547	54
7	079	.27013	.7019	540	53
8	107	044	.6976	532	52
9	135	076	.6933	524	51
10	.26163	.27107	3.6891	.96517	**50**
11	191	138	.6848	509	49
12	219	169	.6806	502	48
13	247	201	.6764	494	47
14	275	232	.6722	486	46
15	.26303	.27263	3.6680	.96479	**45**
16	331	294	.6638	471	44
17	359	326	.6596	463	43
18	387	357	.6554	456	42
19	415	388	.6512	448	41
20	.26443	.27419	3.6470	.96440	**40**
21	471	451	.6429	433	39
22	500	482	.6387	425	38
23	528	513	.6346	417	37
24	556	545	.6305	410	36
25	.26584	.27576	3.6264	.96402	**35**
26	612	607	.6222	394	34
27	640	638	.6181	386	33
28	668	670	.6140	379	32
29	696	701	.6100	371	31
30	.26724	.27732	3.6059	.96363	**30**
31	752	764	.6018	355	29
32	780	795	.5978	347	28
33	808	826	.5937	340	27
34	836	858	.5897	332	26
35	.26864	.27889	3.5856	.96324	**25**
36	892	921	.5816	316	24
37	920	952	.5776	308	23
38	948	.27983	.5736	301	22
39	.26976	.28015	.5696	293	21
40	.27004	.28046	3.5656	.96285	**20**
41	032	077	.5616	277	19
42	060	109	.5576	269	18
43	088	140	.5536	261	17
44	116	172	.5497	253	16
45	.27144	.28203	3.5457	.96246	**15**
46	172	234	.5418	238	14
47	200	266	.5379	230	13
48	228	297	.5339	222	12
49	256	329	.5300	214	11
50	.27284	.28360	3.5261	.96206	**10**
51	312	391	.5222	198	9
52	340	423	.5183	190	8
53	368	454	.5144	182	7
54	396	486	.5105	174	6
55	.27424	.28517	3.5067	.96166	**5**
56	452	549	.5028	158	4
57	480	580	.4989	150	3
58	508	612	.4951	142	2
59	536	643	.4912	134	1
60	.27564	.28675	3.4874	.96126	**0**
	Cos	Ctn	Tan	Sin	′

74°

16°—Natural Trigonometric Functions—17°

16°

′	Sin	Tan	Ctn	Cos	
0	.27564	.28675	3.4874	.96126	**60**
1	592	706	.4836	118	59
2	620	738	.4798	110	58
3	648	769	.4760	102	57
4	676	801	.4722	094	56
5	.27704	.28832	3.4684	.96086	**55**
6	731	864	.4646	078	54
7	759	895	.4608	070	53
8	787	927	.4570	062	52
9	815	958	.4533	054	51
10	.27843	.28990	3.4495	.96046	**50**
11	871	.29021	.4458	037	49
12	899	053	.4420	029	48
13	927	084	.4383	021	47
14	955	116	.4346	013	46
15	.27983	.29147	3.4308	.96005	**45**
16	.28011	179	.4271	.95997	44
17	039	210	.4234	989	43
18	067	242	.4197	981	42
19	095	274	.4160	972	41
20	.28123	.29305	3.4124	.95964	**40**
21	150	337	.4087	956	39
22	178	368	.4050	948	38
23	206	400	.4014	940	37
24	234	432	.3977	931	36
25	.28262	.29463	3.3941	.95923	**35**
26	290	495	.3904	915	34
27	318	526	.3868	907	33
28	346	558	.3832	898	32
29	374	590	.3796	890	31
30	.28402	.29621	3.3759	.95882	**30**
31	429	653	.3723	874	29
32	457	685	.3687	865	28
33	485	716	.3652	857	27
34	513	748	.3616	849	26
35	.28541	.29780	3.3580	.95841	**25**
36	569	811	.3544	832	24
37	597	843	.3509	824	23
38	625	875	.3473	816	22
39	652	906	.3438	807	21
40	.28680	.29938	3.3402	.95799	**20**
41	708	.29970	.3367	791	19
42	736	.30001	.3332	782	18
43	764	033	.3297	774	17
44	792	065	.3261	766	16
45	.28820	.30097	3.3226	.95757	**15**
46	847	128	.3191	749	14
47	875	160	.3156	740	13
48	903	192	.3122	732	12
49	931	224	.3087	724	11
50	.28959	.30255	3.3052	.95715	**10**
51	.28987	287	.3017	707	9
52	.29015	319	.2983	698	8
53	042	351	.2948	690	7
54	070	382	.2914	681	6
55	.29098	.30414	3.2879	.95673	**5**
56	126	446	.2845	664	4
57	154	478	.2811	656	3
58	182	509	.2777	647	2
59	209	541	.2743	639	1
60	.29237	.30573	3.2709	.95630	**0**
	Cos	**Ctn**	**Tan**	**Sin**	**′**

73°

17°

′	Sin	Tan	Ctn	Cos	
0	.29237	.30573	3.2709	.95630	**60**
1	265	605	.2675	622	59
2	293	637	.2641	613	58
3	321	669	.2607	605	57
4	348	700	.2573	596	56
5	.29376	.30732	3.2539	.95588	**55**
6	404	764	.2506	579	54
7	432	796	.2472	571	53
8	460	828	.2438	562	52
9	487	860	.2405	554	51
10	.29515	.30891	3.2371	.95545	**50**
11	543	923	.2338	536	49
12	571	955	.2305	528	48
13	599	.30987	.2272	519	47
14	626	.31019	.2238	511	46
15	.29654	.31051	3.2205	.95502	**45**
16	682	083	.2172	493	44
17	710	115	.2139	485	43
18	737	147	.2106	476	42
19	765	178	.2073	467	41
20	.29793	.31210	3.2041	.95459	**40**
21	821	242	.2008	450	39
22	849	274	.1975	441	38
23	876	306	.1943	433	37
24	904	338	.1910	424	36
25	.29932	.31370	3.1878	.95415	**35**
26	960	402	.1845	407	34
27	.29987	434	.1813	398	33
28	.30015	466	.1780	389	32
29	043	498	.1748	380	31
30	.30071	.31530	3.1716	.95372	**30**
31	098	562	.1684	363	29
32	126	594	.1652	354	28
33	154	626	.1620	345	27
34	182	658	.1588	337	26
35	.30209	.31690	3.1556	.95328	**25**
36	237	722	.1524	319	24
37	265	754	.1492	310	23
38	292	786	.1460	301	22
39	320	818	.1429	293	21
40	.30348	.31850	3.1397	.95284	**20**
41	376	882	.1366	275	19
42	403	914	.1334	266	18
43	431	946	.1303	257	17
44	459	.31978	.1271	248	16
45	.30486	.32010	3.1240	.95240	**15**
46	514	042	.1209	231	14
47	542	074	.1178	222	13
48	570	106	.1146	213	12
49	597	139	.1115	204	11
50	.30625	.32171	3.1084	.95195	**10**
51	653	203	.1053	186	9
52	680	235	.1022	177	8
53	708	267	.0991	168	7
54	736	299	.0961	159	6
55	.30763	.32331	3.0930	.95150	**5**
56	791	363	.0899	142	4
57	819	396	.0868	133	3
58	846	428	.0838	124	2
59	874	460	.0807	115	1
60	.30902	.32492	3.0777	.95106	**0**
	Cos	**Ctn**	**Tan**	**Sin**	**′**

72°

18°—Natural Trigonometric Functions—19°

'	Sin	Tan	Ctn	Cos	
0	.30902	.32492	3.0777	.95106	**60**
1	929	524	.0746	097	59
2	957	556	.0716	088	58
3	.30985	588	.0686	079	57
4	.31012	621	.0655	070	56
5	.31040	.32653	3.0625	.95061	**55**
6	068	685	.0595	052	54
7	095	717	.0565	043	53
8	123	749	.0535	033	52
9	151	782	.0505	024	51
10	.31178	.32814	3.0475	.95015	**50**
11	206	846	.0445	.95006	49
12	233	878	.0415	.94997	48
13	261	911	.0385	988	47
14	289	943	.0356	979	46
15	.31316	.32975	3.0326	.94970	**45**
16	344	.33007	.0296	961	44
17	372	040	.0267	952	43
18	399	072	.0237	943	42
19	427	104	.0208	933	41
20	.31454	.33136	3.0178	.94924	**40**
21	482	169	.0149	915	39
22	510	201	.0120	906	38
23	537	233	.0090	897	37
24	565	266	.0061	888	36
25	.31593	.33298	3.0032	.94878	**35**
26	620	330	3.0003	869	34
27	648	363	2.9974	860	33
28	675	395	.9945	851	32
29	703	427	.9916	842	31
30	.31730	.33460	2.9887	.94832	**30**
31	758	492	.9858	823	29
32	786	524	.9829	814	28
33	813	557	.9800	805	27
34	841	589	.9772	795	26
35	.31868	.33621	2.9743	.94786	**25**
36	896	654	.9714	777	24
37	923	686	.9686	768	23
38	951	718	.9657	758	22
39	.31979	751	.9629	749	21
40	.32006	.33783	2.9600	.94740	**20**
41	034	816	.9572	730	19
42	061	848	.9544	721	18
43	089	881	.9515	712	17
44	116	913	.9487	702	16
45	.32144	.33945	2.9459	.94693	**15**
46	171	.33978	.9431	684	14
47	199	.34010	.9403	674	13
48	227	043	.9375	665	12
49	254	075	.9347	656	11
50	.32282	.34108	2.9319	.94646	**10**
51	309	140	.9291	637	9
52	337	173	.9263	627	8
53	364	205	.9235	618	7
54	392	238	.9208	609	6
55	.32419	.34270	2.9180	.94599	**5**
56	447	303	.9152	590	4
57	474	335	.9125	580	3
58	502	368	.9097	571	2
59	529	400	.9070	561	1
60	.32557	.34433	2.9042	.94552	**0**
	Cos	Ctn	Tan	Sin	'

71°

'	Sin	Tan	Ctn	Cos	
0	.32557	.34433	2.9042	.94552	**60**
1	584	465	.9015	542	59
2	612	498	.8987	533	58
3	639	530	.8960	523	57
4	667	563	.8933	514	56
5	.32694	.34596	2.8905	.94504	**55**
6	722	628	.8878	495	54
7	749	661	.8851	485	53
8	777	693	.8824	476	52
9	804	726	.8797	466	51
10	.32832	.34758	2.8770	.94457	**50**
11	859	791	.8743	447	49
12	887	824	.8716	438	48
13	914	856	.8689	428	47
14	942	889	.8662	418	46
15	.32969	.34922	2.8636	.94409	**45**
16	.32997	954	.8609	399	44
17	.33024	.34987	.8582	390	43
18	051	.35020	.8556	380	42
19	079	052	.8529	370	41
20	.33106	.35085	2.8502	.94361	**40**
21	134	118	.8476	351	39
22	161	150	.8449	342	38
23	189	183	.8423	332	37
24	216	216	.8397	322	36
25	.33244	.35248	2.8370	.94313	**35**
26	271	281	.8344	303	34
27	298	314	.8318	293	33
28	326	346	.8291	284	32
29	353	379	.8265	274	31
30	.33381	.35412	2.8239	.94264	**30**
31	408	445	.8213	254	29
32	436	477	.8187	245	28
33	463	510	.8161	235	27
34	490	543	.8135	225	26
35	.33518	.35576	2.8109	.94215	**25**
36	545	608	.8083	206	24
37	573	641	.8057	196	23
38	600	674	.8032	186	22
39	627	707	.8006	176	21
40	.33655	.35740	2.7980	.94167	**20**
41	682	772	.7955	157	19
42	710	805	.7929	147	18
43	737	838	.7903	137	17
44	764	871	.7878	127	16
45	.33792	.35904	2.7852	.94118	**15**
46	819	937	.7827	108	14
47	846	.35969	.7801	098	13
48	874	.36002	.7776	088	12
49	901	035	.7751	078	11
50	.33929	.36068	2.7725	.94068	**10**
51	956	101	.7700	058	9
52	.33983	134	.7675	049	8
53	.34011	167	.7650	039	7
54	038	199	.7625	029	6
55	.34065	.36232	2.7600	.94019	**5**
56	093	265	.7575	.94009	4
57	120	298	.7550	.93999	3
58	147	331	.7525	989	2
59	175	364	.7500	979	1
60	.34202	.36397	2.7475	.93969	**0**
	Cos	Ctn	Tan	Sin	'

70°

20°—Natural Trigonometric Functions—21°

′	Sin	Tan	Ctn	Cos	
0	.34202	.36397	2.7475	.93969	60
1	229	430	.7450	959	59
2	257	463	.7425	949	58
3	284	496	.7400	939	57
4	311	529	.7376	929	56
5	.34339	.36562	2.7351	.93919	55
6	366	595	.7326	909	54
7	393	628	.7302	899	53
8	421	661	.7277	889	52
9	448	694	.7253	879	51
10	.34475	.36727	2.7228	.93869	50
11	503	760	.7204	859	49
12	530	793	.7179	849	48
13	557	826	.7155	839	47
14	584	859	.7130	829	46
15	.34612	.36892	2.7106	.93819	45
16	639	925	.7082	809	44
17	666	958	.7058	799	43
18	694	.36991	.7034	789	42
19	721	.37024	.7009	779	41
20	.34748	.37057	2.6985	.93769	40
21	775	090	.6961	759	39
22	803	123	.6937	748	38
23	830	157	.6913	738	37
24	857	190	.6889	728	36
25	.34884	.37223	2.6865	.93718	35
26	912	256	.6841	708	34
27	939	289	.6818	698	33
28	966	322	.6794	688	32
29	.34993	355	.6770	677	31
30	.35021	.37388	2.6746	.93667	30
31	048	422	.6723	657	29
32	075	455	.6699	647	28
33	102	488	.6675	637	27
34	130	521	.6652	626	26
35	.35157	.37554	2.6628	.93616	25
36	184	588	.6605	606	24
37	211	621	.6581	596	23
38	239	654	.6558	585	22
39	266	687	.6534	575	21
40	.35293	.37720	2.6511	.93565	20
41	320	754	.6488	555	19
42	347	787	.6464	544	18
43	375	820	.6441	534	17
44	402	853	.6418	524	16
45	.35429	.37887	2.6395	.93514	15
46	456	920	.6371	503	14
47	484	953	.6348	493	13
48	511	.37986	.6325	483	12
49	538	.38020	.6302	472	11
50	.35565	.38053	2.6279	.93462	10
51	592	086	.6256	452	9
52	619	120	.6233	441	8
53	647	153	.6210	431	7
54	674	186	.6187	420	6
55	.35701	.38220	2.6165	.93410	5
56	728	253	.6142	400	4
57	755	286	.6119	389	3
58	782	320	.6096	379	2
59	810	353	.6074	368	1
60	.35837	.38386	2.6051	.93358	0
	Cos	Ctn	Tan	Sin	′

69°

′	Sin	Tan	Ctn	Cos	
0	.35837	.38386	2.6051	.93358	60
1	864	420	.6028	348	59
2	891	453	.6006	337	58
3	918	487	.5983	327	57
4	945	520	.5961	316	56
5	.35973	.38553	2.5938	.93306	55
6	.36000	587	.5916	295	54
7	027	620	.5893	285	53
8	054	654	.5871	274	52
9	081	687	.5848	264	51
10	.36108	.38721	2.5826	.93253	50
11	135	754	.5804	243	49
12	162	787	.5782	232	48
13	190	821	.5759	222	47
14	217	854	.5737	211	46
15	.36244	.38888	2.5715	.93201	45
16	271	921	.5693	190	44
17	298	955	.5671	180	43
18	325	.38988	.5649	169	42
19	352	.39022	.5627	159	41
20	.36379	.39055	2.5605	.93148	40
21	406	089	.5583	137	39
22	434	122	.5561	127	38
23	461	156	.5539	116	37
24	488	190	.5517	106	36
25	.36515	.39223	2.5495	.93095	35
26	542	257	.5473	084	34
27	569	290	.5452	074	33
28	596	324	.5430	063	32
29	623	357	.5408	052	31
30	.36650	.39391	2.5386	.93042	30
31	677	425	.5365	031	29
32	704	458	.5343	020	28
33	731	492	.5322	.93010	27
34	758	526	.5300	.92999	26
35	.36785	.39559	2.5279	.92988	25
36	812	593	.5257	978	24
37	839	626	.5236	967	23
38	867	660	.5214	956	22
39	894	694	.5193	945	21
40	.36921	.39727	2.5172	.92935	20
41	948	761	.5150	924	19
42	.36975	795	.5129	913	18
43	.37002	829	.5108	902	17
44	029	862	.5086	892	16
45	.37056	.39896	2.5065	.92881	15
46	083	930	.5044	870	14
47	110	963	.5023	859	13
48	137	.39997	.5002	849	12
49	164	.40031	.4981	838	11
50	.37191	.40065	2.4960	.92827	10
51	218	098	.4939	816	9
52	245	132	.4918	805	8
53	272	166	.4897	794	7
54	299	200	.4876	784	6
55	.37326	.40234	2.4855	.92773	5
56	353	267	.4834	762	4
57	380	301	.4813	751	3
58	407	335	.4792	740	2
59	434	369	.4772	729	1
60	.37461	.40403	2.4751	.92718	0
	Cos	Ctn	Tan	Sin	′

68°

′	Sin	Tan	Ctn	Cos	
0	.37461	.40403	2.4751	.92718	60
1	488	436	.4730	707	59
2	515	470	.4709	697	58
3	542	504	.4689	686	57
4	569	538	.4668	675	56
5	.37595	.40572	2.4648	.92664	55
6	622	606	.4627	653	54
7	649	640	.4606	642	53
8	676	674	.4586	631	52
9	703	707	.4566	620	51
10	.37730	.40741	2.4545	.92609	50
11	757	775	.4525	598	49
12	784	809	.4504	587	48
13	811	843	.4484	576	47
14	838	877	.4464	565	46
15	.37865	.40911	2.4443	.92554	45
16	892	945	.4423	543	44
17	919	.40979	.4403	532	43
18	946	.41013	.4383	521	42
19	973	047	.4362	510	41
20	.37999	.41081	2.4342	.92499	40
21	.38026	115	.4322	488	39
22	053	149	.4302	477	38
23	080	183	.4282	466	37
24	107	217	.4262	455	36
25	.38134	.41251	2.4242	.92444	35
26	161	285	.4222	432	34
27	188	319	.4202	421	33
28	215	353	.4182	410	32
29	241	387	.4162	399	31
30	.38268	.41421	2.4142	.92388	30
31	295	455	.4122	377	29
32	322	490	.4102	366	28
33	349	524	.4083	355	27
34	376	558	.4063	343	26
35	.38403	.41592	2.4043	.92332	25
36	430	626	.4023	321	24
37	456	660	.4004	310	23
38	483	694	.3984	299	22
39	510	728	.3964	287	21
40	.38537	.41763	2.3945	.92276	20
41	564	797	.3925	265	19
42	591	831	.3906	254	18
43	617	865	.3886	243	17
44	644	899	.3867	231	16
45	.38671	.41933	2.3847	.92220	15
46	698	.41968	.3828	209	14
47	725	.42002	.3808	198	13
48	752	036	.3789	186	12
49	778	070	.3770	175	11
50	.38805	.42105	2.3750	.92164	10
51	832	139	.3731	152	9
52	859	173	.3712	141	8
53	886	207	.3693	130	7
54	912	242	.3673	119	6
55	.38939	.42276	2.3654	.92107	5
56	966	310	.3635	096	4
57	.38993	345	.3616	085	3
58	.39020	379	.3597	073	2
59	046	413	.3578	062	1
60	.39073	.42447	2.3559	.92050	0
	Cos	Ctn	Tan	Sin	′

67°

′	Sin	Tan	Ctn	Cos	
0	.39073	.42447	2.3559	.92050	60
1	100	482	.3539	039	59
2	127	516	.3520	028	58
3	153	551	.3501	016	57
4	180	585	.3483	.92005	56
5	.39207	.42619	2.3464	.91994	55
6	234	654	.3445	982	54
7	260	688	.3426	971	53
8	287	722	.3407	959	52
9	314	757	.3388	948	51
10	.39341	.42791	2.3369	.91936	50
11	367	826	.3351	925	49
12	394	860	.3332	914	48
13	421	894	.3313	902	47
14	448	929	.3294	891	46
15	.39474	.42963	2.3276	.91879	45
16	501	.42998	.3257	868	44
17	528	.43032	.3238	856	43
18	555	067	.3220	845	42
19	581	101	.3201	833	41
20	.39608	.43136	2.3183	.91822	40
21	635	170	.3164	810	39
22	661	205	.3146	799	38
23	688	239	.3127	787	37
24	715	274	.3109	775	36
25	.39741	.43308	2.3090	.91764	35
26	768	343	.3072	752	34
27	795	378	.3053	741	33
28	822	412	.3035	729	32
29	848	447	.3017	718	31
30	.39875	.43481	2.2998	.91706	30
31	902	516	.2980	694	29
32	928	550	.2962	683	28
33	955	585	.2944	671	27
34	.39982	620	.2925	660	26
35	.40008	.43654	2.2907	.91648	25
36	035	689	.2889	636	24
37	062	724	.2871	625	23
38	088	758	.2853	613	22
39	115	793	.2835	601	21
40	.40141	.43828	2.2817	.91590	20
41	168	862	.2799	578	19
42	195	897	.2781	566	18
43	221	932	.2763	555	17
44	248	.43966	.2745	543	16
45	.40275	.44001	2.2727	.91531	15
46	301	036	.2709	519	14
47	328	071	.2691	508	13
48	355	105	.2673	496	12
49	381	140	.2655	484	11
50	.40408	.44175	2.2637	.91472	10
51	434	210	.2620	461	9
52	461	244	.2602	449	8
53	488	279	.2584	437	7
54	514	314	.2566	425	6
55	.40541	.44349	2.2549	.91414	5
56	567	384	.2531	402	4
57	594	418	.2513	390	3
58	621	453	.2496	378	2
59	647	488	.2478	366	1
60	.40674	.44523	2.2460	.91355	0
	Cos	Ctn	Tan	Sin	′

66°

24°—Natural Trigonometric Functions—25°

′	Sin	Tan	Ctn	Cos	
0	.40674	.44523	2.2460	.91355	60
1	700	558	.2443	343	59
2	727	593	.2425	331	58
3	753	627	.2408	319	57
4	780	662	.2390	307	56
5	.40806	.44697	2.2373	.91295	55
6	833	732	.2355	283	54
7	860	767	.2338	272	53
8	886	802	.2320	260	52
9	913	837	.2303	248	51
10	.40939	.44872	2.2286	.91236	50
11	966	907	.2268	224	49
12	.40992	942	.2251	212	48
13	.41019	.44977	.2234	200	47
14	045	.45012	.2216	188	46
15	.41072	.45047	2.2199	.91176	45
16	098	082	.2182	164	44
17	125	117	.2165	152	43
18	151	152	.2148	140	42
19	178	187	.2130	128	41
20	.41204	.45222	2.2113	.91116	40
21	231	257	.2096	104	39
22	257	292	.2079	092	38
23	284	327	.2062	080	37
24	310	362	.2045	068	36
25	.41337	.45397	2.2028	.91056	35
26	363	432	.2011	044	34
27	390	467	.1994	032	33
28	416	502	.1977	020	32
29	443	538	.1960	.91008	31
30	.41469	.45573	2.1943	.90996	30
31	496	608	.1926	984	29
32	522	643	.1909	972	28
33	549	678	.1892	960	27
34	575	713	.1876	948	26
35	.41602	.45748	2.1859	.90936	25
36	628	784	.1842	924	24
37	655	819	.1825	911	23
38	681	854	.1808	899	22
39	707	889	.1792	887	21
40	.41734	.45924	2.1775	.90875	20
41	760	960	.1758	863	19
42	787	.45995	.1742	851	18
43	813	.46030	.1725	839	17
44	840	065	.1708	826	16
45	.41866	.46101	2.1692	.90814	15
46	892	136	.1675	802	14
47	919	171	.1659	790	13
48	945	206	.1642	778	12
49	972	242	.1625	766	11
50	.41998	.46277	2.1609	.90753	10
51	.42024	312	.1592	741	9
52	051	348	.1576	729	8
53	077	383	.1560	717	7
54	104	418	.1543	704	6
55	.42130	.46454	2.1527	.90692	5
56	156	489	.1510	680	4
57	183	525	.1494	668	3
58	209	560	.1478	655	2
59	235	595	.1461	643	1
60	.42262	.46631	2.1445	.90631	0
	Cos	Ctn	Tan	Sin	′

65°

′	Sin	Tan	Ctn	Cos	
0	.42262	.46631	2.1445	.90631	60
1	288	666	.1429	618	59
2	315	702	.1413	606	58
3	341	737	.1396	594	57
4	367	772	.1380	582	56
5	.42394	.46808	2.1364	.90569	55
6	420	843	.1348	557	54
7	446	879	.1332	545	53
8	473	914	.1315	532	52
9	499	950	.1299	520	51
10	.42525	.46985	2.1283	.90507	50
11	552	.47021	.1267	495	49
12	578	056	.1251	483	48
13	604	092	.1235	470	47
14	631	128	.1219	458	46
15	.42657	.47163	2.1203	.90446	45
16	683	199	.1187	433	44
17	709	234	.1171	421	43
18	736	270	.1155	408	42
19	762	305	.1139	396	41
20	.42788	.47341	2.1123	.90383	40
21	815	377	.1107	371	39
22	841	412	.1092	358	38
23	867	448	.1076	346	37
24	894	483	.1060	334	36
25	.42920	.47519	2.1044	.90321	35
26	946	555	.1028	309	34
27	972	590	.1013	296	33
28	.42999	626	.0997	284	32
29	.43025	662	.0981	271	31
30	.43051	.47698	2.0965	.90259	30
31	077	733	.0950	246	29
32	104	769	.0934	233	28
33	130	805	.0918	221	27
34	156	840	.0903	208	26
35	.43182	.47876	2.0887	.90196	25
36	209	912	.0872	183	24
37	235	948	.0856	171	23
38	261	.47984	.0840	158	22
39	287	.48019	.0825	146	21
40	.43313	.48055	2.0809	.90133	20
41	340	091	.0794	120	19
42	366	127	.0778	108	18
43	392	163	.0763	095	17
44	418	198	.0748	082	16
45	.43445	.48234	2.0732	.90070	15
46	471	270	.0717	057	14
47	497	306	.0701	045	13
48	523	342	.0686	032	12
49	549	378	.0671	019	11
50	.43575	.48414	2.0655	.90007	10
51	602	450	.0640	.89994	9
52	628	486	.0625	981	8
53	654	521	.0609	968	7
54	680	557	.0594	956	6
55	.43706	.48593	2.0579	.89943	5
56	733	629	.0564	930	4
57	759	665	.0549	918	3
58	785	701	.0533	905	2
59	811	737	.0518	892	1
60	.43837	.48773	2.0503	.89879	0
	Cos	Ctn	Tan	Sin	′

64°

26°—Natural Trigonometric Functions—27°

′	Sin	Tan	Ctn	Cos	
0	.43837	.48773	2.0503	.89879	**60**
1	863	809	.0488	867	59
2	889	845	.0473	854	58
3	916	881	.0458	841	57
4	942	917	.0443	828	56
5	.43968	.48953	2.0428	.89816	**55**
6	.43994	.48989	.0413	803	54
7	.44020	.49026	.0398	790	53
8	046	062	.0383	777	52
9	072	098	.0368	764	51
10	.44098	.49134	2.0353	.89752	**50**
11	124	170	.0338	739	49
12	151	206	.0323	726	48
13	177	242	.0308	713	47
14	203	278	.0293	700	46
15	.44229	.49315	2.0278	.89687	**45**
16	255	351	.0263	674	44
17	281	387	.0248	662	43
18	307	423	.0233	649	42
19	333	459	.0219	636	41
20	.44359	.49495	2.0204	.89623	**40**
21	385	532	.0189	610	39
22	411	568	.0174	597	38
23	437	604	.0160	584	37
24	464	640	.0145	571	36
25	.44490	.49677	2.0130	.89558	**35**
26	516	713	.0115	545	34
27	542	749	.0101	532	33
28	568	786	.0086	519	32
29	594	822	.0072	506	31
30	.44620	.49858	2.0057	.89493	**30**
31	646	894	.0042	480	29
32	672	931	.0028	467	28
33	698	.49967	2.0013	454	27
34	724	.50004	1.9999	441	26
35	.44750	.50040	1.9984	.89428	**25**
36	776	076	.9970	415	24
37	802	113	.9955	402	23
38	828	149	.9941	389	22
39	854	185	.9926	376	21
40	.44880	.50222	1.9912	.89363	**20**
41	906	258	.9897	350	19
42	932	295	.9883	337	18
43	958	331	.9868	324	17
44	.44984	368	.9854	311	16
45	.45010	.50404	1.9840	.89298	**15**
46	036	441	.9825	285	14
47	062	477	.9811	272	13
48	088	514	.9797	259	12
49	114	550	.9782	245	11
50	.45140	.50587	1.9768	.89232	**10**
51	166	623	.9754	219	9
52	192	660	.9740	206	8
53	218	696	.9725	193	7
54	243	733	.9711	180	6
55	.45269	.50769	1.9697	.89167	**5**
56	295	806	.9683	153	4
57	321	843	.9669	140	3
58	347	879	.9654	127	2
59	373	916	.9640	114	1
60	.45399	.50953	1.9626	.89101	**0**
	Cos	Ctn	Tan	Sin	′

63°

′	Sin	Tan	Ctn	Cos	
0	.45399	.50953	1.9626	.89101	**60**
1	425	.50989	.9612	087	59
2	451	.51026	.9598	074	58
3	477	063	.9584	061	57
4	503	099	.9570	048	56
5	.45529	.51136	1.9556	.89035	**55**
6	554	173	.9542	021	54
7	580	209	.9528	.89008	53
8	606	246	.9514	.88995	52
9	632	283	.9500	981	51
10	.45658	.51319	1.9486	.88968	**50**
11	684	356	.9472	955	49
12	710	393	.9458	942	48
13	736	430	.9444	928	47
14	762	467	.9430	915	46
15	.45787	.51503	1.9416	.88902	**45**
16	813	540	.9402	888	44
17	839	577	.9388	875	43
18	865	614	.9375	862	42
19	891	651	.9361	848	41
20	.45917	.51688	1.9347	.88835	**40**
21	942	724	.9333	822	39
22	968	761	.9319	808	38
23	.45994	798	.9306	795	37
24	.46020	835	.9292	782	36
25	.46046	.51872	1.9278	.88768	**35**
26	072	909	.9265	755	34
27	097	946	.9251	741	33
28	123	.51983	.9237	728	32
29	149	.52020	.9223	715	31
30	.46175	.52057	1.9210	.88701	**30**
31	201	094	.9196	688	29
32	226	131	.9183	674	28
33	252	168	.9169	661	27
34	278	205	.9155	647	26
35	.46304	.52242	1.9142	.88634	**25**
36	330	279	.9128	620	24
37	355	316	.9115	607	23
38	381	353	.9101	593	22
39	407	390	.9088	580	21
40	.46433	.52427	1.9074	.88566	**20**
41	458	464	.9061	553	19
42	484	501	.9047	539	18
43	510	538	.9034	526	17
44	536	575	.9020	512	16
45	.46561	.52613	1.9007	.88499	**15**
46	587	650	.8993	485	14
47	613	687	.8980	472	13
48	639	724	.8967	458	12
49	664	761	.8953	445	11
50	.46690	.52798	1.8940	.88431	**10**
51	716	836	.8927	417	9
52	742	873	.8913	404	8
53	767	910	.8900	390	7
54	793	947	.8887	377	6
55	.46819	.52985	1.8873	.88363	**5**
56	844	.53022	.8860	349	4
57	870	059	.8847	336	3
58	896	096	.8834	322	2
59	921	134	.8820	308	1
60	.46947	.53171	1.8807	.88295	**0**
	Cos	Ctn	Tan	Sin	′

62°

28°—Natural Trigonometric Functions—29°

′	Sin	Tan	Ctn	Cos	
0	.46947	.53171	1.8807	.88295	**60**
1	973	208	.8794	281	59
2	.46999	246	.8781	267	58
3	.47024	283	.8768	254	57
4	050	320	.8755	240	56
5	.47076	.53358	1.8741	.88226	**55**
6	101	395	.8728	213	54
7	127	432	.8715	199	53
8	153	470	.8702	185	52
9	178	507	.8689	172	51
10	.47204	.53545	1.8676	.88158	**50**
11	229	582	.8663	144	49
12	255	620	.8650	130	48
13	281	657	.8637	117	47
14	306	694	.8624	103	46
15	.47332	.53732	1.8611	.88089	**45**
16	358	769	.8598	075	44
17	383	807	.8585	062	43
18	409	844	.8572	048	42
19	434	882	.8559	034	41
20	.47460	.53920	1.8546	.88020	**40**
21	486	957	.8533	.88006	39
22	511	.53995	.8520	.87993	38
23	537	.54032	.8507	979	37
24	562	070	.8495	965	36
25	.47588	.54107	1.8482	.87951	**35**
26	614	145	.8469	937	34
27	639	183	.8456	923	33
28	665	220	.8443	909	32
29	690	258	.8430	896	31
30	.47716	.54296	1.8418	.87882	**30**
31	741	333	.8405	868	29
32	767	371	.8392	854	28
33	793	409	.8379	840	27
34	818	446	.8367	826	26
35	.47844	.54484	1.8354	.87812	**25**
36	869	522	.8341	798	24
37	895	560	.8329	784	23
38	920	597	.8316	770	22
39	946	635	.8303	756	21
40	.47971	.54673	1.8291	.87743	**20**
41	.47997	711	.8278	729	19
42	.48022	748	.8265	715	18
43	048	786	.8253	701	17
44	073	824	.8240	687	16
45	.48099	.54862	1.8228	.87673	**15**
46	124	900	.8215	659	14
47	150	938	.8202	645	13
48	175	.54975	.8190	631	12
49	201	.55013	.8177	617	11
50	.48226	.55051	1.8165	.87603	**10**
51	252	089	.8152	589	9
52	277	127	.8140	575	8
53	303	165	.8127	561	7
54	328	203	.8115	546	6
55	.48354	.55241	1.8103	.87532	**5**
56	379	279	.8090	518	4
57	405	317	.8078	504	3
58	430	355	.8065	490	2
59	456	393	.8053	476	1
60	.48481	.55431	1.8040	.87462	**0**
	Cos	Ctn	Tan	Sin	′

61°

′	Sin	Tan	Ctn	Cos	
0	.48481	.55431	1.8040	.87462	**60**
1	506	469	.8028	448	59
2	532	507	.8016	434	58
3	557	545	.8003	420	57
4	583	583	.7991	406	56
5	.48608	.55621	1.7979	.87391	**55**
6	634	659	.7966	377	54
7	659	697	.7954	363	53
8	684	736	.7942	349	52
9	710	774	.7930	335	51
10	.48735	.55812	1.7917	.87321	**50**
11	761	850	.7905	306	49
12	786	888	.7893	292	48
13	811	926	.7881	278	47
14	837	.55964	.7868	264	46
15	.48862	.56003	1.7856	.87250	**45**
16	888	041	.7844	235	44
17	913	079	.7832	221	43
18	938	117	.7820	207	42
19	964	156	.7808	193	41
20	.48989	.56194	1.7796	.87178	**40**
21	.49014	232	.7783	164	39
22	040	270	.7771	150	38
23	065	309	.7759	136	37
24	090	347	.7747	121	36
25	.49116	.56385	1.7735	.87107	**35**
26	141	424	.7723	093	34
27	166	462	.7711	079	33
28	192	501	.7699	064	32
29	217	539	.7687	050	31
30	.49242	.56577	1.7675	.87036	**30**
31	268	616	.7663	021	29
32	293	654	.7651	.87007	28
33	318	693	.7639	.86993	27
34	344	731	.7627	978	26
35	.49369	.56769	1.7615	.86964	**25**
36	394	808	.7603	949	24
37	419	846	.7591	935	23
38	445	885	.7579	921	22
39	470	923	.7567	906	21
40	.49495	.56962	1.7556	.86892	**20**
41	521	.57000	.7544	878	19
42	546	039	.7532	863	18
43	571	078	.7520	849	17
44	596	116	.7508	834	16
45	.49622	.57155	1.7496	.86820	**15**
46	647	193	.7485	805	14
47	672	232	.7473	791	13
48	697	271	.7461	777	12
49	723	309	.7449	762	11
50	.49748	.57348	1.7437	.86748	**10**
51	773	386	.7426	733	9
52	798	425	.7414	719	8
53	824	464	.7402	704	7
54	849	503	.7391	690	6
55	.49874	.57541	1.7379	.86675	**5**
56	899	580	.7367	661	4
57	924	619	.7355	646	3
58	950	657	.7344	632	2
59	.49975	696	.7332	617	1
60	.50000	.57735	1.7321	.86603	**0**
	Cos	Ctn	Tan	Sin	′

60°

′	Sin	Tan	Ctn	Cos	
0	.50000	.57735	1.7321	.86603	**60**
1	025	774	.7309	588	59
2	050	813	.7297	573	58
3	076	851	.7286	559	57
4	101	890	.7274	544	56
5	.50126	.57929	1.7262	.86530	**55**
6	151	.57968	.7251	515	54
7	176	.58007	.7239	501	53
8	201	046	.7228	486	52
9	227	085	.7216	471	51
10	.50252	.58124	1.7205	.86457	**50**
11	277	162	.7193	442	49
12	302	201	.7182	427	48
13	327	240	.7170	413	47
14	352	279	.7159	398	46
15	.50377	.58318	1.7147	.86384	**45**
16	403	357	.7136	369	44
17	428	396	.7124	354	43
18	453	435	.7113	340	42
19	478	474	.7102	325	41
20	.50503	.58513	1.7090	.86310	**40**
21	528	552	.7079	295	39
22	553	591	.7067	281	38
23	578	631	.7056	266	37
24	603	670	.7045	251	36
25	.50628	.58709	1.7033	.86237	**35**
26	654	748	.7022	222	34
27	679	787	.7011	207	33
28	704	826	.6999	192	32
29	729	865	.6988	178	31
30	.50754	.58905	1.6977	.86163	**30**
31	779	944	.6965	148	29
32	804	.58983	.6954	133	28
33	829	.59022	.6943	119	27
34	854	061	.6932	104	26
35	.50879	.59101	1.6920	.86089	**25**
36	904	140	.6909	074	24
37	929	179	.6898	059	23
38	954	218	.6887	045	22
39	.50979	258	.6875	030	21
40	.51004	.59297	1.6864	.86015	**20**
41	029	336	.6853	.86000	19
42	054	376	.6842	.85985	18
43	079	415	.6831	970	17
44	104	454	.6820	956	16
45	.51129	.59494	1.6808	.85941	**15**
46	154	533	.6797	926	14
47	179	573	.6786	911	13
48	204	612	.6775	896	12
49	229	651	.6764	881	11
50	.51254	.59691	1.6753	.85866	**10**
51	279	730	.6742	851	9
52	304	770	.6731	836	8
53	329	809	.6720	821	7
54	354	849	.6709	806	6
55	.51379	.59888	1.6698	.85792	**5**
56	404	928	.6687	777	4
57	429	.59967	.6676	762	3
58	454	.60007	.6665	747	2
59	479	046	.6654	732	1
60	.51504	.60086	1.6643	.85717	**0**
	Cos	**Ctn**	**Tan**	**Sin**	**′**

59°

′	Sin	Tan	Ctn	Cos	
0	.51504	.60086	1.6643	.85717	**60**
1	529	126	.6632	702	59
2	554	165	.6621	687	58
3	579	205	.6610	672	57
4	604	245	.6599	657	56
5	.51628	.60284	1.6588	.85642	**55**
6	653	324	.6577	627	54
7	678	364	.6566	612	53
8	703	403	.6555	597	52
9	728	443	.6545	582	51
10	.51753	.60483	1.6534	.85567	**50**
11	778	522	.6523	551	49
12	803	562	.6512	536	48
13	828	602	.6501	521	47
14	852	642	.6490	506	46
15	.51877	.60681	1.6479	.85491	**45**
16	902	721	.6469	476	44
17	927	761	.6458	461	43
18	952	801	.6447	446	42
19	.51977	841	.6436	431	41
20	.52002	.60881	1.6426	.85416	**40**
21	026	921	.6415	401	39
22	051	.60960	.6404	385	38
23	076	.61000	.6393	370	37
24	101	040	.6383	355	36
25	.52126	.61080	1.6372	.85340	**35**
26	151	120	.6361	325	34
27	175	160	.6351	310	33
28	200	200	.6340	294	32
29	225	240	.6329	279	31
30	.52250	.61280	1.6319	.85264	**30**
31	275	320	.6308	249	29
32	299	360	.6297	234	28
33	324	400	.6287	218	27
34	349	440	.6276	203	26
35	.52374	.61480	1.6265	.85188	**25**
36	399	520	.6255	173	24
37	423	561	.6244	157	23
38	448	601	.6234	142	22
39	473	641	.6223	127	21
40	.52498	.61681	1.6212	.85112	**20**
41	522	721	.6202	096	19
42	547	761	.6191	081	18
43	572	801	.6181	066	17
44	597	842	.6170	051	16
45	.52621	.61882	1.6160	.85035	**15**
46	646	922	.6149	020	14
47	671	.61962	.6139	.85005	13
48	696	.62003	.6128	.84989	12
49	720	043	.6118	974	11
50	.52745	.62083	1.6107	.84959	**10**
51	770	124	.6097	943	9
52	794	164	.6087	928	8
53	819	204	.6076	913	7
54	844	245	.6066	897	6
55	.52869	.62285	1.6055	.84882	**5**
56	893	325	.6045	866	4
57	918	366	.6034	851	3
58	943	406	.6024	836	2
59	967	446	.6014	820	1
60	.52992	.62487	1.6003	.84805	**0**
	Cos	**Ctn**	**Tan**	**Sin**	**′**

58°

32°—Natural Trigonometric Functions—33°

'	Sin	Tan	Ctn	Cos	
0	.52992	.62487	1.6003	.84805	**60**
1	.53017	527	.5993	789	59
2	041	568	.5983	774	58
3	066	608	.5972	759	57
4	091	649	.5962	743	56
5	.53115	.62689	1.5952	.84728	**55**
6	140	730	.5941	712	54
7	164	770	.5931	697	53
8	189	811	.5921	681	52
9	214	852	.5911	666	51
10	.53238	.62892	1.5900	.84650	**50**
11	263	933	.5890	635	49
12	288	.62973	.5880	619	48
13	312	.63014	.5869	604	47
14	337	055	.5859	588	46
15	.53361	.63095	1.5849	.84573	**45**
16	386	136	.5839	557	44
17	411	177	.5829	542	43
18	435	217	.5818	526	42
19	460	258	.5808	511	41
20	.53484	.63299	1.5798	.84495	**40**
21	509	340	.5788	480	39
22	534	380	.5778	464	38
23	558	421	.5768	448	37
24	583	462	.5757	433	36
25	.53607	.63503	1.5747	.84417	**35**
26	632	544	.5737	402	34
27	656	584	.5727	386	33
28	681	625	.5717	370	32
29	705	666	.5707	355	31
30	.53730	.63707	1.5697	.84339	**30**
31	754	748	.5687	324	29
32	779	789	.5677	308	28
33	804	830	.5667	292	27
34	828	871	.5657	277	26
35	.53853	.63912	1.5647	.84261	**25**
36	877	953	.5637	245	24
37	902	.63994	.5627	230	23
38	926	.64035	.5617	214	22
39	951	076	.5607	198	21
40	.53975	.64117	1.5597	.84182	**20**
41	.54000	158	.5587	167	19
42	024	199	.5577	151	18
43	049	240	.5567	135	17
44	073	281	.5557	120	16
45	.54097	.64322	1.5547	.84104	**15**
46	122	363	.5537	088	14
47	146	404	.5527	072	13
48	171	446	.5517	057	12
49	195	487	.5507	041	11
50	.54220	.64528	1.5497	.84025	**10**
51	244	569	.5487	.84009	9
52	269	610	.5477	.83994	8
53	293	652	.5468	978	7
54	317	693	.5458	962	6
55	.54342	.64734	1.5448	.83946	**5**
56	366	775	.5438	930	4
57	391	817	.5428	915	3
58	415	858	.5418	899	2
59	440	899	.5408	883	1
60	.54464	.64941	1.5399	.83867	**0**
	Cos	Ctn	Tan	Sin	'

57°

'	Sin	Tan	Ctn	Cos	
0	.54464	.64941	1.5399	.83867	**60**
1	488	.64982	.5389	851	59
2	513	.65024	.5379	835	58
3	537	065	.5369	819	57
4	561	106	.5359	804	56
5	.54586	.65148	1.5350	.83788	**55**
6	610	189	.5340	772	54
7	635	231	.5330	756	53
8	659	272	.5320	740	52
9	683	314	.5311	724	51
10	.54708	.65355	1.5301	.83708	**50**
11	732	397	.5291	692	49
12	756	438	.5282	676	48
13	781	480	.5272	660	47
14	805	521	.5262	645	46
15	.54829	.65563	1.5253	.83629	**45**
16	854	604	.5243	613	44
17	878	646	.5233	597	43
18	902	688	.5224	581	42
19	927	729	.5214	565	41
20	.54951	.65771	1.5204	.83549	**40**
21	975	813	.5195	533	39
22	.54999	854	.5185	517	38
23	.55024	896	.5175	501	37
24	048	938	.5166	485	36
25	.55072	.65980	1.5156	.83469	**35**
26	097	.66021	.5147	453	34
27	121	063	.5137	437	33
28	145	105	.5127	421	32
29	169	147	.5118	405	31
30	.55194	.66189	1.5108	.83389	**30**
31	218	230	.5099	373	29
32	242	272	.5089	356	28
33	266	314	.5080	340	27
34	291	356	.5070	324	26
35	.55315	.66398	1.5061	.83308	**25**
36	339	440	.5051	292	24
37	363	482	.5042	276	23
38	388	524	.5032	260	22
39	412	566	.5023	244	21
40	.55436	.66608	1.5013	.83228	**20**
41	460	650	.5004	212	19
42	484	692	.4994	195	18
43	509	734	.4985	179	17
44	533	776	.4975	163	16
45	.55557	.66818	1.4966	.83147	**15**
46	581	860	.4957	131	14
47	605	902	.4947	115	13
48	630	944	.4938	098	12
49	654	.66986	.4928	082	11
50	.55678	.67028	1.4919	.83066	**10**
51	702	071	.4910	050	9
52	726	113	.4900	034	8
53	750	155	.4891	017	7
54	775	197	.4882	.83001	6
55	.55799	.67239	1.4872	.82985	**5**
56	823	282	.4863	969	4
57	847	324	.4854	953	3
58	871	366	.4844	936	2
59	895	409	.4835	920	1
60	.55919	.67451	1.4826	.82904	**0**
	Cos	Ctn	Tan	Sin	'

56°

′	Sin	Tan	Ctn	Cos	
0	.55919	.67451	1.4826	.82904	**60**
1	943	493	.4816	887	59
2	968	536	.4807	871	58
3	.55992	578	.4798	855	57
4	.56016	620	.4788	839	56
5	.56040	.67663	1.4779	.82822	**55**
6	064	705	.4770	806	54
7	088	748	.4761	790	53
8	112	790	.4751	773	52
9	136	832	.4742	757	51
10	.56160	.67875	1.4733	.82741	**50**
11	184	917	.4724	724	49
12	208	.67960	.4715	708	48
13	232	.68002	.4705	692	47
14	256	045	.4696	675	46
15	.56280	.68088	1.4687	.82659	**45**
16	305	130	.4678	643	44
17	329	173	.4669	626	43
18	353	215	.4659	610	42
19	377	258	.4650	593	41
20	.56401	.68301	1.4641	.82577	**40**
21	425	343	.4632	561	39
22	449	386	.4623	544	38
23	473	429	.4614	528	37
24	497	471	.4605	511	36
25	.56521	.68514	1.4596	.82495	**35**
26	545	557	.4586	478	34
27	569	600	.4577	462	33
28	593	642	.4568	446	32
29	617	685	.4559	429	31
30	.56641	.68728	1.4550	.82413	**30**
31	665	771	.4541	396	29
32	689	814	.4532	380	28
33	713	857	.4523	363	27
34	736	900	.4514	347	26
35	.56760	.68942	1.4505	.82330	**25**
36	784	.68985	.4496	314	24
37	808	.69028	.4487	297	23
38	832	071	.4478	281	22
39	856	114	.4469	264	21
40	.56880	.69157	1.4460	.82248	**20**
41	904	200	.4451	231	19
42	928	243	.4442	214	18
43	952	286	.4433	198	17
44	.56976	329	.4424	181	16
45	.57000	.69372	1.4415	.82165	**15**
46	024	416	.4406	148	14
47	047	459	.4397	132	13
48	071	502	.4388	115	12
49	095	545	.4379	098	11
50	.57119	.69588	1.4370	.82082	**10**
51	143	631	.4361	065	9
52	167	675	.4352	048	8
53	191	718	.4344	032	7
54	215	761	.4335	.82015	6
55	.57238	.69804	1.4326	.81999	**5**
56	262	847	.4317	982	4
57	286	891	.4308	965	3
58	310	934	.4299	949	2
59	334	.69977	.4290	932	1
60	.57358	.70021	1.4281	.81915	**0**
	Cos	Ctn	Tan	Sin	′

55°

′	Sin	Tan	Ctn	Cos	
0	.57358	.70021	1.4281	.81915	**60**
1	381	064	.4273	899	59
2	405	107	.4264	882	58
3	429	151	.4255	865	57
4	453	194	.4246	848	56
5	.57477	.70238	1.4237	.81832	**55**
6	501	281	.4229	815	54
7	524	325	.4220	798	53
8	548	368	.4211	782	52
9	572	412	.4202	765	51
10	.57596	.70455	1.4193	.81748	**50**
11	619	499	.4185	731	49
12	643	542	.4176	714	48
13	667	586	.4167	698	47
14	691	629	.4158	681	46
15	.57715	.70673	1.4150	.81664	**45**
16	738	717	.4141	647	44
17	762	760	.4132	631	43
18	786	804	.4124	614	42
19	810	848	.4115	597	41
20	.57833	.70891	1.4106	.81580	**40**
21	857	935	.4097	563	39
22	881	.70979	.4089	546	38
23	904	.71023	.4080	530	37
24	928	066	.4071	513	36
25	.57952	.71110	1.4063	.81496	**35**
26	976	154	.4054	479	34
27	.57999	198	.4045	462	33
28	.58023	242	.4037	445	32
29	047	285	.4028	428	31
30	.58070	.71329	1.4019	.81412	**30**
31	094	373	.4011	395	29
32	118	417	.4002	378	28
33	141	461	.3994	361	27
34	165	505	.3985	344	26
35	.58189	.71549	1.3976	.81327	**25**
36	212	593	.3968	310	24
37	236	637	.3959	293	23
38	260	681	.3951	276	22
39	283	725	.3942	259	21
40	.58307	.71769	1.3934	.81242	**20**
41	330	813	.3925	225	19
42	354	857	.3916	208	18
43	378	901	.3908	191	17
44	401	946	.3899	174	16
45	.58425	.71990	1.3891	.81157	**15**
46	449	.72034	.3882	140	14
47	472	078	.3874	123	13
48	496	122	.3865	106	12
49	519	167	.3857	089	11
50	.58543	.72211	1.3848	.81072	**10**
51	567	255	.3840	055	9
52	590	299	.3831	038	8
53	614	344	.3823	021	7
54	637	388	.3814	.81004	6
55	.58661	.72432	1.3806	.80987	**5**
56	684	477	.3798	970	4
57	708	521	.3789	953	3
58	731	565	.3781	936	2
59	755	610	.3772	919	1
60	.58779	.72654	1.3764	.80902	**0**
	Cos	Ctn	Tan	Sin	′

54°

36°—Natural Trigonometric Functions—37°

′	Sin	Tan	Ctn	Cos	
0	.58779	.72654	1.3764	.80902	**60**
1	802	699	.3755	885	59
2	826	743	.3747	867	58
3	849	788	.3739	850	57
4	873	832	.3730	833	56
5	.58896	.72877	1.3722	.80816	**55**
6	920	921	.3713	799	54
7	943	.72966	.3705	782	53
8	967	.73010	.3697	765	52
9	.58990	055	.3688	748	51
10	.59014	.73100	1.3680	.80730	**50**
11	037	144	.3672	713	49
12	061	189	.3663	696	48
13	084	234	.3655	679	47
14	108	278	.3647	662	46
15	.59131	.73323	1.3638	.80644	**45**
16	154	368	.3630	627	44
17	178	413	.3622	610	43
18	201	457	.3613	593	42
19	225	502	.3605	576	41
20	.59248	.73547	1.3597	.80558	**40**
21	272	592	.3588	541	39
22	295	637	.3580	524	38
23	318	681	.3572	507	37
24	342	726	.3564	489	36
25	.59365	.73771	1.3555	.80472	**35**
26	389	816	.3547	455	34
27	412	861	.3539	438	33
28	436	906	.3531	420	32
29	459	951	.3522	403	31
30	.59482	.73996	1.3514	.80386	**30**
31	506	.74041	.3506	368	29
32	529	086	.3498	351	28
33	552	131	.3490	334	27
34	576	176	.3481	316	26
35	.59599	.74221	1.3473	.80299	**25**
36	622	267	.3465	282	24
37	646	312	.3457	264	23
38	669	357	.3449	247	22
39	693	402	.3440	230	21
40	.59716	.74447	1.3432	.80212	**20**
41	739	492	.3424	195	19
42	763	538	.3416	178	18
43	786	583	.3408	160	17
44	809	628	.3400	143	16
45	.59832	.74674	1.3392	.80125	**15**
46	856	719	.3384	108	14
47	879	764	.3375	091	13
48	902	810	.3367	073	12
49	926	855	.3359	056	11
50	.59949	.74900	1.3351	.80038	**10**
51	972	946	.3343	021	9
52	.59995	.74991	.3335	.80003	8
53	.60019	.75037	.3327	.79986	7
54	042	082	.3319	968	6
55	.60065	.75128	1.3311	.79951	**5**
56	089	173	.3303	934	4
57	112	219	.3295	916	3
58	135	264	.3287	899	2
59	158	310	.3278	881	1
60	.60182	.75355	1.3270	.79864	**0**
	Cos	**Ctn**	**Tan**	**Sin**	**′**

53°

′	Sin	Tan	Ctn	Cos	
0	.60182	.75355	1.3270	.79864	**60**
1	205	401	.3262	846	59
2	228	447	.3254	829	58
3	251	492	.3246	811	57
4	274	538	.3238	793	56
5	.60298	.75584	1.3230	.79776	**55**
6	321	629	.3222	758	54
7	344	675	.3214	741	53
8	367	721	.3206	723	52
9	390	767	.3198	706	51
10	.60414	.75812	1.3190	.79688	**50**
11	437	858	.3182	671	49
12	460	904	.3175	653	48
13	483	950	.3167	635	47
14	506	.75996	.3159	618	46
15	.60529	.76042	1.3151	.79600	**45**
16	553	088	.3143	583	44
17	576	134	.3135	565	43
18	599	180	.3127	547	42
19	622	226	.3119	530	41
20	.60645	.76272	1.3111	.79512	**40**
21	668	318	.3103	494	39
22	691	364	.3095	477	38
23	714	410	.3087	459	37
24	738	456	.3079	441	36
25	.60761	.76502	1.3072	.79424	**35**
26	784	548	.3064	406	34
27	807	594	.3056	388	33
28	830	640	.3048	371	32
29	853	686	.3040	353	31
30	.60876	.76733	1.3032	.79335	**30**
31	899	779	.3024	318	29
32	922	825	.3017	300	28
33	945	871	.3009	282	27
34	968	918	.3001	264	26
35	.60991	.76964	1.2993	.79247	**25**
36	.61015	.77010	.2985	229	24
37	038	057	.2977	211	23
38	061	103	.2970	193	22
39	084	149	.2962	176	21
40	.61107	.77196	1.2954	.79158	**20**
41	130	242	.2946	140	19
42	153	289	.2938	122	18
43	176	335	.2931	105	17
44	199	382	.2923	087	16
45	.61222	.77428	1.2915	.79069	**15**
46	245	475	.2907	051	14
47	268	521	.2900	033	13
48	291	568	.2892	.79016	12
49	314	615	.2884	.78998	11
50	.61337	.77661	1.2876	.78980	**10**
51	360	708	.2869	962	9
52	383	754	.2861	944	8
53	406	801	.2853	926	7
54	429	848	.2846	908	6
55	.61451	.77895	1.2838	.78891	**5**
56	474	941	.2830	873	4
57	497	.77988	.2822	855	3
58	520	.78035	.2815	837	2
59	543	082	.2807	819	1
60	.61566	.78129	1.2799	.78801	**0**
	Cos	**Ctn**	**Tan**	**Sin**	**′**

52°

38°—Natural Trigonometric Functions—39°

′	Sin	Tan	Ctn	Cos	
0	.61566	.78129	1.2799	.78801	60
1	589	175	.2792	783	59
2	612	222	.2784	765	58
3	635	269	.2776	747	57
4	658	316	.2769	729	56
5	.61681	.78363	1.2761	.78711	55
6	704	410	.2753	694	54
7	726	457	.2746	676	53
8	749	504	.2738	658	52
9	772	551	.2731	640	51
10	.61795	.78598	1.2723	.78622	50
11	818	645	.2715	604	49
12	841	692	.2708	586	48
13	864	739	.2700	568	47
14	887	786	.2693	550	46
15	.61909	.78834	1.2685	.78532	45
16	932	881	.2677	514	44
17	955	928	.2670	496	43
18	.61978	.78975	.2662	478	42
19	.62001	.79022	.2655	460	41
20	.62024	.79070	1.2647	.78442	40
21	046	117	.2640	424	39
22	069	164	.2632	405	38
23	092	212	.2624	387	37
24	115	259	.2617	369	36
25	.62138	.79306	1.2609	.73351	35
26	160	354	.2602	333	34
27	183	401	.2594	315	33
28	206	449	.2587	297	32
29	229	496	.2579	279	31
30	.62251	.79544	1.2572	.78261	30
31	274	591	.2564	243	29
32	297	639	.2557	225	28
33	320	686	.2549	206	27
34	342	734	.2542	188	26
35	.62365	.79781	1.2534	.78170	25
36	388	829	.2527	152	24
37	411	877	.2519	134	23
38	433	924	.2512	116	22
39	456	.79972	.2504	098	21
40	.62479	.80020	1.2497	.78079	20
41	502	067	.2489	061	19
42	524	115	.2482	043	18
43	547	163	.2475	025	17
44	570	211	.2467	.78007	16
45	.62592	.80258	1.2460	.77988	15
46	615	306	.2452	970	14
47	638	354	.2445	952	13
48	660	402	.2437	934	12
49	683	450	.2430	916	11
50	.62706	.80498	1.2423	.77897	10
51	728	546	.2415	879	9
52	751	594	.2408	861	8
53	774	642	.2401	843	7
54	796	690	.2393	824	6
55	.62819	.80738	1.2386	.77806	5
56	842	786	.2378	788	4
57	864	834	.2371	769	3
58	887	882	.2364	751	2
59	909	930	.2356	733	1
60	.62932	.80978	1.2349	.77715	0
	Cos	Ctn	Tan	Sin	′

51°

′	Sin	Tan	Ctn	Cos	
0	.62932	.80978	1.2349	.77715	60
1	955	.81027	.2342	696	59
2	.62977	075	.2334	678	58
3	.63000	123	.2327	660	57
4	022	171	.2320	641	56
5	.63045	.81220	1.2312	.77623	55
6	068	268	.2305	605	54
7	090	316	.2298	586	53
8	113	364	.2290	568	52
9	135	413	.2283	550	51
10	.63158	.81461	1.2276	.77531	50
11	180	510	.2268	513	49
12	203	558	.2261	494	48
13	225	606	.2254	476	47
14	248	655	.2247	458	46
15	.63271	.81703	1.2239	.77439	45
16	293	752	.2232	421	44
17	316	800	.2225	402	43
18	338	849	.2218	384	42
19	361	898	.2210	366	41
20	.63383	.81946	1.2203	.77347	40
21	406	.81995	.2196	329	39
22	428	.82044	.2189	310	38
23	451	092	.2181	292	37
24	473	141	.2174	273	36
25	.63496	.82190	1.2167	.77255	35
26	518	238	.2160	236	34
27	540	287	.2153	218	33
28	563	336	.2145	199	32
29	585	385	.2138	181	31
30	.63608	.82434	1.2131	.77162	30
31	630	483	.2124	144	29
32	653	531	.2117	125	28
33	675	580	.2109	107	27
34	698	629	.2102	088	26
35	.63720	.82678	1.2095	.77070	25
36	742	727	.2088	051	24
37	765	776	.2081	033	23
38	787	825	.2074	.77014	22
39	810	874	.2066	.76996	21
40	.63832	.82923	1.2059	.76977	20
41	854	.82972	.2052	959	19
42	877	.83022	.2045	940	18
43	899	071	.2038	921	17
44	922	120	.2031	903	16
45	.63944	.83169	1.2024	.76884	15
46	966	218	.2017	866	14
47	.63989	268	.2009	847	13
48	.64011	317	.2002	828	12
49	033	366	.1995	810	11
50	.64056	.83415	1.1988	.76791	10
51	078	465	.1981	772	9
52	100	514	.1974	754	8
53	123	564	.1967	735	7
54	145	613	.1960	717	6
55	.64167	.83662	1.1953	.76698	5
56	190	712	.1946	679	4
57	212	761	.1939	661	3
58	234	811	.1932	642	2
59	256	860	.1925	623	1
60	.64279	.83910	1.1918	.76604	0
	Cos	Ctn	Tan	Sin	′

50°

40°—Natural Trigonometric Functions—41°

′	Sin	Tan	Ctn	Cos	
0	.64279	.83910	1.1918	.76604	60
1	301	.83960	.1910	586	59
2	323	.84009	.1903	567	58
3	346	059	.1896	548	57
4	368	108	.1889	530	56
5	.64390	.84158	1.1882	.76511	55
6	412	208	.1875	492	54
7	435	258	.1868	473	53
8	457	307	.1861	455	52
9	479	357	.1854	436	51
10	.64501	.84407	1.1847	.76417	50
11	524	457	.1840	398	49
12	546	507	.1833	380	48
13	568	556	.1826	361	47
14	590	606	.1819	342	46
15	.64612	.84656	1.1812	.76323	45
16	635	706	.1806	304	44
17	657	756	.1799	286	43
18	679	806	.1792	267	42
19	701	856	.1785	248	41
20	.64723	.84906	1.1778	.76229	40
21	746	.84956	.1771	210	39
22	768	.85006	.1764	192	38
23	790	057	.1757	173	37
24	812	107	.1750	154	36
25	.64834	.85157	1.1743	.76135	35
26	856	207	.1736	116	34
27	878	257	.1729	097	33
28	901	308	.1722	078	32
29	923	358	.1715	059	31
30	.64945	.85408	1.1708	.76041	30
31	967	458	.1702	022	29
32	.64989	509	.1695	.76003	28
33	.65011	559	.1688	.75984	27
34	033	609	.1681	965	26
35	.65055	.85660	1.1674	.75946	25
36	077	710	.1667	927	24
37	100	761	.1660	908	23
38	122	811	.1653	889	22
39	144	862	.1647	870	21
40	.65166	.85912	1.1640	.75851	20
41	188	.85963	.1633	832	19
42	210	.86014	.1626	813	18
43	232	064	.1619	794	17
44	254	115	.1612	775	16
45	.65276	.86166	1.1606	.75756	15
46	298	216	.1599	738	14
47	320	267	.1592	719	13
48	342	318	.1585	700	12
49	364	368	.1578	680	11
50	.65386	.86419	1.1571	.75661	10
51	408	470	.1565	642	9
52	430	521	.1558	623	8
53	452	572	.1551	604	7
54	474	623	.1544	585	6
55	.65496	.86674	1.1538	.75566	5
56	518	725	.1531	547	4
57	540	776	.1524	528	3
58	562	827	.1517	509	2
59	584	878	.1510	490	1
60	.65606	.86929	1.1504	.75471	0
	Cos	Ctn	Tan	Sin	′

49°

′	Sin	Tan	Ctn	Cos	
0	.65606	.86929	1.1504	.75471	60
1	628	.86980	.1497	452	59
2	650	.87031	.1490	433	58
3	672	082	.1483	414	57
4	694	133	.1477	395	56
5	.65716	.87184	1.1470	.75375	55
6	738	236	.1463	356	54
7	759	287	.1456	337	53
8	781	338	.1450	318	52
9	803	389	.1443	299	51
10	.65825	.87441	1.1436	.75280	50
11	847	492	.1430	261	49
12	869	543	.1423	241	48
13	891	595	.1416	222	47
14	913	646	.1410	203	46
15	.65935	.87698	1.1403	.75184	45
16	956	749	.1396	165	44
17	.65978	801	.1389	146	43
18	.66000	852	.1383	126	42
19	022	904	.1376	107	41
20	.66044	.87955	1.1369	.75088	40
21	066	.88007	.1363	069	39
22	088	059	.1356	050	38
23	109	110	.1349	030	37
24	131	162	.1343	.75011	36
25	.66153	.88214	1.1336	.74992	35
26	175	265	.1329	973	34
27	197	317	.1323	953	33
28	218	369	.1316	934	32
29	240	421	.1310	915	31
30	.66262	.88473	1.1303	.74896	30
31	284	524	.1296	876	29
32	306	576	.1290	857	28
33	327	628	.1283	838	27
34	349	680	.1276	818	26
35	.66371	.88732	1.1270	.74799	25
36	393	784	.1263	780	24
37	414	836	.1257	760	23
38	436	888	.1250	741	22
39	458	940	.1243	722	21
40	.66480	.88992	1.1237	.74703	20
41	501	.89045	.1230	683	19
42	523	097	.1224	664	18
43	545	149	.1217	644	17
44	566	201	.1211	625	16
45	.66588	.89253	1.1204	.74606	15
46	610	306	.1197	586	14
47	632	358	.1191	567	13
48	653	410	.1184	548	12
49	675	463	.1178	528	11
50	.66697	.89515	1.1171	.74509	10
51	718	567	.1165	489	9
52	740	620	.1158	470	8
53	762	672	.1152	451	7
54	783	725	.1145	431	6
55	.66805	.89777	1.1139	.74412	5
56	827	830	.1132	392	4
57	848	883	.1126	373	3
58	870	935	.1119	353	2
59	891	.89988	.1113	334	1
60	.66913	.90040	1.1106	.74314	0
	Cos	Ctn	Tan	Sin	′

48°

42°—Natural Trigonometric Functions—43°

′	Sin	Tan	Ctn	Cos	
0	.66913	.90040	1.1106	.74314	**60**
1	935	093	.1100	295	59
2	956	146	.1093	276	58
3	978	199	.1087	256	57
4	.66999	251	.1080	237	56
5	.67021	.90304	1.1074	.74217	**55**
6	043	357	.1067	198	54
7	064	410	.1061	178	53
8	086	463	.1054	159	52
9	107	516	.1048	139	51
10	.67129	.90569	1.1041	.74120	**50**
11	151	621	.1035	100	49
12	172	674	.1028	080	48
13	194	727	.1022	061	47
14	215	781	.1016	041	46
15	.67237	.90834	1.1009	.74022	**45**
16	258	887	.1003	.74002	44
17	280	940	.0996	.73983	43
18	301	.90993	.0990	963	42
19	323	.91046	.0983	944	41
20	.67344	.91099	1.0977	.73924	**40**
21	366	153	.0971	904	39
22	387	206	.0964	885	38
23	409	259	.0958	865	37
24	430	313	.0951	846	36
25	.67452	.91366	1.0945	.73826	**35**
26	473	419	.0939	806	34
27	495	473	.0932	787	33
28	516	526	.0926	767	32
29	538	580	.0919	747	31
30	.67559	.91633	1.0913	.73728	**30**
31	580	687	.0907	708	29
32	602	740	.0900	688	28
33	623	794	.0894	669	27
34	645	847	.0888	649	26
35	.67666	.91901	1.0881	.73629	**25**
36	688	.91955	.0875	610	24
37	709	.92008	.0869	590	23
38	730	062	.0862	570	22
39	752	116	.0856	551	21
40	.67773	.92170	1.0850	.73531	**20**
41	795	224	.0843	511	19
42	816	277	.0837	491	18
43	837	331	.0831	472	17
44	859	385	.0824	452	16
45	.67880	.92439	1.0818	.73432	**15**
46	901	493	.0812	413	14
47	923	547	.0805	393	13
48	944	601	.0799	373	12
49	965	655	.0793	353	11
50	.67987	.92709	1.0786	.73333	**10**
51	.68008	763	.0780	314	9
52	029	817	.0774	294	8
53	051	872	.0768	274	7
54	072	926	.0761	254	6
55	.68093	.92980	1.0755	.73234	**5**
56	115	.93034	.0749	215	4
57	136	088	.0742	195	3
58	157	143	.0736	175	2
59	179	197	.0730	155	1
60	.68200	.93252	1.0724	.73135	**0**
	Cos	Ctn	Tan	Sin	′

47°

′	Sin	Tan	Ctn	Cos	
0	.68200	.93252	1.0724	.73135	**60**
1	221	306	.0717	116	59
2	242	360	.0711	096	58
3	264	415	.0705	076	57
4	285	469	.0699	056	56
5	.68306	.93524	1.0692	.73036	**55**
6	327	578	.0686	.73016	54
7	349	633	.0680	.72996	53
8	370	688	.0674	976	52
9	391	742	.0668	957	51
10	.68412	.93797	1.0661	.72937	**50**
11	434	852	.0655	917	49
12	455	906	.0649	897	48
13	476	.93961	.0643	877	47
14	497	.94016	.0637	857	46
15	.68518	.94071	1.0630	.72837	**45**
16	539	125	.0624	817	44
17	561	180	.0618	797	43
18	582	235	.0612	777	42
19	603	290	.0606	757	41
20	.68624	.94345	1.0599	.72737	**40**
21	645	400	.0593	717	39
22	666	455	.0587	697	38
23	688	510	.0581	677	37
24	709	565	.0575	657	36
25	.68730	.94620	1.0569	.72637	**35**
26	751	676	.0562	617	34
27	772	731	.0556	597	33
28	793	786	.0550	577	32
29	814	841	.0544	557	31
30	.68835	.94896	1.0538	.72537	**30**
31	857	.94952	.0532	517	29
32	878	.95007	.0526	497	28
33	899	062	.0519	477	27
34	920	118	.0513	457	26
35	.68941	.95173	1.0507	.72437	**25**
36	962	229	.0501	417	24
37	.68983	284	.0495	397	23
38	.69004	340	.0489	377	22
39	025	395	.0483	357	21
40	.69046	.95451	1.0477	.72337	**20**
41	067	506	.0470	317	19
42	088	562	.0464	297	18
43	109	618	.0458	277	17
44	130	673	.0452	257	16
45	.69151	.95729	1.0446	.72236	**15**
46	172	785	.0440	216	14
47	193	841	.0434	196	13
48	214	897	.0428	176	12
49	235	.95952	.0422	156	11
50	.69256	.96008	1.0416	.72136	**10**
51	277	064	.0410	116	9
52	298	120	.0404	095	8
53	319	176	.0398	075	7
54	340	232	.0392	055	6
55	.69361	.96288	1.0385	.72035	**5**
56	382	344	.0379	.72015	4
57	403	400	.0373	.71995	3
58	424	457	.0367	974	2
59	445	513	.0361	954	1
60	.69466	.96569	1.0355	.71934	**0**
	Cos	Ctn	Tan	Sin	′

46°

44°—Natural Trigonometric Functions

′	Sin	Tan	Ctn	Cos	
0	.69466	.96569	1.0355	.71934	**60**
1	487	625	.0349	914	59
2	508	681	.0343	894	58
3	529	738	.0337	873	57
4	549	794	.0331	853	56
5	.69570	.96850	1.0325	.71833	**55**
6	591	907	.0319	813	54
7	612	.96963	.0313	792	53
8	633	.97020	.0307	772	52
9	654	076	.0301	752	51
10	.69675	.97133	1.0295	.71732	**50**
11	696	189	.0289	711	49
12	717	246	.0283	691	48
13	737	302	.0277	671	47
14	758	359	.0271	650	46
15	.69779	.97416	1.0265	.71630	**45**
16	800	472	.0259	610	44
17	821	529	.0253	590	43
18	842	586	.0247	569	42
19	862	643	.0241	549	41
20	.69883	.97700	1.0235	.71529	**40**
21	904	756	.0230	508	39
22	925	813	.0224	488	38
23	946	870	.0218	468	37
24	966	927	.0212	447	36
25	.69987	.97984	1.0206	.71427	**35**
26	.70008	.98041	.0200	407	34
27	029	098	.0194	386	33
28	049	155	.0188	366	32
29	070	213	.0182	345	31
30	.70091	.98270	1.0176	.71325	**30**
31	112	327	.0170	305	29
32	132	384	.0164	284	28
33	153	441	.0158	264	27
34	174	499	.0152	243	26
35	.70195	.98556	1.0147	.71223	**25**
36	215	613	.0141	203	24
37	236	671	.0135	182	23
38	257	728	.0129	162	22
39	277	786	.0123	141	21
40	.70298	.98843	1.0117	.71121	**20**
41	319	901	.0111	100	19
42	339	.98958	.0105	080	18
43	360	.99016	.0099	059	17
44	381	073	.0094	039	16
45	.70401	.99131	1.0088	.71019	**15**
46	422	189	.0082	.70998	14
47	443	247	.0076	978	13
48	463	304	.0070	957	12
49	484	362	.0064	937	11
50	.70505	.99420	1.0058	.70916	**10**
51	525	478	.0052	896	9
52	546	536	.0047	875	8
53	567	594	.0041	855	7
54	587	652	.0035	834	6
55	.70608	.99710	1.0029	.70813	**5**
56	628	768	.0023	793	4
57	649	826	.0017	772	3
58	670	884	.0012	752	2
59	690	.99942	.0006	731	1
60	.70711	1.0000	1.0000	.70711	**0**
	Cos	Ctn	Tan	Sin	′

45°

V. Logarithms of Trigonometric Functions

FROM

0° TO 90° AT INTERVALS OF ONE MINUTE

TO

FIVE DECIMAL PLACES

From each logarithm given, subtract 10

Auxiliary Table of S and T for A in Minutes

$S = \log \sin A - \log A'$ and $T = \log \tan A - \log A'$

A'	$S+10$	A'	$T+10$	A'	$T+10$
0′ – 13′	6.46373	0′ – 26′	6.46373	131′ – 133′	6.46394
14′ – 42′	72	27′ – 39′	74	134′ – 136′	95
43′ – 58′	71	40′ – 48′	75	137′ – 139′	96
59′ – 71′	6.46370	49′ – 56′	6.46376	140′ – 142′	6.46397
72′ – 81′	69	57′ – 63′	77	143′ – 145′	98
82′ – 91′	68	64′ – 69′	78	146′ – 148′	99
92′ – 99′	6.46367	70′ – 74′	6.46379	149′ – 150′	6.46400
100′ – 107′	66	75′ – 80′	80	151′ – 153′	01
108′ – 115′	65	81′ – 85′	81	154′ – 156′	02
116′ – 121′	6.46364	86′ – 89′	6.46382	157′ – 158′	6.46403
122′ – 128′	63	90′ – 94′	83	159′ – 161′	04
129′ – 134′	62	95′ – 98′	84	162′ – 163′	05
135′ – 140′	6.46361	99′ – 102′	6.46385	164′ – 166′	6.46406
141′ – 146′	60	103′ – 106′	86	167′ – 168′	07
147′ – 151′	59	107′ – 110′	87	169′ – 171′	08
152′ – 157′	6.46358	111′ – 113′	6.46388	172′ – 173′	6.46409
158′ – 162′	57	114′ – 117′	89	174′ – 175′	10
163′ – 167′	56	118′ – 120′	90	176′ – 178′	11
168′ – 171′	6.46355	121′ – 124′	6.46391	179′ – 180′	6.46412
172′ – 176′	54	125′ – 127′	92	181′ – 182′	13
177′ – 181′	53	128′ – 130′	93	183′ – 184′	14

or small angles: $\log \sin A = \log A' + S$ and $\log \tan A = \log A' + T$.
or angles near 90°: $\log \cos A = \log (90° - A)' + S$, $\log \operatorname{ctn} A = \log (90° - A)' + T$ where A' = number of minutes in A, and $(90° - A)'$ = number of minutes $90° - A$.

0° — Logarithms of Trigonometric Functions

′	L Sin	d	L Tan	c d	L Ctn	L Cos	
0	———		———		———	10.00 000	**60**
1	6.46 373	30103	6.46 373	30103	13.53 627	10.00 000	59
2	6.76 476	17609	6.76 476	17609	13.23 524	10.00 000	58
3	6.94 085	12494	6.94 085	12494	13.05 915	10.00 000	57
4	7.06 579	9691	7.06 579	9691	12.93 421	10.00 000	56
5	7.16 270	7918	7.16 270	7918	12.83 730	10.00 000	**55**
6	7.24 188	6694	7.24 188	6694	12.75 812	10.00 000	54
7	7.30 882	5800	7.30 882	5800	12.69 118	10.00 000	53
8	7.36 682	5115	7.36 682	5115	12.63 318	10.00 000	52
9	7.41 797	4576	7.41 797	4576	12.58 203	10.00 000	51
10	7.46 373	4139	7.46 373	4139	12.53 627	10.00 000	**50**
11	7.50 512	3779	7.50 512	3779	12.49 488	10.00 000	49
12	7.54 291	3476	7.54 291	3476	12.45 709	10.00 000	48
13	7.57 767	3218	7.57 767	3219	12.42 233	10.00 000	47
14	7.60 985	2997	7.60 986	2996	12.39 014	10.00 000	46
15	7.63 982	2802	7.63 982	2803	12.36 018	10.00 000	**45**
16	7.66 784	2633	7.66 785	2633	12.33 215	10.00 000	44
17	7.69 417	2483	7.69 418	2482	12.30 582	9.99 999	43
18	7.71 900	2348	7.71 900	2348	12.28 100	9.99 999	42
19	7.74 248	2227	7.74 248	2228	12.25 752	9.99 999	41
20	7.76 475	2119	7.76 476	2119	12.23 524	9.99 999	**40**
21	7.78 594	2021	7.78 595	2020	12.21 405	9.99 999	39
22	7.80 615	1930	7.80 615	1931	12.19 385	9.99 999	38
23	7.82 545	1848	7.82 546	1848	12.17 454	9.99 999	37
24	7.84 393	1773	7.84 394	1773	12.15 606	9.99 999	36
25	7.86 166	1704	7.86 167	1704	12.13 833	9.99 999	**35**
26	7.87 870	1639	7.87 871	1639	12.12 129	9.99 999	34
27	7.89 509	1579	7.89 510	1579	12.10 490	9.99 999	33
28	7.91 088	1524	7.91 089	1524	12.08 911	9.99 999	32
29	7.92 612	1472	7.92 613	1473	12.07 387	9.99 998	31
30	7.94 084	1424	7.94 086	1424	12.05 914	9.99 998	**30**
31	7.95 508	1379	7.95 510	1379	12.04 490	9.99 998	29
32	7.96 887	1336	7.96 889	1336	12.03 111	9.99 998	28
33	7.98 223	1297	7.98 225	1297	12.01 775	9.99 998	27
34	7.99 520	1259	7.99 522	1259	12.00 478	9.99 998	26
35	8.00 779	1223	8.00 781	1223	11.99 219	9.99 998	**25**
36	8.02 002	1190	8.02 004	1190	11.97 996	9.99 998	24
37	8.03 192	1158	8.03 194	1159	11.96 806	9.99 997	23
38	8.04 350	1128	8.04 353	1128	11.95 647	9.99 997	22
39	8.05 478	1100	8.05 481	1100	11.94 519	9.99 997	21
40	8.06 578	1072	8.06 581	1072	11.93 419	9.99 997	**20**
41	8.07 650	1046	8.07 653	1047	11.92 347	9.99 997	19
42	8.08 696	1022	8.08 700	1022	11.91 300	9.99 997	18
43	8.09 718	999	8.09 722	998	11.90 278	9.99 997	17
44	8.10 717	976	8.10 720	976	11.89 280	9.99 996	16
45	8.11 693	954	8.11 696	955	11.88 304	9.99 996	**15**
46	8.12 647	934	8.12 651	934	11.87 349	9.99 996	14
47	8.13 581	914	8.13 585	915	11.86 415	9.99 996	13
48	8.14 495	896	8.14 500	895	11.85 500	9.99 996	12
49	8.15 391	877	8.15 395	878	11.84 605	9.99 996	11
50	8.16 268	860	8.16 273	860	11.83 727	9.99 995	**10**
51	8.17 128	843	8.17 133	843	11.82 867	9.99 995	9
52	8.17 971	827	8.17 976	828	11.82 024	9.99 995	8
53	8.18 798	812	8.18 804	812	11.81 196	9.99 995	7
54	8.19 610	797	8.19 616	797	11.80 384	9.99 995	6
55	8.20 407	782	8.20 413	782	11.79 587	9.99 994	**5**
56	8.21 189	769	8.21 195	769	11.78 805	9.99 994	4
57	8.21 958	755	8.21 964	756	11.78 036	9.99 994	3
58	8.22 713	743	8.22 720	742	11.77 280	9.99 994	2
59	8.23 456	730	8.23 462	730	11.76 538	9.99 994	1
60	8.24 186		8.24 192		11.75 808	9.99 993	**0**
	L Cos	d	L Ctn	c d	L Tan	L Sin	′

89° — Logarithms of Trigonometric Functions

For logarithms of sines or tangents of angles less than 3° (or logarithms of cosines or cotangents of angles greater than 87°), see p. 123.

When the tabular differences are large, that method is usually better. The proportional parts stated for 1° and 2° in this table are sufficient when great accuracy is not required, even if the ordinary method of interpolation is used.

′	L Sin	d	L Tan	c d	L Ctn	L Cos	
0	8.24 186	717	8.24 192	718	11.75 808	9.99 993	60
1	8.24 903	706	8.24 910	706	11.75 090	9.99 993	59
2	8.25 609	695	8.25 616	696	11.74 384	9.99 993	58
3	8.26 304	684	8.26 312	684	11.73 688	9.99 993	57
4	8.26 988	673	8.26 996	673	11.73 004	9.99 992	56
5	8.27 661	663	8.27 669	663	11.72 331	9.99 992	55
6	8.28 324	653	8.28 332	654	11.71 668	9.99 992	54
7	8.28 977	644	8.28 986	643	11.71 014	9.99 992	53
8	8.29 621	634	8.29 629	634	11.70 371	9.99 992	52
9	8.30 255	624	8.30 263	625	11.69 737	9.99 991	51
10	8.30 879	616	8.30 888	617	11.69 112	9.99 991	50
11	8.31 495	608	8.31 505	607	11.68 495	9.99 991	49
12	8.32 103	599	8.32 112	599	11.67 888	9.99 990	48
13	8.32 702	590	8.32 711	591	11.67 289	9.99 990	47
14	8.33 292	583	8.33 302	584	11.66 698	9.99 990	46
15	8.33 875	575	8.33 886	575	11.66 114	9.99 990	45
16	8.34 450	568	8.34 461	568	11.65 539	9.99 989	44
17	8.35 018	560	8.35 029	561	11.64 971	9.99 989	43
18	8.35 578	553	8.35 590	553	11.64 410	9.99 989	42
19	8.36 131	547	8.36 143	546	11.63 857	9.99 989	41
20	8.36 678	539	8.36 689	540	11.63 311	9.99 988	40
21	8.37 217	533	8.37 229	533	11.62 771	9.99 988	39
22	8.37 750	526	8.37 762	527	11.62 238	9.99 988	38
23	8.38 276	520	8.38 289	520	11.61 711	9.99 987	37
24	8.38 796	514	8.38 809	514	11.61 191	9.99 987	36
25	8.39 310	508	8.39 323	509	11.60 677	9.99 987	35
26	8.39 818	502	8.39 832	502	11.60 168	9.99 986	34
27	8.40 320	496	8.40 334	496	11.59 666	9.99 986	33
28	8.40 816	491	8.40 830	491	11.59 170	9.99 986	32
29	8.41 307	485	8.41 321	486	11.58 679	9.99 985	31
30	8.41 792	480	8.41 807	480	11.58 193	9.99 985	30
31	8.42 272	474	8.42 287	475	11.57 713	9.99 985	29
32	8.42 746	470	8.42 762	470	11.57 238	9.99 984	28
33	8.43 216	464	8.43 232	464	11.56 768	9.99 984	27
34	8.43 680	459	8.43 696	460	11.56 304	9.99 984	26
35	8.44 139	455	8.44 156	455	11.55 844	9.99 983	25
36	8.44 594	450	8.44 611	450	11.55 389	9.99 983	24
37	8.45 044	445	8.45 061	446	11.54 939	9.99 983	23
38	8.45 489	441	8.45 507	441	11.54 493	9.99 982	22
39	8.45 930	436	8.45 948	437	11.54 052	9.99 982	21
40	8.46 366	433	8.46 385	432	11.53 615	9.99 982	20
41	8.46 799	427	8.46 817	428	11.53 183	9.99 981	19
42	8.47 226	424	8.47 245	424	11.52 755	9.99 981	18
43	8.47 650	419	8.47 669	420	11.52 331	9.99 981	17
44	8.48 069	416	8.48 089	416	11.51 911	9.99 980	16
45	8.48 485	411	8.48 505	412	11.51 495	9.99 980	15
46	8.48 896	408	8.48 917	408	11.51 083	9.99 979	14
47	8.49 304	404	8.49 325	404	11.50 675	9.99 979	13
48	8.49 708	400	8.49 729	401	11.50 271	9.99 979	12
49	8.50 108	396	8.50 130	397	11.49 870	9.99 978	11
50	8.50 504	393	8.50 527	393	11.49 473	9.99 978	10
51	8.50 897	390	8.50 920	390	11.49 080	9.99 977	9
52	8.51 287	386	8.51 310	386	11.48 690	9.99 977	8
53	8.51 673	382	8.51 696	383	11.48 304	9.99 977	7
54	8.52 055	379	8.52 079	380	11.47 921	9.99 976	6
55	8.52 434	376	8.52 459	376	11.47 541	9.99 976	5
56	8.52 810	373	8.52 835	373	11.47 165	9.99 975	4
57	8.53 183	369	8.53 208	370	11.46 792	9.99 975	3
58	8.53 552	367	8.53 578	367	11.46 422	9.99 974	2
59	8.53 919	363	8.53 945	363	11.46 055	9.99 974	1
60	8.54 282		8.54 308		11.45 692	9.99 974	0
	L Cos	d	L Ctn	c d	L Tan	L Sin	′

Prop. Pts.

	710	690	670	650
2	142	138	134	130
3	213	207	201	195
4	284	276	268	260
5	355	345	335	325
6	426	414	402	390
7	497	483	469	455
8	568	552	536	520
9	639	621	603	585

	630	620	610	600
2	126	124	122	120
3	189	186	183	180
4	252	248	244	240
5	315	310	305	300
6	378	372	366	360
7	441	434	427	420
8	504	496	488	480
9	567	558	549	540

	590	580	570	560
2	118	116	114	112
3	177	174	171	168
4	236	232	228	224
5	295	290	285	280
6	354	348	342	336
7	413	406	399	392
8	472	464	456	448
9	531	522	513	504

	550	540	530	520
2	110	108	106	104
3	165	162	159	156
4	220	216	212	208
5	275	270	265	260
6	330	324	318	312
7	385	378	371	364
8	440	432	424	416
9	495	486	477	468

	510	500	490	480
2	102	100	98	96
3	153	150	147	144
4	204	200	196	192
5	255	250	245	240
6	306	300	294	288
7	357	350	343	336
8	408	400	392	384
9	459	450	441	432

	470	460	450	440
2	94	92	90	88
3	141	138	135	132
4	188	184	180	176
5	235	230	225	220
6	282	276	270	264
7	329	322	315	308
8	376	368	360	352
9	423	414	405	396

	430	420	410	400
2	86	84	82	80
3	129	126	123	120
4	172	168	164	160
5	215	210	205	200
6	258	252	246	240
7	301	294	287	280
8	344	336	328	320
9	387	378	369	360

	390	380	370	360
2	78	76	74	72
3	117	114	111	108
4	156	152	148	144
5	195	190	185	180
6	234	228	222	216
7	273	266	259	252
8	312	304	296	288
9	351	342	333	324

Prop. Pts.

′	L Sin	d	L Tan	c d	L Ctn	L Cos	
0	8.54 282	360	8.54 308	361	11.45 692	9.99 974	60
1	8.54 642	357	8.54 669	358	11.45 331	9.99 973	59
2	8.54 999	355	8.55 027	355	11.44 973	9.99 973	58
3	8.55 354	351	8.55 382	352	11.44 618	9.99 972	57
4	8.55 705	349	8.55 734	349	11.44 266	9.99 972	56
5	8.56 054	346	8.56 083	346	11.43 917	9.99 971	55
6	8.56 400	343	8.56 429	344	11.43 571	9.99 971	54
7	8.56 743	341	8.56 773	341	11.43 227	9.99 970	53
8	8.57 084	337	8.57 114	338	11.42 886	9.99 970	52
9	8.57 421	336	8.57 452	336	11.42 548	9.99 969	51
10	8.57 757	332	8.57 788	333	11.42 212	9.99 969	50
11	8.58 089	330	8.58 121	330	11.41 879	9.99 968	49
12	8.58 419	328	8.58 451	328	11.41 549	9.99 968	48
13	8.58 747	325	8.58 779	326	11.41 221	9.99 967	47
14	8.59 072	323	8.59 105	323	11.40 895	9.99 967	46
15	8.59 395	320	8.59 428	321	11.40 572	9.99 967	45
16	8.59 715	318	8.59 749	319	11.40 251	9.99 966	44
17	8.60 033	316	8.60 068	316	11.39 932	9.99 966	43
18	8.60 349	313	8.60 384	314	11.39 616	9.99 965	42
19	8.60 662	311	8.60 698	311	11.39 302	9.99 964	41
20	8.60 973	309	8.61 009	310	11.38 991	9.99 964	40
21	8.61 282	307	8.61 319	307	11.38 681	9.99 963	39
22	8.61 589	305	8.61 626	305	11.38 374	9.99 963	38
23	8.61 894	302	8.61 931	303	11.38 069	9.99 962	37
24	8.62 196	301	8.62 234	301	11.37 766	9.99 962	36
25	8.62 497	298	8.62 535	299	11.37 465	9.99 961	35
26	8.62 795	296	8.62 834	297	11.37 166	9.99 961	34
27	8.63 091	294	8.63 131	295	11.36 869	9.99 960	33
28	8.63 385	293	8.63 426	292	11.36 574	9.99 960	32
29	8.63 678	290	8.63 718	291	11.36 282	9.99 959	31
30	8.63 968	288	8.64 009	289	11.35 991	9.99 959	30
31	8.64 256	287	8.64 298	287	11.35 702	9.99 958	29
32	8.64 543	284	8.64 585	285	11.35 415	9.99 958	28
33	8.64 827	283	8.64 870	284	11.35 130	9.99 957	27
34	8.65 110	281	8.65 154	281	11.34 846	9.99 956	26
35	8.65 391	279	8.65 435	280	11.34 565	9.99 956	25
36	8.65 670	277	8.65 715	278	11.34 285	9.99 955	24
37	8.65 947	276	8.65 993	276	11.34 007	9.99 955	23
38	8.66 223	274	8.66 269	274	11.33 731	9.99 954	22
39	8.66 497	272	8.66 543	273	11.33 457	9.99 954	21
40	8.66 769	270	8.66 816	271	11.33 184	9.99 953	20
41	8.67 039	269	8.67 087	269	11.32 913	9.99 952	19
42	8.67 308	267	8.67 356	268	11.32 644	9.99 952	18
43	8.67 575	266	8.67 624	266	11.32 376	9.99 951	17
44	8.67 841	263	8.67 890	264	11.32 110	9.99 951	16
45	8.68 104	263	8.68 154	263	11.31 846	9.99 950	15
46	8.68 367	260	8.68 417	261	11.31 583	9.99 949	14
47	8.68 627	259	8.68 678	260	11.31 322	9.99 949	13
48	8.68 886	258	8.68 938	258	11.31 062	9.99 948	12
49	8.69 144	256	8.69 196	257	11.30 804	9.99 948	11
50	8.69 400	254	8.69 453	255	11.30 547	9.99 947	10
51	8.69 654	253	8.69 708	254	11.30 292	9.99 946	9
52	8.69 907	252	8.69 962	252	11.30 038	9.99 946	8
53	8.70 159	250	8.70 214	251	11.29 786	9.99 945	7
54	8.70 409	249	8.70 465	249	11.29 535	9.99 944	6
55	8.70 658	247	8.70 714	248	11.29 286	9.99 944	5
56	8.70 905	246	8.70 962	246	11.29 038	9.99 943	4
57	8.71 151	244	8.71 208	245	11.28 792	9.99 942	3
58	8.71 395	243	8.71 453	244	11.28 547	9.99 942	2
59	8.71 638	242	8.71 697	243	11.28 303	9.99 941	1
60	8.71 880		8.71 940		11.28 060	9.99 940	0
	L Cos	d	L Ctn	c d	L Tan	L Sin	′

Prop. Pts.

	360	355	350
2	72	71.0	70
3	108	106.5	105
4	144	142.0	140
5	180	177.5	175
6	216	213.0	210
7	252	248.5	245
8	288	284.0	280
9	324	319.5	315

	345	340	335
2	69.0	68	67.0
3	103.5	102	100.5
4	138.0	136	134.0
5	172.5	170	167.5
6	207.0	204	201.0
7	241.5	238	234.5
8	276.0	272	268.0
9	310.5	306	301.5

	330	325	320
2	66	65.0	64
3	99	97.5	96
4	132	130.0	128
5	165	162.5	160
6	198	195.0	192
7	231	227.5	224
8	264	260.0	256
9	297	292.5	288

	315	310	305
2	63.0	62	61.0
3	94.5	93	91.5
4	126.0	124	122.0
5	157.5	155	152.5
6	189.0	186	183.0
7	220.5	217	213.5
8	252.0	248	244.0
9	283.5	279	274.5

	300	295	290
2	60	59.0	58
3	90	88.5	87
4	120	118.0	116
5	150	147.5	145
6	180	177.0	174
7	210	206.5	203
8	240	236.0	232
9	270	265.5	261

	285	280	275
2	57.0	56	55.0
3	85.5	84	82.5
4	114.0	112	110.0
5	142.5	140	137.5
6	171.0	168	165.0
7	199.5	196	192.5
8	228.0	224	220.0
9	256.5	252	247.5

	270	265	260
2	54	53.0	52
3	81	79.5	78
4	108	106.0	104
5	135	132.5	130
6	162	159.0	156
7	189	185.5	182
8	216	212.0	208
9	243	238.5	234

	255	250	245
2	51.0	50	49.0
3	76.5	75	73.5
4	102.0	100	98.0
5	127.5	125	122.5
6	153.0	150	147.0
7	178.5	175	171.5
8	204.0	200	196.0
9	229.5	225	220.5

Prop. Pts.

3° — Logarithms of Trigonometric Functions

′	L Sin	d	L Tan	c d	L Ctn	L Cos	
0	8.71 880	240	8.71 940	241	11.28 060	9.99 940	60
1	8.72 120	239	8.72 181	239	11.27 819	9.99 940	59
2	8.72 359	238	8.72 420	239	11.27 580	9.99 939	58
3	8.72 597	237	8.72 659	237	11.27 341	9.99 938	57
4	8.72 834	235	8.72 896	236	11.27 104	9.99 938	56
5	8.73 069	234	8.73 132	234	11.26 868	9.99 937	55
6	8.73 303	232	8.73 366	234	11.26 634	9.99 936	54
7	8.73 535	232	8.73 600	232	11.26 400	9.99 936	53
8	8.73 767	230	8.73 832	231	11.26 168	9.99 935	52
9	8.73 997	229	8.74 063	229	11.25 937	9.99 934	51
10	8.74 226	228	8.74 292	229	11.25 708	9.99 934	50
11	8.74 454	226	8.74 521	227	11.25 479	9.99 933	49
12	8.74 680	226	8.74 748	226	11.25 252	9.99 932	48
13	8.74 906	224	8.74 974	225	11.25 026	9.99 932	47
14	8.75 130	223	8.75 199	224	11.24 801	9.99 931	46
15	8.75 353	222	8.75 423	222	11.24 577	9.99 930	45
16	8.75 575	220	8.75 645	222	11.24 355	9.99 929	44
17	8.75 795	220	8.75 867	220	11.24 133	9.99 929	43
18	8.76 015	219	8.76 087	219	11.23 913	9.99 928	42
19	8.76 234	217	8.76 306	219	11.23 694	9.99 927	41
20	8.76 451	216	8.76 525	217	11.23 475	9.99 926	40
21	8.76 667	216	8.76 742	216	11.23 258	9.99 926	39
22	8.76 883	214	8.76 958	215	11.23 042	9.99 925	38
23	8.77 097	213	8.77 173	214	11.22 827	9.99 924	37
24	8.77 310	212	8.77 387	213	11.22 613	9.99 923	36
25	8.77 522	211	8.77 600	211	11.22 400	9.99 923	35
26	8.77 733	210	8.77 811	211	11.22 189	9.99 922	34
27	8.77 943	209	8.78 022	210	11.21 978	9.99 921	33
28	8.78 152	208	8.78 232	209	11.21 768	9.99 920	32
29	8.78 360	208	8.78 441	208	11.21 559	9.99 920	31
30	8.78 568	206	8.78 649	206	11.21 351	9.99 919	30
31	8.78 774	205	8.78 855	206	11.21 145	9.99 918	29
32	8.78 979	204	8.79 061	205	11.20 939	9.99 917	28
33	8.79 183	203	8.79 266	204	11.20 734	9.99 917	27
34	8.79 386	202	8.79 470	203	11.20 530	9.99 916	26
35	8.79 588	201	8.79 673	202	11.20 327	9.99 915	25
36	8.79 789	201	8.79 875	201	11.20 125	9.99 914	24
37	8.79 990	199	8.80 076	201	11.19 924	9.99 913	23
38	8.80 189	199	8.80 277	199	11.19 723	9.99 913	22
39	8.80 388	197	8.80 476	198	11.19 524	9.99 912	21
40	8.80 585	197	8.80 674	198	11.19 326	9.99 911	20
41	8.80 782	196	8.80 872	196	11.19 128	9.99 910	19
42	8.80 978	195	8.81 068	196	11.18 932	9.99 909	18
43	8.81 173	194	8.81 264	195	11.18 736	9.99 909	17
44	8.81 367	193	8.81 459	194	11.18 541	9.99 908	16
45	8.81 560	192	8.81 653	193	11.18 347	9.99 907	15
46	8.81 752	192	8.81 846	192	11.18 154	9.99 906	14
47	8.81 944	190	8.82 038	192	11.17 962	9.99 905	13
48	8.82 134	190	8.82 230	190	11.17 770	9.99 904	12
49	8.82 324	189	8.82 420	190	11.17 580	9.99 904	11
50	8.82 513	188	8.82 610	189	11.17 390	9.99 903	10
51	8.82 701	187	8.82 799	188	11.17 201	9.99 902	9
52	8 82 888	187	8.82 987	188	11.17 013	9.99 901	8
53	8.83 075	186	8.83 175	186	11.16 825	9.99 900	7
54	8.83 261	185	8.83 361	186	11.16 639	9.99 899	6
55	8.83 446	184	8.83 547	185	11.16 453	9.99 898	5
56	8.83 630	183	8.83 732	184	11.16 268	9.99 898	4
57	8.83 813	183	8.83 916	184	11.16 084	9.99 897	3
58	8.83 996	181	8.84 100	182	11.15 900	9.99 896	2
59	8.84 177	181	8.84 282	182	11.15 718	9.99 895	1
60	8.84 358		8.84 464		11.15 536	9.99 894	0
	L Cos	d	L Ctn	c d	L Tan	L Sin	′

Prop. Pts.

	240	235	230
2	48	47.0	46
3	72	70.5	69
4	96	94.0	92
5	120	117.5	115
6	144	141.0	138
7	168	164.5	161
8	192	188.0	184
9	216	211.5	207

	225	220	215
2	45.0	44.0	43.0
3	67.5	66.0	64.5
4	90.0	88.0	86.0
5	112.5	110.0	107.5
6	135.0	132.0	129.0
7	157.5	154.0	150.5
8	180.0	176.0	172.0
9	202.5	198.0	193.5

	213	211	208
2	42.6	42.2	41.6
3	63.9	63.3	62.4
4	85.2	84.4	83.2
5	106.5	105.5	104.0
6	127.8	126.6	124.8
7	149.1	147.7	145.6
8	170.4	168.8	166.4
9	191.7	189.9	187.2

	206	203	201
2	41.2	40.6	40.2
3	61.8	60.9	60.3
4	82.4	81.2	80.4
5	103.0	101.5	100.5
6	123.6	121.8	120.6
7	144.2	142.1	140.7
8	164.8	162.4	160.8
9	185.4	182.7	180.9

	199	197	195
2	39.8	39.4	39.0
3	59.7	59.1	58.5
4	79.6	78.8	78.0
5	99.5	98.5	97.5
6	119.4	118.2	117.0
7	139.3	137.9	136.5
8	159.2	157.6	156.0
9	179.1	177.3	175.5

	193	192	190
2	38.6	38.4	38.0
3	57.9	57.6	57.0
4	77.2	76.8	76.0
5	96.5	96.0	95.0
6	115.8	115.2	114.0
7	135.1	134.4	133.0
8	154.4	153.6	152.0
9	173.7	172.8	171.0

	188	186	184
2	37.6	37.2	36.8
3	56.4	55.8	55.2
4	75.2	74.4	73.6
5	94.0	93.0	92.0
6	112.8	111.6	110.4
7	131.6	130.2	128.8
8	150.4	148.8	147.2
9	169.2	167.4	165.6

	183	182	181
2	36.6	36.4	36.2
3	54.9	54.6	54.3
4	73.2	72.8	72.4
5	91.5	91.0	90.5
6	109.8	109.2	108.6
7	128.1	127.4	126.7
8	146.4	145.6	144.8
9	164.7	163.8	162.9

Prop. Pts.

86° — Logarithms of Trigonometric Functions

′	L Sin	d	L Tan	c d	L Ctn	L Cos	
0	8.84 358	181	8.84 464	182	11.15 536	9.99 894	60
1	8.84 539	179	8.84 646	180	11.15 354	9.99 893	59
2	8.84 718	179	8.84 826	180	11.15 174	9.99 892	58
3	8.84 897	178	8.85 006	179	11.14 994	9.99 891	57
4	8.85 075	177	8.85 185	178	11.14 815	9.99 891	56
5	8.85 252	177	8.85 363	177	11.14 637	9.99 890	55
6	8.85 429	176	8.85 540	177	11.14 460	9.99 889	54
7	8.85 605	175	8.85 717	176	11.14 283	9.99 888	53
8	8.85 780	175	8.85 893	176	11.14 107	9.99 887	52
9	8.85 955	173	8.86 069	174	11.13 931	9.99 886	51
10	8.86 128	173	8.86 243	174	11.13 757	9.99 885	50
11	8.86 301	173	8.86 417	174	11.13 583	9.99 884	49
12	8.86 474	171	8.86 591	172	11.13 409	9.99 883	48
13	8.86 645	171	8.86 763	172	11.13 237	9.99 882	47
14	8.86 816	171	8.86 935	171	11.13 065	9.99 881	46
15	8.86 987	169	8.87 106	171	11.12 894	9.99 880	45
16	8.87 156	169	8.87 277	170	11.12 723	9.99 879	44
17	8.87 325	169	8.87 447	169	11.12 553	9.99 879	43
18	8.87 494	167	8.87 616	169	11.12 384	9.99 878	42
19	8.87 661	168	8.87 785	168	11.12 215	9.99 877	41
20	8.87 829	166	8.87 953	167	11.12 047	9.99 876	40
21	8.87 995	166	8.88 120	167	11.11 880	9.99 875	39
22	8.88 161	165	8.88 287	166	11.11 713	9.99 874	38
23	8.88 326	164	8.88 453	165	11.11 547	9.99 873	37
24	8.88 490	164	8.88 618	165	11.11 382	9.99 872	36
25	8.88 654	163	8.88 783	165	11.11 217	9.99 871	35
26	8.88 817	163	8.88 948	163	11.11 052	9.99 870	34
27	8.88 980	162	8.89 111	163	11.10 889	9.99 869	33
28	8.89 142	162	8.89 274	163	11.10 726	9.99 868	32
29	8.89 304	160	8.89 437	161	11.10 563	9.99 867	31
30	8.89 464	161	8.89 598	162	11.10 402	9.99 866	30
31	8.89 625	159	8.89 760	160	11.10 240	9.99 865	29
32	8.89 784	159	8.89 920	160	11.10 080	9.99 864	28
33	8.89 943	159	8.90 080	160	11.09 920	9.99 863	27
34	8.90 102	158	8.90 240	159	11.09 760	9.99 862	26
35	8.90 260	157	8.90 399	158	11.09 601	9.99 861	25
36	8.90 417	157	8.90 557	158	11.09 443	9.99 860	24
37	8.90 574	156	8.90 715	157	11.09 285	9.99 859	23
38	8.90 730	155	8.90 872	157	11.09 128	9.99 858	22
39	8.90 885	155	8.91 029	156	11.08 971	9.99 857	21
40	8.91 040	155	8.91 185	155	11.08 815	9.99 856	20
41	8.91 195	154	8.91 340	155	11.08 660	9.99 855	19
42	8.91 349	153	8.91 495	155	11.08 505	9.99 854	18
43	8.91 502	153	8.91 650	153	11.08 350	9.99 853	17
44	8.91 655	152	8.91 803	154	11.08 197	9.99 852	16
45	8.91 807	152	8.91 957	153	11.08 043	9.99 851	15
46	8.91 959	151	8.92 110	152	11.07 890	9.99 850	14
47	8.92 110	151	8.92 262	152	11.07 738	9.99 848	13
48	8.92 261	150	8.92 414	151	11.07 586	9.99 847	12
49	8.92 411	150	8.92 565	151	11.07 435	9.99 846	11
50	8.92 561	149	8.92 716	150	11.07 284	9.99 845	10
51	8.92 710	149	8.92 866	150	11.07 134	9.99 844	9
52	8.92 859	148	8.93 016	149	11.06 984	9.99 843	8
53	8.93 007	147	8.93 165	148	11.06 835	9.99 842	7
54	8.93 154	147	8.93 313	149	11.06 687	9.99 841	6
55	8.93 301	147	8.93 462	147	11.06 538	9.99 840	5
56	8.93 448	146	8.93 609	147	11.06 391	9.99 839	4
57	8.93 594	146	8.93 756	147	11.06 244	9.99 838	3
58	8.93 740	145	8.93 903	146	11.06 097	9.99 837	2
59	8.93 885	145	8.94 049	146	11.05 951	9.99 836	1
60	8.94 030		8.94 195		11.05 805	9.99 834	0
	L Cos	d	L Ctn	c d	L Tan	L Sin	′

Prop. Pts.

	181	180	179
2	36.2	36.0	35.8
3	54.3	54.0	53.7
4	72.4	72.0	71.6
5	90.5	90.0	89.5
6	108.6	108.0	107.4
7	126.7	126.0	125.3
8	144.8	144.0	143.2
9	162.9	162.0	161.1

	177	175	173
2	35.4	35.0	34.6
3	53.1	52.5	51.9
4	70.8	70.0	69.2
5	88.5	87.5	86.5
6	106.2	105.0	103.8
7	123.9	122.5	121.1
8	141.6	140.0	138.4
9	159.3	157.5	155.7

	171	170	169
2	34.2	34.0	33.8
3	51.3	51.0	50.7
4	68.4	68.0	67.6
5	85.5	85.0	84.5
6	102.6	102.0	101.4
7	119.7	119.0	118.3
8	136.8	136.0	135.2
9	153.9	153.0	152.1

	167	165	163
2	33.4	33.0	32.6
3	50.1	49.5	48.9
4	66.8	66.0	65.2
5	83.5	82.5	81.5
6	100.2	99.0	97.8
7	116.9	115.5	114.1
8	133.6	132.0	130.4
9	150.3	148.5	146.7

	161	160	159
2	32.2	32.0	31.8
3	48.3	48.0	47.7
4	64.4	64.0	63.6
5	80.5	80.0	79.5
6	96.6	96.0	95.4
7	112.7	112.0	111.3
8	128.8	128.0	127.2
9	144.9	144.0	143.1

	157	155	153
2	31.4	31.0	30.6
3	47.1	46.5	45.9
4	62.8	62.0	61.2
5	78.5	77.5	76.5
6	94.2	93.0	91.8
7	109.9	108.5	107.1
8	125.6	124.0	122.4
9	141.3	139.5	137.7

	151	150	149
2	30.2	30.0	29.8
3	45.3	45.0	44.7
4	60.4	60.0	59.6
5	75.5	75.0	74.5
6	90.6	90.0	89.4
7	105.7	105.0	104.3
8	120.8	120.0	119.2
9	135.9	135.0	134.1

	147	145	144
2	29.4	29.0	28.8
3	44.1	43.5	43.2
4	58.8	58.0	57.6
5	73.5	72.5	72.0
6	88.2	87.0	86.4
7	102.9	101.5	100.8
8	117.6	116.0	115.2
9	132.3	130.5	129.6

Prop. Pts.

′	L Sin	d	L Tan	c d	L Ctn	L Cos	
0	8.94 030	144	8.94 195	145	11.05 805	9.99 834	60
1	8.94 174	143	8.94 340	145	11.05 660	9.99 833	59
2	8.94 317	144	8.94 485	145	11.05 515	9.99 832	58
3	8.94 461	142	8.94 630	143	11.05 370	9.99 831	57
4	8.94 603	143	8.94 773	144	11.05 227	9.99 830	56
5	8.94 746	141	8.94 917	143	11.05 083	9.99 829	55
6	8.94 887	142	8.95 060	142	11.04 940	9.99 828	54
7	8.95 029	141	8.95 202	142	11.04 798	9.99 827	53
8	8.95 170	140	8.95 344	142	11.04 656	9.99 825	52
9	8.95 310	140	8.95 486	141	11.04 514	9.99 824	51
10	8.95 450	139	8.95 627	140	11.04 373	9.99 823	50
11	8.95 589	139	8.95 767	141	11.04 233	9.99 822	49
12	8.95 728	139	8.95 908	139	11.04 092	9.99 821	48
13	8.95 867	138	8.96 047	140	11.03 953	9.99 820	47
14	8.96 005	138	8.96 187	138	11.03 813	9.99 819	46
15	8.96 143	137	8.96 325	139	11.03 675	9.99 817	45
16	8.96 280	137	8.96 464	138	11.03 536	9.99 816	44
17	8.96 417	136	8.96 602	137	11.03 398	9.99 815	43
18	8.96 553	136	8.96 739	138	11.03 261	9.99 814	42
19	8.96 689	136	8.96 877	136	11.03 123	9.99 813	41
20	8.96 825	135	8.97 013	137	11.02 987	9.99 812	40
21	8.96 960	135	8.97 150	135	11.02 850	9.99 810	39
22	8.97 095	134	8.97 285	136	11.02 715	9.99 809	38
23	8.97 229	134	8.97 421	135	11.02 579	9.99 808	37
24	8.97 363	133	8.97 556	135	11.02 444	9.99 807	36
25	8.97 496	133	8.97 691	134	11.02 309	9.99 806	35
26	8.97 629	133	8.97 825	134	11.02 175	9.99 804	34
27	8.97 762	132	8.97 959	133	11.02 041	9.99 803	33
28	8.97 894	132	8.98 092	133	11.01 908	9.99 802	32
29	8.98 026	131	8.98 225	133	11.01 775	9.99 801	31
30	8.98 157	131	8.98 358	132	11.01 642	9.99 800	30
31	8.98 288	131	8.98 490	132	11.01 510	9.99 798	29
32	8.98 419	130	8.98 622	131	11.01 378	9.99 797	28
33	8.98 549	130	8.98 753	131	11.01 247	9.99 796	27
34	8.98 679	129	8.98 884	131	11.01 116	9.99 795	26
35	8.98 808	129	8.99 015	130	11.00 985	9.99 793	25
36	8.98 937	129	8.99 145	130	11.00 855	9.99 792	24
37	8.99 066	128	8.99 275	130	11.00 725	9.99 791	23
38	8.99 194	128	8.99 405	129	11.00 595	9.99 790	22
39	8.99 322	128	8.99 534	128	11.00 466	9.99 788	21
40	8.99 450	127	8.99 662	129	11.00 338	9.99 787	20
41	8.99 577	127	8.99 791	128	11.00 209	9.99 786	19
42	8.99 704	126	8.99 919	127	11.00 081	9.99 785	18
43	8.99 830	126	9.00 046	128	10.99 954	9.99 783	17
44	8.99 956	126	9.00 174	127	10.99 826	9.99 782	16
45	9.00 082	125	9.00 301	126	10.99 699	9.99 781	15
46	9.00 207	125	9.00 427	126	10.99 573	9.99 780	14
47	9.00 332	124	9.00 553	126	10.99 447	9.99 778	13
48	9.00 456	125	9.00 679	126	10.99 321	9.99 777	12
49	9.00 581	123	9.00 805	125	10.99 195	9.99 776	11
50	9.00 704	124	9.00 930	125	10.99 070	9.99 775	10
51	9.00 828	123	9.01 055	124	10.98 945	9.99 773	9
52	9.00 951	123	9.01 179	124	10.98 821	9.99 772	8
53	9.01 074	122	9.01 303	124	10.98 697	9.99 771	7
54	9.01 196	122	9.01 427	123	10.98 573	9.99 769	6
55	9.01 318	122	9.01 550	123	10.98 450	9.99 768	5
56	9.01 440	121	9.01 673	123	10.98 327	9.99 767	4
57	9.01 561	121	9.01 796	122	10.98 204	9.99 765	3
58	9.01 682	121	9.01 918	122	10.98 082	9.99 764	2
59	9.01 803	120	9.02 040	122	10.97 960	9.99 763	1
60	9.01 923		9.02 162		10.97 838	9.99 761	0
	L Cos	d	L Ctn	c d	L Tan	L Sin	′

Prop. Pts.

	143	142	141
2	28.6	28.4	28.2
3	42.9	42.6	42.3
4	57.2	56.8	56.4
5	71.5	71.0	70.5
6	85.8	85.2	84.6
7	100.1	99.4	98.7
8	114.4	113.6	112.8
9	128.7	127.8	126.9

	140	139	138
2	28.0	27.8	27.6
3	42.0	41.7	41.4
4	56.0	55.6	55.2
5	70.0	69.5	69.0
6	84.0	83.4	82.8
7	98.0	97.3	96.6
8	112.0	111.2	110.4
9	126.0	125.1	124.2

	137	136	135
2	27.4	27.2	27.0
3	41.1	40.8	40.5
4	54.8	54.4	54.0
5	68.5	68.0	67.5
6	82.2	81.6	81.0
7	95.9	95.2	94.5
8	109.6	108.8	108.0
9	123.3	122.4	121.5

	134	133	132
2	26.8	26.6	26.4
3	40.2	39.9	39.6
4	53.6	53.2	52.8
5	67.0	66.5	66.0
6	80.4	79.8	79.2
7	93.8	93.1	92.4
8	107.2	106.4	105.6
9	120.6	119.7	118.8

	131	130	129
2	26.2	26.0	25.8
3	39.3	39.0	38.7
4	52.4	52.0	51.6
5	65.5	65.0	64.5
6	78.6	78.0	77.4
7	91.7	91.0	90.3
8	104.8	104.0	103.2
9	117.9	117.0	116.1

	128	127	126
2	25.6	25.4	25.2
3	38.4	38.1	37.8
4	51.2	50.8	50.4
5	64.0	63.5	63.0
6	76.8	76.2	75.6
7	89.6	88.9	88.2
8	102.4	101.6	100.8
9	115.2	114.3	113.4

	125	124	123
2	25.0	24.8	24.6
3	37.5	37.2	36.9
4	50.0	49.6	49.2
5	62.5	62.0	61.5
6	75.0	74.4	73.8
7	87.5	86.8	86.1
8	100.0	99.2	98.4
9	112.5	111.6	110.7

	122	121	120
2	24.4	24.2	24.0
3	36.6	36.3	36.0
4	48.8	48.4	48.0
5	61.0	60.5	60.0
6	73.2	72.6	72.0
7	85.4	84.7	84.0
8	97.6	96.8	96.0
9	109.8	108.9	108.0

Prop. Pts.

′	L Sin	d	L Tan	c d	L Ctn	L Cos	
0	9.01 923	120	9.02 162	121	10.97 838	9.99 761	60
1	9.02 043	120	9.02 283	121	10.97 717	9.99 760	59
2	9.02 163	120	9.02 404	121	10.97 596	9.99 759	58
3	9.02 283	119	9.02 525	120	10.97 475	9.99 757	57
4	9.02 402	118	9.02 645	121	10.97 355	9.99 756	56
5	9.02 520	119	9.02 766	119	10.97 234	9.99 755	55
6	9.02 639	118	9.02 885	120	10.97 115	9.99 753	54
7	9.02 757	117	9.03 005	119	10.96 995	9.99 752	53
8	9.02 874	118	9.03 124	118	10.96 876	9.99 751	52
9	9.02 992	117	9.03 242	119	10.96 758	9.99 749	51
10	9.03 109	117	9.03 361	118	10.96 639	9.99 748	50
11	9.03 226	116	9.03 479	118	10.96 521	9.99 747	49
12	9.03 342	116	9.03 597	117	10.96 403	9.99 745	48
13	9.03 458	116	9.03 714	118	10.96 286	9.99 744	47
14	9.03 574	116	9.03 832	116	10.96 168	9.99 742	46
15	9.03 690	115	9.03 948	117	10.96 052	9.99 741	45
16	9.03 805	115	9.04 065	116	10.95 935	9.99 740	44
17	9.03 920	114	9.04 181	116	10.95 819	9.99 738	43
18	9.04 034	115	9.04 297	116	10.95 703	9.99 737	42
19	9.04 149	113	9.04 413	115	10.95 587	9.99 736	41
20	9.04 262	114	9.04 528	115	10.95 472	9.99 734	40
21	9.04 376	114	9.04 643	115	10.95 357	9.99 733	39
22	9.04 490	113	9.04 758	115	10.95 242	9.99 731	38
23	9.04 603	112	9.04 873	114	10.95 127	9.99 730	37
24	9.04 715	113	9.04 987	114	10.95 013	9.99 728	36
25	9.04 828	112	9.05 101	113	10.94 899	9.99 727	35
26	9.04 940	112	9.05 214	114	10.94 786	9.99 726	34
27	9.05 052	112	9.05 328	113	10.94 672	9.99 724	33
28	9.05 164	111	9.05 441	112	10.94 559	9.99 723	32
29	9.05 275	111	9.05 553	113	10.94 447	9.99 721	31
30	9.05 386	111	9.05 666	112	10.94 334	9.99 720	30
31	9.05 497	110	9.05 778	112	10.94 222	9.99 718	29
32	9.05 607	110	9.05 890	112	10.94 110	9.99 717	28
33	9.05 717	110	9.06 002	111	10.93 998	9.99 716	27
34	9.05 827	110	9.06 113	111	10.93 887	9.99 714	26
35	9.05 937	109	9.06 224	111	10.93 776	9.99 713	25
36	9.06 046	109	9.06 335	110	10.93 665	9.99 711	24
37	9.06 155	109	9.06 445	111	10.93 555	9.99 710	23
38	9.06 264	108	9.06 556	110	10.93 444	9.99 708	22
39	9.06 372	109	9.06 666	109	10.93 334	9.99 707	21
40	9.06 481	108	9.06 775	110	10.93 225	9.99 705	20
41	9.06 589	107	9.06 885	109	10.93 115	9.99 704	19
42	9.06 696	108	9.06 994	109	10.93 006	9.99 702	18
43	9.06 804	107	9.07 103	108	10.92 897	9.99 701	17
44	9.06 911	107	9.07 211	109	10.92 789	9.99 699	16
45	9.07 018	106	9.07 320	108	10.92 680	9.99 698	15
46	9.07 124	107	9.07 428	108	10.92 572	9.99 696	14
47	9.07 231	106	9.07 536	107	10.92 464	9.99 695	13
48	9.07 337	105	9.07 643	108	10.92 357	9.99 693	12
49	9.07 442	106	9.07 751	107	10.92 249	9.99 692	11
50	9.07 548	105	9.07 858	106	10.92 142	9.99 690	10
51	9.07 653	105	9.07 964	107	10.92 036	9.99 689	9
52	9.07 758	105	9.08 071	106	10.91 929	9.99 687	8
53	9.07 863	105	9.08 177	106	10.91 823	9.99 686	7
54	9.07 968	104	9.08 283	106	10.91 717	9.99 684	6
55	9.08 072	104	9.08 389	106	10.91 611	9.99 683	5
56	9.08 176	104	9.08 495	105	10.91 505	9.99 681	4
57	9.08 280	103	9.08 600	105	10.91 400	9.99 680	3
58	9.08 383	103	9.08 705	105	10.91 295	9.99 678	2
59	9.08 486	103	9.08 810	104	10.91 190	9.99 677	1
60	9.08 589		9.08 914		10.91 086	9.99 675	0
	L Cos	d	L Ctn	c d	L Tan	L Sin	′

Prop. Pts.

	121	120	119
2	24.2	24.0	23.8
3	36.3	36.0	35.7
4	48.4	48.0	47.6
5	60.5	60.0	59.5
6	72.6	72.0	71.4
7	84.7	84.0	83.3
8	96.8	96.0	95.2
9	108.9	108.0	107.1

	118	117	116
2	23.6	23.4	23.2
3	35.4	35.1	34.8
4	47.2	46.8	46.4
5	59.0	58.5	58.0
6	70.8	70.2	69.6
7	82.6	81.9	81.2
8	94.4	93.6	92.8
9	106.2	105.3	104.4

	115	114	113
2	23.0	22.8	22.6
3	34.5	34.2	33.9
4	46.0	45.6	45.2
5	57.5	57.0	56.5
6	69.0	68.4	67.8
7	80.5	79.8	79.1
8	92.0	91.2	90.4
9	103.5	102.6	101.7

	112	111	110
2	22.4	22.2	22.0
3	33.6	33.3	33.0
4	44.8	44.4	44.0
5	56.0	55.5	55.0
6	67.2	66.6	66.0
7	78.4	77.7	77.0
8	89.6	88.8	88.0
9	100.8	99.9	99.0

	109	108	107
2	21.8	21.6	21.4
3	32.7	32.4	32.1
4	43.6	43.2	42.8
5	54.5	54.0	53.5
6	65.4	64.8	64.2
7	76.3	75.6	74.9
8	87.2	86.4	85.6
9	98.1	97.2	96.3

	106	105	104
2	21.2	21.0	20.8
3	31.8	31.5	31.2
4	42.4	42.0	41.6
5	53.0	52.5	52.0
6	63.6	63.0	62.4
7	74.2	73.5	72.8
8	84.8	84.0	83.2
9	95.4	94.5	93.6

From the top:

For **6°+** or **186°+**, read as printed; for **96°+** or **276°+**, read co-function.

From the bottom:

For **83°+** or **263°+**, read as printed; for **173°+** or **353°+**, read co-function.

′	L Sin	d	L Tan	c d	L Ctn	L Cos	
0	9.08 589	103	9.08 914	105	10.91 086	9.99 675	**60**
1	9.08 692	103	9.09 019	104	10.90 981	9.99 674	59
2	9.08 795	102	9.09 123	104	10.90 877	9.99 672	58
3	9.08 897	102	9.09 227	103	10.90 773	9.99 670	57
4	9.08 999	102	9.09 330	104	10.90 670	9.99 669	56
5	9.09 101	101	9.09 434	103	10.90 566	9.99 667	**55**
6	9.09 202	102	9.09 537	103	10.90 463	9.99 666	54
7	9.09 304	101	9.09 640	102	10.90 360	9.99 664	53
8	9.09 405	101	9.09 742	103	10.90 258	9.99 663	52
9	9.09 506	100	9.09 845	102	10.90 155	9.99 661	51
10	9.09 606	101	9.09 947	102	10.90 053	9.99 659	**50**
11	9.09 707	100	9.10 049	101	10.89 951	9.99 658	49
12	9.09 807	100	9.10 150	102	10.89 850	9.99 656	48
13	9.09 907	99	9.10 252	101	10.89 748	9.99 655	47
14	9.10 006	100	9.10 353	101	10.89 647	9.99 653	46
15	9.10 106	99	9.10 454	101	10.89 546	9.99 651	**45**
16	9.10 205	99	9.10 555	101	10.89 445	9.99 650	44
17	9.10 304	98	9.10 656	100	10.89 344	9.99 648	43
18	9.10 402	99	9.10 756	100	10.89 244	9.99 647	42
19	9.10 501	98	9.10 856	100	10.89 144	9.99 645	41
20	9.10 599	98	9.10 956	100	10.89 044	9.99 643	**40**
21	9.10 697	98	9.11 056	99	10.88 944	9.99 642	39
22	9.10 795	98	9.11 155	99	10.88 845	9.99 640	38
23	9.10 893	97	9.11 254	99	10.88 746	9.99 638	37
24	9.10 990	97	9.11 353	99	10.88 647	9.99 637	36
25	9.11 087	97	9.11 452	99	10.88 548	9.99 635	**35**
26	9.11 184	97	9.11 551	98	10.88 449	9.99 633	34
27	9.11 281	96	9.11 649	98	10.88 351	9.99 632	33
28	9.11 377	97	9.11 747	98	10.88 253	9.99 630	32
29	9.11 474	96	9.11 845	98	10.88 155	9.99 629	31
30	9.11 570	96	9.11 943	97	10.88 057	9.99 627	**30**
31	9.11 666	95	9.12 040	98	10.87 960	9.99 625	29
32	9.11 761	96	9.12 138	97	10.87 862	9.99 624	28
33	9.11 857	95	9.12 235	97	10.87 765	9.99 622	27
34	9.11 952	95	9.12 332	96	10.87 668	9.99 620	26
35	9.12 047	95	9.12 428	97	10.87 572	9.99 618	**25**
36	9.12 142	94	9.12 525	96	10.87 475	9.99 617	24
37	9.12 236	95	9.12 621	96	10.87 379	9.99 615	23
38	9.12 331	94	9.12 717	96	10.87 283	9.99 613	22
39	9.12 425	94	9.12 813	96	10.87 187	9.99 612	21
40	9.12 519	93	9.12 909	95	10.87 091	9.99 610	**20**
41	9.12 612	94	9.13 004	95	10.86 996	9.99 608	19
42	9.12 706	93	9.13 099	95	10.86 901	9.99 607	18
43	9.12 799	93	9.13 194	95	10.86 806	9.99 605	17
44	9.12 892	93	9.13 289	95	10.86 711	9.99 603	16
45	9.12 985	93	9.13 384	94	10.86 616	9.99 601	**15**
46	9.13 078	93	9.13 478	95	10.86 522	9.99 600	14
47	9.13 171	92	9.13 573	94	10.86 427	9.99 598	13
48	9.13 263	92	9.13 667	94	10.86 333	9.99 596	12
49	9.13 355	92	9.13 761	93	10.86 239	9.99 595	11
50	9.13 447	92	9.13 854	94	10.86 146	9.99 593	**10**
51	9.13 539	91	9.13 948	93	10.86 052	9.99 591	9
52	9.13 630	92	9.14 041	93	10.85 959	9.99 589	8
53	9.13 722	91	9.14 134	93	10.85 866	9.99 588	7
54	9.13 813	91	9.14 227	93	10.85 773	9.99 586	6
55	9.13 904	90	9.14 320	92	10.85 680	9.99 584	**5**
56	9.13 994	91	9.14 412	92	10.85 588	9.99 582	4
57	9.14 085	90	9.14 504	93	10.85 496	9.99 581	3
58	9.14 175	91	9.14 597	91	10.85 403	9.99 579	2
59	9.14 266	90	9.14 688	92	10.85 312	9.99 577	1
60	9.14 356		9.14 780		10.85 220	9.99 575	**0**
	L Cos	d	L Ctn	c d	L Tan	L Sin	′

Prop. Pts.

	105	104	103
2	21.0	20.8	20.6
3	31.5	31.2	30.9
4	42.0	41.6	41.2
5	52.5	52.0	51.5
6	63.0	62.4	61.8
7	73.5	72.8	72.1
8	84.0	83.2	82.4
9	94.5	93.6	92.7

	102	101	99
2	20.4	20.2	19.8
3	30.6	30.3	29.7
4	40.8	40.4	39.6
5	51.0	50.5	49.5
6	61.2	60.6	59.4
7	71.4	70.7	69.3
8	81.6	80.8	79.2
9	91.8	90.9	89.1

	98	97	96
2	19.6	19.4	19.2
3	29.4	29.1	28.8
4	39.2	38.8	38.4
5	49.0	48.5	48.0
6	58.8	58.2	57.6
7	68.6	67.9	67.2
8	78.4	77.6	76.8
9	88.2	87.3	86.4

	95	94	93
2	19.0	18.8	18.6
3	28.5	28.2	27.9
4	38.0	37.6	37.2
5	47.5	47.0	46.5
6	57.0	56.4	55.8
7	66.5	65.8	65.1
8	76.0	75.2	74.4
9	85.5	84.6	83.7

	92	91	90
2	18.4	18.2	18.0
3	27.6	27.3	27.0
4	36.8	36.4	36.0
5	46.0	45.5	45.0
6	55.2	54.6	54.0
7	64.4	63.7	63.0
8	73.6	72.8	72.0
9	82.8	81.9	81.0

From the top:

For **7°+** or **187°+**, read as printed; for **97°+** or **277°+**, read co-function.

From the bottom:

For **82°+** or **262°+**, read as printed; for **172°+** or **352°+**, read co-function.

′	L Sin	d	L Tan	c d	L Ctn	L Cos	
0	9.14 356	89	9.14 780	92	10.85 220	9.99 575	60
1	9.14 445	90	9.14 872	91	10.85 128	9.99 574	59
2	9.14 535	89	9.14 963	91	10.85 037	9.99 572	58
3	9.14 624	90	9.15 054	91	10.84 946	9.99 570	57
4	9.14 714	89	9.15 145	91	10.84 855	9.99 568	56
5	9.14 803	88	9.15 236	91	10.84 764	9.99 566	55
6	9.14 891	89	9.15 327	90	10.84 673	9.99 565	54
7	9.14 980	89	9.15 417	91	10.84 583	9.99 563	53
8	9.15 069	88	9.15 508	90	10.84 492	9.99 561	52
9	9.15 157	88	9.15 598	90	10.84 402	9.99 559	51
10	9.15 245	88	9.15 688	89	10.84 312	9.99 557	50
11	9.15 333	88	9.15 777	90	10.84 223	9.99 556	49
12	9.15 421	87	9.15 867	89	10.84 133	9.99 554	48
13	9.15 508	88	9.15 956	90	10.84 044	9.99 552	47
14	9.15 596	87	9.16 046	89	10.83 954	9.99 550	46
15	9.15 683	87	9.16 135	89	10.83 865	9.99 548	45
16	9.15 770	87	9.16 224	88	10.83 776	9.99 546	44
17	9.15 857	87	9.16 312	89	10.83 688	9.99 545	43
18	9.15 944	86	9.16 401	88	10.83 599	9.99 543	42
19	9.16 030	86	9.16 489	88	10.83 511	9.99 541	41
20	9.16 116	87	9.16 577	88	10.83 423	9.99 539	40
21	9.16 203	86	9.16 665	88	10.83 335	9.99 537	39
22	9.16 289	85	9.16 753	88	10.83 247	9.99 535	38
23	9.16 374	86	9.16 841	87	10.83 159	9.99 533	37
24	9.16 460	85	9.16 928	88	10.83 072	9.99 532	36
25	9.16 545	86	9.17 016	87	10.82 984	9.99 530	35
26	9.16 631	85	9.17 103	87	10.82 897	9.99 528	34
27	9.16 716	85	9.17 190	87	10.82 810	9.99 526	33
28	9.16 801	85	9.17 277	86	10.82 723	9.99 524	32
29	9.16 886	84	9.17 363	87	10.82 637	9.99 522	31
30	9.16 970	85	9.17 450	86	10.82 550	9.99 520	30
31	9.17 055	84	9.17 536	86	10.82 464	9.99 518	29
32	9.17 139	84	9.17 622	86	10.82 378	9.99 517	28
33	9.17 223	84	9.17 708	86	10.82 292	9.99 515	27
34	9.17 307	84	9.17 794	86	10.82 206	9.99 513	26
35	9.17 391	83	9.17 880	85	10.82 120	9.99 511	25
36	9.17 474	84	9.17 965	86	10.82 035	9.99 509	24
37	9.17 558	83	9.18 051	85	10.81 949	9.99 507	23
38	9.17 641	83	9.18 136	85	10.81 864	9.99 505	22
39	9.17 724	83	9.18 221	85	10.81 779	9.99 503	21
40	9.17 807	83	9.18 306	85	10.81 694	9.99 501	20
41	9.17 890	83	9.18 391	84	10.81 609	9.99 499	19
42	9.17 973	82	9.18 475	85	10.81 525	9.99 497	18
43	9.18 055	82	9.18 560	84	10.81 440	9.99 495	17
44	9.18 137	83	9.18 644	84	10.81 356	9.99 494	16
45	9.18 220	82	9.18 728	84	10.81 272	9.99 492	15
46	9.18 302	81	9.18 812	84	10.81 188	9.99 490	14
47	9.18 383	82	9.18 896	83	10.81 104	9.99 488	13
48	9.18 465	82	9.18 979	84	10.81 021	9.99 486	12
49	9.18 547	81	9.19 063	83	10.80 937	9.99 484	11
50	9.18 628	81	9.19 146	83	10.80 854	9.99 482	10
51	9.18 709	81	9.19 229	83	10.80 771	9.99 480	9
52	9.18 790	81	9.19 312	83	10.80 688	9.99 478	8
53	9.18 871	81	9.19 395	83	10.80 605	9.99 476	7
54	9.18 952	81	9.19 478	83	10.80 522	9.99 474	6
55	9.19 033	80	9.19 561	82	10.80 439	9.99 472	5
56	9.19 113	80	9.19 643	82	10.80 357	9.99 470	4
57	9.19 193	80	9.19 725	82	10.80 275	9.99 468	3
58	9.19 273	80	9.19 807	82	10.80 193	9.99 466	2
59	9.19 353	80	9.19 889	82	10.80 111	9.99 464	1
60	9.19 433		9.19 971		10.80 029	9.99 462	0
	L Cos	d	L Ctn	c d	L Tan	L Sin	′

Prop. Pts.

	92	91	90
2	18.4	18.2	18.0
3	27.6	27.3	27.0
4	36.8	36.4	36.0
5	46.0	45.5	45.0
6	55.2	54.6	54.0
7	64.4	63.7	63.0
8	73.6	72.8	72.0
9	82.8	81.9	81.0

	89	88	87
2	17.8	17.6	17.4
3	26.7	26.4	26.1
4	35.6	35.2	34.8
5	44.5	44.0	43.5
6	53.4	52.8	52.2
7	62.3	61.6	60.9
8	71.2	70.4	69.6
9	80.1	79.2	78.3

	86	85	84
2	17.2	17.0	16.8
3	25.8	25.5	25.2
4	34.4	34.0	33.6
5	43.0	42.5	42.0
6	51.6	51.0	50.4
7	60.2	59.5	58.8
8	68.8	68.0	67.2
9	77.4	76.5	75.6

	83	82	81
2	16.6	16.4	16.2
3	24.9	24.6	24.3
4	33.2	32.8	32.4
5	41.5	41.0	40.5
6	49.8	49.2	48.6
7	58.1	57.4	56.7
8	66.4	65.6	64.8
9	74.7	73.8	72.9

From the top:

For **8°+** or **188°+**, read as printed; for **98°+** or **278°+**, read co-function.

From the bottom:

For **81°+** or **261°+**, read as printed; for **171°+** or **351°+**, read co-function.

Prop. Pts.

9° — Logarithms of Trigonometric Functions

′	L Sin	d	L Tan	c d	L Ctn	L Cos	
0	9.19 433	80	9.19 971	82	10.80 029	9.99 462	60
1	9.19 513	79	9.20 053	81	10.79 947	9.99 460	59
2	9.19 592	80	9.20 134	82	10.79 866	9.99 458	58
3	9.19 672	79	9.20 216	81	10.79 784	9.99 456	57
4	9.19 751	79	9.20 297	81	10.79 703	9.99 454	56
5	9.19 830	79	9.20 378	81	10.79 622	9.99 452	55
6	9.19 909	79	9.20 459	81	10.79 541	9.99 450	54
7	9.19 988	79	9.20 540	81	10.79 460	9.99 448	53
8	9.20 067	78	9.20 621	80	10.79 379	9.99 446	52
9	9.20 145	78	9.20 701	81	10.79 299	9.99 444	51
10	9.20 223	79	9.20 782	80	10.79 218	9.99 442	50
11	9.20 302	78	9.20 862	80	10.79 138	9.99 440	49
12	9.20 380	78	9.20 942	80	10.79 058	9.99 438	48
13	9.20 458	77	9.21 022	80	10.78 978	9.99 436	47
14	9.20 535	78	9.21 102	80	10.78 898	9.99 434	46
15	9.20 613	78	9.21 182	79	10.78 818	9.99 432	45
16	9.20 691	77	9.21 261	80	10.78 739	9.99 429	44
17	9.20 768	77	9.21 341	79	10.78 659	9.99 427	43
18	9.20 845	77	9.21 420	79	10.78 580	9.99 425	42
19	9.20 922	77	9.21 499	79	10.78 501	9.99 423	41
20	9.20 999	77	9.21 578	79	10.78 422	9.99 421	40
21	9.21 076	77	9.21 657	79	10.78 343	9.99 419	39
22	9.21 153	76	9.21 736	78	10.78 264	9.99 417	38
23	9.21 229	77	9.21 814	79	10.78 186	9.99 415	37
24	9.21 306	76	9.21 893	78	10.78 107	9.99 413	36
25	9.21 382	76	9.21 971	78	10.78 029	9.99 411	35
26	9.21 458	76	9.22 049	78	10.77 951	9.99 409	34
27	9.21 534	76	9.22 127	78	10.77 873	9.99 407	33
28	9.21 610	75	9.22 205	78	10.77 795	9.99 404	32
29	9.21 685	76	9.22 283	78	10.77 717	9.99 402	31
30	9.21 761	75	9.22 361	77	10.77 639	9.99 400	30
31	9.21 836	76	9.22 438	78	10.77 562	9.99 398	29
32	9.21 912	75	9.22 516	77	10.77 484	9.99 396	28
33	9.21 987	75	9.22 593	77	10.77 407	9.99 394	27
34	9.22 062	75	9.22 670	77	10.77 330	9.99 392	26
35	9.22 137	74	9.22 747	77	10.77 253	9.99 390	25
36	9.22 211	75	9.22 824	77	10.77 176	9.99 388	24
37	9.22 286	75	9.22 901	76	10.77 099	9.99 385	23
38	9.22 361	74	9.22 977	77	10.77 023	9.99 383	22
39	9.22 435	74	9.23 054	76	10.76 946	9.99 381	21
40	9.22 509	74	9.23 130	76	10.76 870	9.99 379	20
41	9.22 583	74	9.23 206	77	10.76 794	9.99 377	19
42	9.22 657	74	9.23 283	76	10.76 717	9.99 375	18
43	9.22 731	74	9.23 359	76	10.76 641	9.99 372	17
44	9.22 805	78	9.23 435	75	10.76 565	9.99 370	16
45	9.22 878	74	9.23 510	76	10.76 490	9.99 368	15
46	9.22 952	73	9.23 586	75	10.76 414	9.99 366	14
47	9.23 025	73	9.23 661	76	10.76 339	9.99 364	13
48	9.23 098	73	9.23 737	75	10.76 263	9.99 362	12
49	9.23 171	73	9.23 812	75	10.76 188	9.99 359	11
50	9.23 244	73	9.23 887	75	10.76 113	9.99 357	10
51	9.23 317	73	9.23 962	75	10.76 038	9.99 355	9
52	9.23 390	72	9.24 037	75	10.75 963	9.99 353	8
53	9.23 462	73	9.24 112	74	10.75 888	9.99 351	7
54	9.23 535	72	9.24 186	75	10.75 814	9.99 348	6
55	9.23 607	72	9.24 261	74	10.75 739	9.99 346	5
56	9.23 679	73	9.24 335	75	10.75 665	9.99 344	4
57	9.23 752	71	9.24 410	74	10.75 590	9.99 342	3
58	9.23 823	72	9.24 484	74	10.75 516	9.99 340	2
59	9.23 895	72	9.24 558	74	10.75 442	9.99 337	1
60	9.23 967		9.24 632		10.75 368	9.99 335	0
	L Cos	d	L Ctn	c d	L Tan	L Sin	′

Prop. Pts.

	82	81	80
2	16.4	16.2	16.0
3	24.6	24.3	24.0
4	32.8	32.4	32.0
5	41.0	40.5	40.0
6	49.2	48.6	48.0
7	57.4	56.7	56.0
8	65.6	64.8	64.0
9	73.8	72.9	72.0

	79	78	77
2	15.8	15.6	15.4
3	23.7	23.4	23.1
4	31.6	31.2	30.8
5	39.5	39.0	38.5
6	47.4	46.8	46.2
7	55.3	54.6	53.9
8	63.2	62.4	61.6
9	71.1	70.2	69.3

	76	75	74
2	15.2	15.0	14.8
3	22.8	22.5	22.2
4	30.4	30.0	29.6
5	38.0	37.5	37.0
6	45.6	45.0	44.4
7	53.2	52.5	51.8
8	60.8	60.0	59.2
9	68.4	67.5	66.6

	73	72	71
2	14.6	14.4	14.2
3	21.9	21.6	21.3
4	29.2	28.8	28.4
5	36.5	36.0	35.5
6	43.8	43.2	42.6
7	51.1	50.4	49.7
8	58.4	57.6	56.8
9	65.7	64.8	63.9

From the top:

For **9°+**, or **189°+**, read as printed; for **99°+** or **279°+**, read co-function.

From the bottom:

For **80°+** or **260°+**, read as printed; for **170°+** or **350°+**, read co-function.

Prop. Pts.

80° — Logarithms of Trigonometric Functions

′	L Sin	d	L Tan	c d	L Ctn	L Cos	d	
0	9.23 967	72	9.24 632	74	10.75 368	9.99 335	2	60
1	9.24 039	71	9.24 706	73	10.75 294	9.99 333	2	59
2	9.24 110	71	9.24 779	74	10.75 221	9.99 331	3	58
3	9.24 181	72	9.24 853	73	10.75 147	9.99 328	2	57
4	9.24 253	71	9.24 926	74	10.75 074	9.99 326	2	56
5	9.24 324	71	9.25 000	73	10.75 000	9.99 324	2	55
6	9.24 395	71	9.25 073	73	10.74 927	9.99 322	3	54
7	9.24 466	70	9.25 146	73	10.74 854	9.99 319	2	53
8	9.24 536	71	9.25 219	73	10.74 781	9.99 317	2	52
9	9.24 607	70	9.25 292	73	10.74 708	9.99 315	2	51
10	9.24 677	71	9.25 365	72	10.74 635	9.99 313	3	50
11	9.24 748	70	9.25 437	73	10.74 563	9.99 310	2	49
12	9.24 818	70	9.25 510	72	10.74 490	9.99 308	2	48
13	9.24 888	70	9.25 582	73	10.74 418	9.99 306	2	47
14	9.24 958	70	9.25 655	72	10.74 345	9.99 304	3	46
15	9.25 028	70	9.25 727	72	10.74 273	9.99 301	2	45
16	9.25 098	70	9.25 799	72	10.74 201	9.99 299	2	44
17	9.25 168	69	9.25 871	72	10.74 129	9.99 297	3	43
18	9.25 237	70	9.25 943	72	10.74 057	9.99 294	2	42
19	9.25 307	69	9.26 015	71	10.73 985	9.99 292	2	41
20	9.25 376	69	9.26 086	72	10.73 914	9.99 290	2	40
21	9.25 445	69	9.26 158	71	10.73 842	9.99 288	3	39
22	9.25 514	69	9.26 229	72	10.73 771	9.99 285	2	38
23	9.25 583	69	9.26 301	71	10.73 699	9.99 283	2	37
24	9.25 652	69	9.26 372	71	10.73 628	9.99 281	3	36
25	9.25 721	69	9.26 443	71	10.73 557	9.99 278	2	35
26	9.25 790	68	9.26 514	71	10.73 486	9.99 276	2	34
27	9.25 858	69	9.26 585	70	10.73 415	9.99 274	3	33
28	9.25 927	68	9.26 655	71	10.73 345	9.99 271	2	32
29	9.25 995	68	9.26 726	71	10.73 274	9.99 269	2	31
30	9.26 063	68	9.26 797	70	10.73 203	9.99 267	3	30
31	9.26 131	68	9.26 867	70	10.73 133	9.99 264	2	29
32	9.26 199	68	9.26 937	71	10.73 063	9.99 262	2	28
33	9.26 267	68	9.27 008	70	10.72 992	9.99 260	3	27
34	9.26 335	68	9.27 078	70	10.72 922	9.99 257	2	26
35	9.26 403	67	9.27 148	70	10.72 852	9.99 255	3	25
36	9.26 470	68	9.27 218	70	10.72 782	9.99 252	2	24
37	9.26 538	67	9.27 288	69	10.72 712	9.99 250	2	23
38	9.26 605	67	9.27 357	70	10.72 643	9.99 248	3	22
39	9.26 672	67	9.27 427	69	10.72 573	9.99 245	2	21
40	9.26 739	67	9.27 496	70	10.72 504	9.99 243	2	20
41	9.26 806	67	9.27 566	69	10.72 434	9.99 241	3	19
42	9.26 873	67	9.27 635	69	10.72 365	9.99 238	2	18
43	9.26 940	67	9.27 704	69	10.72 296	9.99 236	3	17
44	9.27 007	66	9.27 773	69	10.72 227	9.99 233	2	16
45	9.27 073	67	9.27 842	69	10.72 158	9.99 231	2	15
46	9.27 140	66	9.27 911	69	10.72 089	9.99 229	3	14
47	9.27 206	67	9.27 980	69	10.72 020	9.99 226	2	13
48	9.27 273	66	9.28 049	68	10.71 951	9.99 224	3	12
49	9.27 339	66	9.28 117	69	10.71 883	9.99 221	2	11
50	9.27 405	66	9.28 186	68	10.71 814	9.99 219	2	10
51	9.27 471	66	9.28 254	69	10.71 746	9.99 217	3	9
52	9.27 537	65	9.28 323	68	10.71 677	9.99 214	2	8
53	9.27 602	66	9.28 391	68	10.71 609	9.99 212	3	7
54	9.27 668	66	9.28 459	68	10.71 541	9.99 209	2	6
55	9.27 734	65	9.28 527	68	10.71 473	9.99 207	3	5
56	9.27 799	65	9.28 595	67	10.71 405	9.99 204	2	4
57	9.27 864	66	9.28 662	68	10.71 338	9.99 202	2	3
58	9.27 930	65	9.28 730	68	10.71 270	9.99 200	3	2
59	9.27 995	65	9.28 798	67	10.71 202	9.99 197	2	1
60	9.28 060		9.28 865		10.71 135	9.99 195		0
	L Cos	d	L Ctn	c d	L Tan	L Sin	d	′

Prop. Pts.

	74	73	72
2	14.8	14.6	14.4
3	22.2	21.9	21.6
4	29.6	29.2	28.8
5	37.0	36.5	36.0
6	44.4	43.8	43.2
7	51.8	51.1	50.4
8	59.2	58.4	57.6
9	66.6	65.7	64.8

	71	70	69
2	14.2	14.0	13.8
3	21.3	21.0	20.7
4	28.4	28.0	27.6
5	35.5	35.0	34.5
6	42.6	42.0	41.4
7	49.7	49.0	48.3
8	56.8	56.0	55.2
9	63.9	63.0	62.1

	68	67	66
2	13.6	13.4	13.2
3	20.4	20.1	19.8
4	27.2	26.8	26.4
5	34.0	33.5	33.0
6	40.8	40.2	39.6
7	47.6	46.9	46.2
8	54.4	53.6	52.8
9	61.2	60.3	59.4

	65	3	2
2	13.0	0.6	0.4
3	19.5	0.9	0.6
4	26.0	1.2	0.8
5	32.5	1.5	1.0
6	39.0	1.8	1.2
7	45.5	2.1	1.4
8	52.0	2.4	1.6
9	58.5	2.7	1.8

From the top:

For **10°+** or **190°+**, read as printed; for **100°+** or **280°+**, read co-function.

From the bottom:

For **79°+** or **259°+**, read as printed; for **169°+** or **349°+**, read co-function.

Prop. Pts.

′	L Sin	d	L Tan	cd	L Ctn	L Cos	d	
0	9.28 060	65	9.28 865	68	10.71 135	9.99 195	3	60
1	9.28 125	65	9.28 933	67	10.71 067	9.99 192	2	59
2	9.28 190	64	9.29 000	67	10.71 000	9.99 190	3	58
3	9.28 254	65	9.29 067	67	10.70 933	9.99 187	2	57
4	9.28 319	65	9.29 134	67	10.70 866	9.99 185	3	56
5	9.28 384	64	9.29 201	67	10.70 799	9.99 182	2	55
6	9.28 448	64	9.29 268	67	10.70 732	9.99 180	3	54
7	9.28 512	65	9.29 335	67	10.70 665	9.99 177	2	53
8	9.28 577	64	9.29 402	66	10.70 598	9.99 175	3	52
9	9.28 641	64	9.29 468	67	10.70 532	9.99 172	2	51
10	9.28 705	64	9.29 535	66	10.70 465	9.99 170	3	50
11	9.28 769	64	9.29 601	67	10.70 399	9.99 167	2	49
12	9.28 833	63	9.29 668	66	10.70 332	9.99 165	3	48
13	9.28 896	64	9.29 734	66	10.70 266	9.99 162	2	47
14	9.28 960	64	9.29 800	66	10.70 200	9.99 160	3	46
15	9.29 024	63	9.29 866	66	10.70 134	9.99 157	2	45
16	9.29 087	63	9.29 932	66	10.70 068	9.99 155	3	44
17	9.29 150	64	9.29 998	66	10.70 002	9.99 152	2	43
18	9.29 214	63	9.30 064	66	10.69 936	9.99 150	3	42
19	9.29 277	63	9.30 130	65	10.69 870	9.99 147	2	41
20	9.29 340	63	9.30 195	66	10.69 805	9.99 145	3	40
21	9.29 403	63	9.30 261	65	10.69 739	9.99 142	2	39
22	9.29 466	63	9.30 326	65	10.69 674	9.99 140	3	38
23	9.29 529	62	9.30 391	66	10.69 609	9.99 137	2	37
24	9.29 591	63	9.30 457	65	10.69 543	9.99 135	3	36
25	9.29 654	62	9.30 522	65	10.69 478	9.99 132	2	35
26	9.29 716	63	9.30 587	65	10.69 413	9.99 130	3	34
27	9.29 779	62	9.30 652	65	10.69 348	9.99 127	3	33
28	9.29 841	62	9.30 717	65	10.69 283	9.99 124	2	32
29	9.29 903	63	9.30 782	64	10.69 218	9.99 122	3	31
30	9.29 966	62	9.30 846	65	10.69 154	9.99 119	2	30
31	9.30 028	62	9.30 911	64	10.69 089	9.99 117	3	29
32	9.30 090	61	9.30 975	65	10.69 025	9.99 114	2	28
33	9.30 151	62	9.31 040	64	10.68 960	9.99 112	3	27
34	9.30 213	62	9.31 104	64	10.68 896	9.99 109	3	26
35	9.30 275	61	9.31 168	65	10.68 832	9.99 106	2	25
36	9.30 336	62	9.31 233	64	10.68 767	9.99 104	3	24
37	9.30 398	61	9.31 297	64	10.68 703	9.99 101	2	23
38	9.30 459	62	9.31 361	64	10.68 639	9.99 099	3	22
39	9.30 521	61	9.31 425	64	10.68 575	9.99 096	3	21
40	9.30 582	61	9.31 489	63	10.68 511	9.99 093	2	20
41	9.30 643	61	9.31 552	64	10.68 448	9.99 091	3	19
42	9.30 704	61	9.31 616	63	10.68 384	9.99 088	2	18
43	9.30 765	61	9.31 679	64	10.68 321	9.99 086	3	17
44	9.30 826	61	9.31 743	63	10.68 257	9.99 083	3	16
45	9.30 887	60	9.31 806	64	10.68 194	9.99 080	2	15
46	9.30 947	61	9.31 870	63	10.68 130	9.99 078	3	14
47	9.31 008	60	9.31 933	63	10.68 067	9.99 075	3	13
48	9.31 068	61	9.31 996	63	10.68 004	9.99 072	2	12
49	9.31 129	60	9.32 059	63	10.67 941	9.99 070	3	11
50	9.31 189	61	9.32 122	63	10.67 878	9.99 067	3	10
51	9.31 250	60	9.32 185	63	10.67 815	9.99 064	2	9
52	9.31 310	60	9.32 248	63	10.67 752	9.99 062	3	8
53	9.31 370	60	9.32 311	62	10.67 689	9.99 059	3	7
54	9.31 430	60	9.32 373	63	10.67 627	9.99 056	2	6
55	9.31 490	59	9.32 436	62	10.67 564	9.99 054	3	5
56	9.31 549	60	9.32 498	63	10.67 502	9.99 051	3	4
57	9.31 609	60	9.32 561	62	10.67 439	9.99 048	2	3
58	9.31 669	59	9.32 623	62	10.67 377	9.99 046	3	2
59	9.31 728	60	9.32 685	62	10.67 315	9.99 043	3	1
60	9.31 788		9.32 747		10.67 253	9.99 040		0
	L Cos	d	L Ctn	cd	L Tan	L Sin	d	′

Prop. Pts.

	68	67	66
2	13.6	13.4	13.2
3	20.4	20.1	19.8
4	27.2	26.8	26.4
5	34.0	33.5	33.0
6	40.8	40.2	39.6
7	47.6	46.9	46.2
8	54.4	53.6	52.8
9	61.2	60.3	59.4

	65	64	63
2	13.0	12.8	12.6
3	19.5	19.2	18.9
4	26.0	25.6	25.2
5	32.5	32.0	31.5
6	39.0	38.4	37.8
7	45.5	44.8	44.1
8	52.0	51.2	50.4
9	58.5	57.6	56.7

	62	61	60
2	12.4	12.2	12.0
3	18.6	18.3	18.0
4	24.8	24.4	24.0
5	31.0	30.5	30.0
6	37.2	36.6	36.0
7	43.4	42.7	42.0
8	49.6	48.8	48.0
9	55.8	54.9	54.0

	59	3	2
2	11.8	0.6	0.4
3	17.7	0.9	0.6
4	23.6	1.2	0.8
5	29.5	1.5	1.0
6	35.4	1.8	1.2
7	41.3	2.1	1.4
8	47.2	2.4	1.6
9	53.1	2.7	1.8

From the top:

For **11°+** or **191°+**, read as printed; for **101°+** or **281°+**, read co-function.

From the bottom:

For **78°+** or **258°+**, read as printed; for **168°+** or **348°+**, read co-function.

'	L Sin	d	L Tan	c d	L Ctn	L Cos	d	
0	9.31 788	59	9.32 747	63	10.67 253	9.99 040	2	60
1	9.31 847	60	9.32 810	62	10.67 190	9.99 038	3	59
2	9.31 907	59	9.32 872	61	10.67 128	9.99 035	3	58
3	9.31 966	59	9.32 933	62	10.67 067	9.99 032	2	57
4	9.32 025	59	9.32 995	62	10.67 005	9.99 030	3	56
5	9.32 084	59	9.33 057	62	10.66 943	9.99 027	3	55
6	9.32 143	59	9.33 119	61	10.66 881	9.99 024	2	54
7	9.32 202	59	9.33 180	62	10.66 820	9.99 022	3	53
8	9.32 261	58	9.33 242	61	10.66 758	9.99 019	3	52
9	9.32 319	59	9.33 303	62	10.66 697	9.99 016	3	51
10	9.32 378	59	9.33 365	61	10.66 635	9.99 013	2	50
11	9.32 437	58	9.33 426	61	10.66 574	9.99 011	3	49
12	9.32 495	58	9.33 487	61	10.66 513	9.99 008	3	48
13	9.32 553	59	9.33 548	61	10.66 452	9.99 005	3	47
14	9.32 612	58	9.33 609	61	10.66 391	9.99 002	2	46
15	9.32 670	58	9.33 670	61	10.66 330	9.99 000	3	45
16	9.32 728	58	9.33 731	61	10.66 269	9.98 997	3	44
17	9.32 786	58	9.33 792	61	10.66 208	9.98 994	3	43
18	9.32 844	58	9.33 853	60	10.66 147	9.98 991	2	42
19	9.32 902	58	9.33 913	61	10.66 087	9.98 989	3	41
20	9.32 960	58	9.33 974	60	10.66 026	9.98 986	3	40
21	9.33 018	57	9.34 034	61	10.65 966	9.98 983	3	39
22	9.33 075	58	9.34 095	60	10.65 905	9.98 980	2	38
23	9.33 133	57	9.34 155	60	10.65 845	9.98 978	3	37
24	9.33 190	58	9.34 215	61	10.65 785	9.98 975	3	36
25	9.33 248	57	9.34 276	60	10.65 724	9.98 972	3	35
26	9.33 305	57	9.34 336	60	10.65 664	9.98 969	2	34
27	9.33 362	58	9.34 396	60	10.65 604	9.98 967	3	33
28	9.33 420	57	9.34 456	60	10.65 544	9.98 964	3	32
29	9.33 477	57	9.34 516	60	10.65 484	9.98 961	3	31
30	9.33 534	57	9.34 576	59	10.65 424	9.98 958	3	30
31	9.33 591	56	9.34 635	60	10.65 365	9.98 955	2	29
32	9.33 647	57	9.34 695	60	10.65 305	9.98 953	3	28
33	9.33 704	57	9.34 755	59	10.65 245	9.98 950	3	27
34	9.33 761	57	9.34 814	60	10.65 186	9.98 947	3	26
35	9.33 818	56	9.34 874	59	10.65 126	9.98 944	3	25
36	9.33 874	57	9.34 933	59	10.65 067	9.98 941	3	24
37	9.33 931	56	9.34 992	59	10.65 008	9.98 938	2	23
38	9.33 987	56	9.35 051	60	10.64 949	9.98 936	3	22
39	9.34 043	57	9.35 111	59	10.64 889	9.98 933	3	21
40	9.34 100	56	9.35 170	59	10.64 830	9.98 930	3	20
41	9.34 156	56	9.35 229	59	10.64 771	9.98 927	3	19
42	9.34 212	56	9.35 288	59	10.64 712	9.98 924	3	18
43	9.34 268	56	9.35 347	58	10.64 653	9.98 921	2	17
44	9.34 324	56	9.35 405	59	10.64 595	9.98 919	3	16
45	9.34 380	56	9.35 464	59	10.64 536	9.98 916	3	15
46	9.34 436	55	9.35 523	58	10.64 477	9.98 913	3	14
47	9.34 491	56	9.35 581	59	10.64 419	9.98 910	3	13
48	9.34 547	55	9.35 640	58	10.64 360	9.98 907	3	12
49	9.34 602	56	9.35 698	59	10.64 302	9.98 904	3	11
50	9.34 658	55	9.35 757	58	10.64 243	9.98 901	3	10
51	9.34 713	56	9.35 815	58	10.64 185	9.98 898	2	9
52	9.34 769	55	9.35 873	58	10.64 127	9.98 896	3	8
53	9.34 824	55	9.35 931	58	10.64 069	9.98 893	3	7
54	9.34 879	55	9.35 989	58	10.64 011	9.98 890	3	6
55	9.34 934	55	9.36 047	58	10.63 953	9.98 887	3	5
56	9.34 989	55	9.36 105	58	10.63 895	9.98 884	3	4
57	9.35 044	55	9.36 163	58	10.63 837	9.98 881	3	3
58	9.35 099	55	9.36 221	58	10.63 779	9.98 878	3	2
59	9.35 154	55	9.36 279	57	10.63 721	9.98 875	3	1
60	9.35 209		9.36 336		10.63 664	9.98 872		0
	L Cos	d	L Ctn	c d	L Tan	L Sin	d	'

Prop. Pts.

	63	62	61
2	12.6	12.4	12.2
3	18.9	18.6	18.3
4	25.2	24.8	24.4
5	31.5	31.0	30.5
6	37.8	37.2	36.6
7	44.1	43.4	42.7
8	50.4	49.6	48.8
9	56.7	55.8	54.9

	60	59	58
2	12.0	11.8	11.6
3	18.0	17.7	17.4
4	24.0	23.6	23.2
5	30.0	29.5	29.0
6	36.0	35.4	34.8
7	42.0	41.3	40.6
8	48.0	47.2	46.4
9	54.0	53.1	52.2

	57	56
2	11.4	11.2
3	17.1	16.8
4	22.8	22.4
5	28.5	28.0
6	34.2	33.6
7	39.9	39.2
8	45.6	44.8
9	51.3	50.4

	55	3	2
2	11.0	0.6	0.4
3	16.5	0.9	0.6
4	22.0	1.2	0.8
5	27.5	1.5	1.0
6	33.0	1.8	1.2
7	38.5	2.1	1.4
8	44.0	2.4	1.6
9	49.5	2.7	1.8

From the top:
For **12°+** or **192°+**, read as printed; for **102°+** or **282°+**, read co-function.

From the bottom:
For **77°+** or **257°+**, read as printed; for **167°+** or **347°+**, read co-function.

Prop. Pts.

′	L Sin	d	L Tan	c d	L Ctn	L Cos	d	
	L Cos	d	L Ctn	c d	L Tan	L Sin	d	′
0	9.35 209	54	9.36 336	58	10.63 664	9.98 872	3	60
1	9.35 263	55	9.36 394	58	10.63 606	9.98 869	2	59
2	9.35 318	55	9.36 452	57	10.63 548	9.98 867	3	58
3	9.35 373	54	9.36 509	57	10.63 491	9.98 864	3	57
4	9.35 427	54	9.36 566	58	10.63 434	9.98 861	3	56
5	9.35 481	55	9.36 624	57	10.63 376	9.98 858	3	55
6	9.35 536	54	9.36 681	57	10.63 319	9.98 855	3	54
7	9.35 590	54	9.36 738	57	10.63 262	9.98 852	3	53
8	9.35 644	54	9.36 795	57	10.63 205	9.98 849	3	52
9	9.35 698	54	9.36 852	57	10.63 148	9.98 846	3	51
10	9.35 752	54	9.36 909	57	10.63 091	9.98 843	3	50
11	9.35 806	54	9.36 966	57	10.63 034	9.98 840	3	49
12	9.35 860	54	9.37 023	57	10.62 977	9.98 837	3	48
13	9.35 914	54	9.37 080	57	10.62 920	9.98 834	3	47
14	9.35 968	54	9.37 137	56	10.62 863	9.98 831	3	46
15	9.36 022	53	9.37 193	57	10.62 807	9.98 828	3	45
16	9.36 075	54	9.37 250	56	10.62 750	9.98 825	3	44
17	9.36 129	53	9.37 306	57	10.62 694	9.98 822	3	43
18	9.36 182	54	9.37 363	56	10.62 637	9.98 819	3	42
19	9.36 236	53	9.37 419	57	10.62 581	9.98 816	3	41
20	9.36 289	53	9.37 476	56	10.62 524	9.98 813	3	40
21	9.36 342	53	9.37 532	56	10.62 468	9.98 810	3	39
22	9.36 395	54	9.37 588	56	10.62 412	9.98 807	3	38
23	9.36 449	53	9.37 644	56	10.62 356	9.98 804	3	37
24	9.36 502	53	9.37 700	56	10.62 300	9.98 801	3	36
25	9.36 555	53	9.37 756	56	10.62 244	9.98 798	3	35
26	9.36 608	52	9.37 812	56	10.62 188	9.98 795	3	34
27	9.36 660	53	9.37 868	56	10.62 132	9.98 792	3	33
28	9.36 713	53	9.37 924	56	10.62 076	9.98 789	3	32
29	9.36 766	53	9.37 980	55	10.62 020	9.98 786	3	31
30	9.36 819	52	9.38 035	56	10.61 965	9.98 783	3	30
31	9.36 871	53	9.38 091	56	10.61 909	9.98 780	3	29
32	9.36 924	52	9.38 147	55	10.61 853	9.98 777	3	28
33	9.36 976	52	9.38 202	55	10.61 798	9.98 774	3	27
34	9.37 028	53	9.38 257	56	10.61 743	9.98 771	3	26
35	9.37 081	52	9.38 313	55	10.61 687	9.98 768	3	25
36	9.37 133	52	9.38 368	55	10.61 632	9.98 765	3	24
37	9.37 185	52	9.38 423	56	10.61 577	9.98 762	3	23
38	9.37 237	52	9.38 479	55	10.61 521	9.98 759	3	22
39	9.37 289	52	9.38 534	55	10.61 466	9.98 756	3	21
40	9.37 341	52	9.38 589	55	10.61 411	9.98 753	3	20
41	9.37 393	52	9.38 644	55	10.61 356	9.98 750	4	19
42	9.37 445	52	9.38 699	55	10.61 301	9.98 746	3	18
43	9.37 497	52	9.38 754	54	10.61 246	9.98 743	3	17
44	9.37 549	51	9.38 808	55	10.61 192	9.98 740	3	16
45	9.37 600	52	9.38 863	55	10.61 137	9.98 737	3	15
46	9.37 652	51	9.38 918	54	10.61 082	9.98 734	3	14
47	9.37 703	52	9.38 972	55	10.61 028	9.98 731	3	13
48	9.37 755	51	9.39 027	55	10.60 973	9.98 728	3	12
49	9.37 806	52	9.39 082	54	10.60 918	9.98 725	3	11
50	9.37 858	51	9.39 136	54	10.60 864	9.98 722	3	10
51	9.37 909	51	9.39 190	55	10.60 810	9.98 719	4	9
52	9.37 960	51	9.39 245	54	10.60 755	9.98 715	3	8
53	9.38 011	51	9.39 299	54	10.60 701	9.98 712	3	7
54	9.38 062	51	9.39 353	54	10.60 647	9.98 709	3	6
55	9.38 113	51	9.39 407	54	10.60 593	9.98 706	3	5
56	9.38 164	51	9.39 461	54	10.60 539	9.98 703	3	4
57	9.38 215	51	9.39 515	54	10.60 485	9.98 700	3	3
58	9.38 266	51	9.39 569	54	10.60 431	9.98 697	3	2
59	9.38 317	51	9.39 623	54	10.60 377	9.98 694	4	1
60	9.38 368		9.39 677		10.60 323	9.98 690		0

Prop. Pts.

	58	57	56
2	11.6	11.4	11.2
3	17.4	17.1	16.8
4	23.2	22.8	22.4
5	29.0	28.5	28.0
6	34.8	34.2	33.6
7	40.6	39.9	39.2
8	46.4	45.6	44.8
9	52.2	51.3	50.4

	55	54	53
2	11.0	10.8	10.6
3	16.5	16.2	15.9
4	22.0	21.6	21.2
5	27.5	27.0	26.5
6	33.0	32.4	31.8
7	38.5	37.8	37.1
8	44.0	43.2	42.4
9	49.5	48.6	47.7

	52	51
2	10.4	10.2
3	15.6	15.3
4	20.8	20.4
5	26.0	25.5
6	31.2	30.6
7	36.4	35.7
8	41.6	40.8
9	46.8	45.9

	4	3	2
2	0.8	0.6	0.4
3	1.2	0.9	0.6
4	1.6	1.2	0.8
5	2.0	1.5	1.0
6	2.4	1.8	1.2
7	2.8	2.1	1.4
8	3.2	2.4	1.6
9	3.6	2.7	1.8

From the top:

For **13°+** or **193°+**, read as printed; for **103°+** or **283°+**, read co-function.

From the bottom:

For **76°+** or **256°+**, read as printed; for **166°+** or **346°+**, read co-function.

Prop. Pts.

′	L Sin	d	L Tan	c d	L Ctn	L Cos	d	
0	9.38 368	50	9.39 677	54	10.60 323	9.98 690	3	60
1	9.38 418	51	9.39 731	54	10.60 269	9.98 687	3	59
2	9.38 469	50	9.39 785	53	10.60 215	9.98 684	3	58
3	9.38 519	51	9.39 838	54	10.60 162	9.98 681	3	57
4	9.38 570	50	9.39 892	53	10.60 108	9.98 678	3	56
5	9.38 620	50	9.39 945	54	10.60 055	9.98 675	4	55
6	9.38 670	51	9.39 999	53	10.60 001	9.98 671	3	54
7	9.38 721	50	9.40 052	54	10.59 948	9.98 668	3	53
8	9.38 771	50	9.40 106	53	10.59 894	9.98 665	3	52
9	9.38 821	50	9.40 159	53	10.59 841	9.98 662	3	51
10	9.38 871	50	9.40 212	54	10.59 788	9.98 659	3	50
11	9.38 921	50	9.40 266	53	10.59 734	9.98 656	4	49
12	9.38 971	50	9.40 319	53	10.59 681	9.98 652	3	48
13	9.39 021	50	9.40 372	53	10.59 628	9.98 649	3	47
14	9.39 071	50	9.40 425	53	10.59 575	9.98 646	3	46
15	9.39 121	49	9.40 478	53	10.59 522	9.98 643	3	45
16	9.39 170	50	9.40 531	53	10.59 469	9.98 640	4	44
17	9.39 220	50	9.40 584	52	10.59 416	9.98 636	3	43
18	9.39 270	49	9.40 636	53	10.59 364	9.98 633	3	42
19	9.39 319	50	9.40 689	53	10.59 311	9.98 630	3	41
20	9.39 369	49	9.40 742	53	10.59 258	9.98 627	4	40
21	9.39 418	49	9.40 795	52	10.59 205	9.98 623	3	39
22	9.39 467	50	9.40 847	53	10.59 153	9.98 620	3	38
23	9.39 517	49	9.40 900	52	10.59 100	9.98 617	3	37
24	9.39 566	49	9.40 952	53	10.59 048	9.98 614	4	36
25	9.39 615	49	9.41 005	52	10.58 995	9.98 610	3	35
26	9.39 664	49	9.41 057	52	10.58 943	9.98 607	3	34
27	9.39 713	49	9.41 109	52	10.58 891	9.98 604	3	33
28	9.39 762	49	9.41 161	53	10.58 839	9.98 601	4	32
29	9.39 811	49	9.41 214	52	10.58 786	9.98 597	3	31
30	9.39 860	49	9.41 266	52	10.58 734	9.98 594	3	30
31	9.39 909	49	9.41 318	52	10.58 682	9.98 591	3	29
32	9.39 958	48	9.41 370	52	10.58 630	9.98 588	4	28
33	9.40 006	49	9.41 422	52	10.58 578	9.98 584	3	27
34	9.40 055	48	9.41 474	52	10.58 526	9.98 581	3	26
35	9.40 103	49	9.41 526	52	10.58 474	9.98 578	4	25
36	9.40 152	48	9.41 578	51	10.58 422	9.98 574	3	24
37	9.40 200	49	9.41 629	52	10.58 371	9.98 571	3	23
38	9.40 249	48	9.41 681	52	10.58 319	9.98 568	3	22
39	9.40 297	49	9.41 733	51	10.58 267	9.98 565	4	21
40	9.40 346	48	9.41 784	52	10.58 216	9.98 561	3	20
41	9.40 394	48	9.41 836	51	10.58 164	9.98 558	3	19
42	9.40 442	48	9.41 887	52	10.58 113	9.98 555	4	18
43	9.40 490	48	9.41 939	51	10.58 061	9.98 551	3	17
44	9.40 538	48	9.41 990	51	10.58 010	9.98 548	3	16
45	9.40 586	48	9.42 041	52	10.57 959	9.98 545	4	15
46	9.40 634	48	9.42 093	51	10.57 907	9.98 541	3	14
47	9.40 682	48	9.42 144	51	10.57 856	9.98 538	3	13
48	9.40 730	48	9.42 195	51	10.57 805	9.98 535	4	12
49	9.40 778	47	9.42 246	51	10.57 754	9.98 531	3	11
50	9.40 825	48	9.42 297	51	10.57 703	9.98 528	3	10
51	9.40 873	48	9.42 348	51	10.57 652	9.98 525	4	9
52	9.40 921	47	9.42 399	51	10.57 601	9.98 521	3	8
53	9.40 968	48	9.42 450	51	10.57 550	9.98 518	3	7
54	9.41 016	47	9.42 501	51	10.57 499	9.98 515	4	6
55	9.41 063	48	9.42 552	51	10.57 448	9.98 511	3	5
56	9.41 111	47	9.42 603	50	10.57 397	9.98 508	3	4
57	9.41 158	47	9.42 653	51	10.57 347	9.98 505	4	3
58	9.41 205	47	9.42 704	51	10.57 296	9.98 501	3	2
59	9.41 252	48	9.42 755	50	10.57 245	9.98 498	4	1
60	9.41 300		9.42 805		10.57 195	9.98 494		0
	L Cos	d	L Ctn	c d	L Tan	L Sin	d	′

Prop. Pts.

	54	53	52
2	10.8	10.6	10.4
3	16.2	15.9	15.6
4	21.6	21.2	20.8
5	27.0	26.5	26.0
6	32.4	31.8	31.2
7	37.8	37.1	36.4
8	43.2	42.4	41.6
9	48.6	47.7	46.8

	51	50	49
2	10.2	10.0	9.8
3	15.3	15.0	14.7
4	20.4	20.0	19.6
5	25.5	25.0	24.5
6	30.6	30.0	29.4
7	35.7	35.0	34.3
8	40.8	40.0	39.2
9	45.9	45.0	44.1

	48	47
2	9.6	9.4
3	14.4	14.1
4	19.2	18.8
5	24.0	23.5
6	28.8	28.2
7	33.6	32.9
8	38.4	37.6
9	43.2	42.3

	4	3
2	0.8	0.6
3	1.2	0.9
4	1.6	1.2
5	2.0	1.5
6	2.4	1.8
7	2.8	2.1
8	3.2	2.4
9	3.6	2.7

From the top:
For **14°+** or **194°+**, read as printed; for **104°+** or **284°+**, read co-function.

From the bottom:
For **75°+** or **255°+**, read as printed; for **165°+** or **345°+**, read co-function.

Prop. Pts.

′	L Sin	d	L Tan	cd	L Ctn	L Cos	d	
0	9.41 300		9.42 805		10.57 195	9.98 494		60
1	9.41 347	47	9.42 856	51	10.57 144	9.98 491	3	59
2	9.41 394	47	9.42 906	50	10.57 094	9.98 488	3	58
3	9.41 441	47	9.42 957	51	10.57 043	9.98 484	4	57
4	9.41 488	47	9.43 007	50	10.56 993	9.98 481	3	56
5	9.41 535	47	9.43 057	50	10.56 943	9.98 477	4	55
6	9.41 582	47	9.43 108	51	10.56 892	9.98 474	3	54
7	9.41 628	46	9.43 158	50	10.56 842	9.98 471	3	53
8	9.41 675	47	9.43 208	50	10.56 792	9.98 467	4	52
9	9.41 722	47	9.43 258	50	10.56 742	9.98 464	3	51
10	9.41 768	46	9.43 308	50	10.56 692	9.98 460	4	50
11	9.41 815	47	9.43 358	50	10.56 642	9.98 457	3	49
12	9.41 861	46	9.43 408	50	10.56 592	9.98 453	4	48
13	9.41 908	47	9.43 458	50	10.56 542	9.98 450	3	47
14	9.41 954	46	9.43 508	50	10.56 492	9.98 447	3	46
15	9.42 001	47	9.43 558	50	10.56 442	9.98 443	4	45
16	9.42 047	46	9.43 607	49	10.56 393	9.98 440	3	44
17	9.42 093	46	9.43 657	50	10.56 343	9.98 436	4	43
18	9.42 140	47	9.43 707	50	10.56 293	9.98 433	3	42
19	9.42 186	46	9.43 756	49	10.56 244	9.98 429	4	41
20	9.42 232	46	9.43 806	50	10.56 194	9.98 426	3	40
21	9.42 278	46	9.43 855	49	10.56 145	9.98 422	4	39
22	9.42 324	46	9.43 905	50	10.56 095	9.98 419	3	38
23	9.42 370	46	9.43 954	49	10.56 046	9.98 415	4	37
24	9.42 416	46	9.44 004	50	10.55 996	9.98 412	3	36
25	9.42 461	45	9.44 053	49	10.55 947	9.98 409	3	35
26	9.42 507	46	9.44 102	49	10.55 898	9.98 405	4	34
27	9.42 553	46	9.44 151	49	10.55 849	9.98 402	3	33
28	9.42 599	46	9.44 201	50	10.55 799	9.98 398	4	32
29	9.42 644	45	9.44 250	49	10.55 750	9.98 395	3	31
30	9.42 690	46	9.44 299	49	10.55 701	9.98 391	4	30
31	9.42 735	45	9.44 348	49	10.55 652	9.98 388	3	29
32	9.42 781	46	9.44 397	49	10.55 603	9.98 384	4	28
33	9.42 826	45	9.44 446	49	10.55 554	9.98 381	3	27
34	9.42 872	46	9.44 495	49	10.55 505	9.98 377	4	26
35	9.42 917	45	9.44 544	49	10.55 456	9.98 373	4	25
36	9.42 962	45	9.44 592	48	10.55 408	9.98 370	3	24
37	9.43 008	46	9.44 641	49	10.55 359	9.98 366	4	23
38	9.43 053	45	9.44 690	49	10.55 310	9.98 363	3	22
39	9.43 098	45	9.44 738	48	10.55 262	9.98 359	4	21
40	9.43 143	45	9.44 787	49	10.55 213	9.98 356	3	20
41	9.43 188	45	9.44 836	49	10.55 164	9.98 352	4	19
42	9.43 233	45	9.44 884	48	10.55 116	9.98 349	3	18
43	9.43 278	45	9.44 933	49	10.55 067	9.98 345	4	17
44	9.43 323	45	9.44 981	48	10.55 019	9.98 342	3	16
45	9.43 367	44	9.45 029	48	10.54 971	9.98 338	4	15
46	9.43 412	45	9.45 078	49	10.54 922	9.98 334	4	14
47	9.43 457	45	9.45 126	48	10.54 874	9.98 331	3	13
48	9.43 502	45	9.45 174	48	10.54 826	9.98 327	4	12
49	9.43 546	44	9.45 222	48	10.54 778	9.98 324	3	11
50	9.43 591	45	9.45 271	49	10.54 729	9.98 320	4	10
51	9.43 635	44	9.45 319	48	10.54 681	9.98 317	3	9
52	9.43 680	45	9.45 367	48	10.54 633	9.98 313	4	8
53	9.43 724	44	9.45 415	48	10.54 585	9.98 309	4	7
54	9.43 769	45	9.45 463	48	10.54 537	9.98 306	3	6
55	9.43 813	44	9.45 511	48	10.54 489	9.98 302	4	5
56	9.43 857	44	9.45 559	48	10.54 441	9.98 299	3	4
57	9.43 901	44	9.45 606	47	10.54 394	9.98 295	4	3
58	9.43 946	45	9.45 654	48	10.54 346	9.98 291	4	2
59	9.43 990	44	9.45 702	48	10.54 298	9.98 288	3	1
60	9.44 034	44	9.45 750	48	10.54 250	9.98 284	4	0
	L Cos	d	L Ctn	cd	L Tan	L Sin	d	′

Prop. Pts.

	51	50	49
2	10.2	10.0	9.8
3	15.3	15.0	14.7
4	20.4	20.0	19.6
5	25.5	25.0	24.5
6	30.6	30.0	29.4
7	35.7	35.0	34.3
8	40.8	40.0	39.2
9	45.9	45.0	44.1

	48	47	46
2	9.6	9.4	9.2
3	14.4	14.1	13.8
4	19.2	18.8	18.4
5	24.0	23.5	23.0
6	28.8	28.2	27.6
7	33.6	32.9	32.2
8	38.4	37.6	36.8
9	43.2	42.3	41.4

	45	44
2	9.0	8.8
3	13.5	13.2
4	18.0	17.6
5	22.5	22.0
6	27.0	26.4
7	31.5	30.8
8	36.0	35.2
9	40.5	39.6

	4	3
2	0.8	0.6
3	1.2	0.9
4	1.6	1.2
5	2.0	1.5
6	2.4	1.8
7	2.8	2.1
8	3.2	2.4
9	3.6	2.7

From the top:

For **15°+** or **195°+**, read as printed; for **105°+** or **285°+**, read co-function.

From the bottom:

For **74°+** or **254°+**, read as printed; for **164°+** or **344°+**, read co-function.

Prop. Pts.

16° — Logarithms of Trigonometric Functions

′	L Sin	d	L Tan	cd	L Ctn	L Cos	d	
0	9.44 034	44	9.45 750	47	10.54 250	9.98 284	3	60
1	9.44 078	44	9.45 797	48	10.54 203	9.98 281	4	59
2	9.44 122	44	9.45 845	47	10.54 155	9.98 277	4	58
3	9.44 166	44	9.45 892	48	10.54 108	9.98 273	3	57
4	9.44 210	43	9.45 940	47	10.54 060	9.98 270	4	56
5	9.44 253	44	9.45 987	48	10.54 013	9.98 266	4	55
6	9.44 297	44	9.46 035	47	10.53 965	9.98 262	3	54
7	9.44 341	44	9.46 082	48	10.53 918	9.98 259	4	53
8	9.44 385	43	9.46 130	47	10.53 870	9.98 255	4	52
9	9.44 428	44	9.46 177	47	10.53 823	9.98 251	3	51
10	9.44 472	44	9.46 224	47	10.53 776	9.98 248	4	50
11	9.44 516	43	9.46 271	48	10.53 729	9.98 244	4	49
12	9.44 559	43	9.46 319	47	10.53 681	9.98 240	3	48
13	9.44 602	44	9.46 366	47	10.53 634	9.98 237	4	47
14	9.44 646	43	9.46 413	47	10.53 587	9.98 233	4	46
15	9.44 689	44	9.46 460	47	10.53 540	9.98 229	3	45
16	9.44 733	43	9.46 507	47	10.53 493	9.98 226	4	44
17	9.44 776	43	9.46 554	47	10.53 446	9.98 222	4	43
18	9.44 819	43	9.46 601	47	10.53 399	9.98 218	3	42
19	9.44 862	43	9.46 648	46	10.53 352	9.98 215	4	41
20	9.44 905	43	9.46 694	47	10.53 306	9.98 211	4	40
21	9.44 948	44	9.46 741	47	10.53 259	9.98 207	3	39
22	9.44 992	43	9.46 788	47	10.53 212	9.98 204	4	38
23	9.45 035	42	9.46 835	46	10.53 165	9.98 200	4	37
24	9.45 077	43	9.46 881	47	10.53 119	9.98 196	4	36
25	9.45 120	43	9.46 928	47	10.53 072	9.98 192	3	35
26	9.45 163	43	9.46 975	46	10.53 025	9.98 189	4	34
27	9.45 206	43	9.47 021	47	10.52 979	9.98 185	4	33
28	9.45 249	43	9.47 068	46	10.52 932	9.98 181	4	32
29	9.45 292	42	9.47 114	46	10.52 886	9.98 177	3	31
30	9.45 334	43	9.47 160	47	10.52 840	9.98 174	4	30
31	9.45 377	42	9.47 207	46	10.52 793	9.98 170	4	29
32	9.45 419	43	9.47 253	46	10.52 747	9.98 166	4	28
33	9.45 462	42	9.47 299	47	10.52 701	9.98 162	3	27
34	9.45 504	43	9.47 346	46	10.52 654	9.98 159	4	26
35	9.45 547	42	9.47 392	46	10.52 608	9.98 155	4	25
36	9.45 589	43	9.47 438	46	10.52 562	9.98 151	4	24
37	9.45 632	42	9.47 484	46	10.52 516	9.98 147	3	23
38	9.45 674	42	9.47 530	46	10.52 470	9.98 144	4	22
39	9.45 716	42	9.47 576	46	10.52 424	9.98 140	4	21
40	9.45 758	43	9.47 622	46	10.52 378	9.98 136	4	20
41	9.45 801	42	9.47 668	46	10.52 332	9.98 132	3	19
42	9.45 843	42	9.47 714	46	10.52 286	9.98 129	4	18
43	9.45 885	42	9.47 760	46	10.52 240	9.98 125	4	17
44	9.45 927	42	9.47 806	46	10.52 194	9.98 121	4	16
45	9.45 969	42	9.47 852	45	10.52 148	9.98 117	4	15
46	9.46 011	42	9.47 897	46	10.52 103	9.98 113	3	14
47	9.46 053	42	9.47 943	46	10.52 057	9.98 110	4	13
48	9.46 095	41	9.47 989	46	10.52 011	9.98 106	4	12
49	9.46 136	42	9.48 035	45	10.51 965	9.98 102	4	11
50	9.46 178	42	9.48 080	46	10.51 920	9.98 098	4	10
51	9.46 220	42	9.48 126	45	10.51 874	9.98 094	4	9
52	9.46 262	41	9.48 171	46	10.51 829	9.98 090	3	8
53	9.46 303	42	9.48 217	45	10.51 783	9.98 087	4	7
54	9.46 345	41	9.48 262	45	10.51 738	9.98 083	4	6
55	9.46 386	42	9.48 307	46	10.51 693	9.98 079	4	5
56	9.46 428	41	9.48 353	45	10.51 647	9.98 075	4	4
57	9.46 469	42	9.48 398	45	10.51 602	9.98 071	4	3
58	9.46 511	41	9.48 443	46	10.51 557	9.98 067	4	2
59	9.46 552	42	9.48 489	45	10.51 511	9.98 063	3	1
60	9.46 594		9.48 534		10.51 466	9.98 060		0
	L Cos	d	L Ctn	cd	L Tan	L Sin	d	′

Prop. Pts.

	48	47	46
2	9.6	9.4	9.2
3	14.4	14.1	13.8
4	19.2	18.8	18.4
5	24.0	23.5	23.0
6	28.8	28.2	27.6
7	33.6	32.9	32.2
8	38.4	37.6	36.8
9	43.2	42.3	41.4

	45	44	43
2	9.0	8.8	8.6
3	13.5	13.2	12.9
4	18.0	17.6	17.2
5	22.5	22.0	21.5
6	27.0	26.4	25.8
7	31.5	30.8	30.1
8	36.0	35.2	34.4
9	40.5	39.6	38.7

	42	41
2	8.4	8.2
3	12.6	12.3
4	16.8	16.4
5	21.0	20.5
6	25.2	24.6
7	29.4	28.7
8	33.6	32.8
9	37.8	36.9

	4	3
2	0.8	0.6
3	1.2	0.9
4	1.6	1.2
5	2.0	1.5
6	2.4	1.8
7	2.8	2.1
8	3.2	2.4
9	3.6	2.7

From the top:

For **16°+** or **196°+**, read as printed; for **106°+** or **286°+**, read co-function.

From the bottom:

For **73°+** or **253°+**, read as printed; for **163°+** or **343°+**, read co-function.

Prop. Pts.

73° — Logarithms of Trigonometric Functions

′	L Sin	d	L Tan	c d	L Ctn	L Cos	d	
0	9.46 594	41	9.48 534	45	10.51 466	9.98 060	4	60
1	9.46 635	41	9.48 579	45	10.51 421	9.98 056	4	59
2	9.46 676	41	9.48 624	45	10.51 376	9.98 052	4	58
3	9.46 717	41	9.48 669	45	10.51 331	9.98 048	4	57
4	9.46 758	42	9.48 714	45	10.51 286	9.98 044	4	56
5	9.46 800	41	9.48 759	45	10.51 241	9.98 040	4	55
6	9.46 841	41	9.48 804	45	10.51 196	9.98 036	4	54
7	9.46 882	41	9.48 849	45	10.51 151	9.98 032	3	53
8	9.46 923	41	9.48 894	45	10.51 106	9.98 029	4	52
9	9.46 964	41	9.48 939	45	10.51 061	9.98 025	4	51
10	9.47 005	40	9.48 984	45	10.51 016	9.98 021	4	50
11	9.47 045	41	9.49 029	44	10.50 971	9.98 017	4	49
12	9.47 086	41	9.49 073	45	10.50 927	9.98 013	4	48
13	9.47 127	41	9.49 118	45	10.50 882	9.98 009	4	47
14	9.47 168	41	9.49 163	44	10.50 837	9.98 005	4	46
15	9.47 209	40	9.49 207	45	10.50 793	9.98 001	4	45
16	9.47 249	41	9.49 252	44	10.50 748	9.97 997	4	44
17	9.47 290	40	9.49 296	45	10.50 704	9.97 993	4	43
18	9.47 330	41	9.49 341	44	10.50 659	9.97 989	3	42
19	9.47 371	40	9.49 385	45	10.50 615	9.97 986	4	41
20	9.47 411	41	9.49 430	44	10.50 570	9.97 982	4	40
21	9.47 452	40	9.49 474	45	10.50 526	9.97 978	4	39
22	9.47 492	41	9.49 519	44	10.50 481	9.97 974	4	38
23	9.47 533	40	9.49 563	44	10.50 437	9.97 970	4	37
24	9.47 573	40	9.49 607	45	10.50 393	9.97 966	4	36
25	9.47 613	41	9.49 652	44	10.50 348	9.97 962	4	35
26	9.47 654	40	9.49 696	44	10.50 304	9.97 958	4	34
27	9.47 694	40	9.49 740	44	10.50 260	9.97 954	4	33
28	9.47 734	40	9.49 784	44	10.50 216	9.97 950	4	32
29	9.47 774	40	9.49 828	44	10.50 172	9.97 946	4	31
30	9.47 814	40	9.49 872	44	10.50 128	9.97 942	4	30
31	9.47 854	40	9.49 916	44	10.50 084	9.97 938	4	29
32	9.47 894	40	9.49 960	44	10.50 040	9.97 934	4	28
33	9.47 934	40	9.50 004	44	10.49 996	9.97 930	4	27
34	9.47 974	40	9.50 048	44	10.49 952	9.97 926	4	26
35	9.48 014	40	9.50 092	44	10.49 908	9.97 922	4	25
36	9.48 054	40	9.50 136	44	10.49 864	9.97 918	4	24
37	9.48 094	39	9.50 180	43	10.49 820	9.97 914	4	23
38	9.48 133	40	9.50 223	44	10.49 777	9.97 910	4	22
39	9.48 173	40	9.50 267	44	10.49 733	9.97 906	4	21
40	9.48 213	39	9.50 311	44	10.49 689	9.97 902	4	20
41	9.48 252	40	9.50 355	43	10.49 645	9.97 898	4	19
42	9.48 292	40	9.50 398	44	10.49 602	9.97 894	4	18
43	9.48 332	39	9.50 442	43	10.49 558	9.97 890	4	17
44	9.48 371	40	9.50 485	44	10.49 515	9.97 886	4	16
45	9.48 411	39	9.50 529	43	10.49 471	9.97 882	4	15
46	9.48 450	40	9.50 572	44	10.49 428	9.97 878	4	14
47	9.48 490	39	9.50 616	43	10.49 384	9.97 874	4	13
48	9.48 529	39	9.50 659	44	10.49 341	9.97 870	4	12
49	9.48 568	39	9.50 703	43	10.49 297	9.97 866	5	11
50	9.48 607	40	9.50 746	43	10.49 254	9.97 861	4	10
51	9.48 647	39	9.50 789	44	10.49 211	9.97 857	4	9
52	9.48 686	39	9.50 833	43	10.49 167	9.97 853	4	8
53	9.48 725	39	9.50 876	43	10.49 124	9.97 849	4	7
54	9.48 764	39	9.50 919	43	10.49 081	9.97 845	4	6
55	9.48 803	39	9.50 962	43	10.49 038	9.97 841	4	5
56	9.48 842	39	9.51 005	43	10.48 995	9.97 837	4	4
57	9.48 881	39	9.51 048	44	10.48 952	9.97 833	4	3
58	9.48 920	39	9.51 092	43	10.48 908	9.97 829	4	2
59	9.48 959	39	9.51 135	43	10.48 865	9.97 825	4	1
60	9.48 998		9.51 178		10.48 822	9.97 821		0
	L Cos	d	L Ctn	c d	L Tan	L Sin	d	′

Prop. Pts.

	45	44	43
2	9.0	8.8	8.6
3	13.5	13.2	12.9
4	18.0	17.6	17.2
5	22.5	22.0	21.5
6	27.0	26.4	25.8
7	31.5	30.8	30.1
8	36.0	35.2	34.4
9	40.5	39.6	38.7

	42	41	40
2	8.4	8.2	8.0
3	12.6	12.3	12.0
4	16.8	16.4	16.0
5	21.0	20.5	20.0
6	25.2	24.6	24.0
7	29.4	28.7	28.0
8	33.6	32.8	32.0
9	37.8	36.9	36.0

	39	5
2	7.8	1.0
3	11.7	1.5
4	15.6	2.0
5	19.5	2.5
6	23.4	3.0
7	27.3	3.5
8	31.2	4.0
9	35.1	4.5

	4	3
2	0.8	0.6
3	1.2	0.9
4	1.6	1.2
5	2.0	1.5
6	2.4	1.8
7	2.8	2.1
8	3.2	2.4
9	3.6	2.7

From the top:

For **17°+** or **197°+**, read as printed; for **107°+** or **287°+**, read co-function.

From the bottom:

For **72°+** or **252°+**, read as printed; for **162°+** or **342°+**, read co-function.

′	L Sin	d	L Tan	cd	L Ctn	L Cos	d	
0	9.48 998	39	9.51 178	43	10.48 822	9.97 821	4	**60**
1	9.49 037	39	9.51 221	43	10.48 779	9.97 817	5	59
2	9.49 076	39	9.51 264	42	10.48 736	9.97 812	4	58
3	9.49 115	38	9.51 306	43	10.48 694	9.97 808	4	57
4	9.49 153	39	9.51 349	43	10.48 651	9.97 804	4	56
5	9.49 192	39	9.51 392	43	10.48 608	9.97 800	4	**55**
6	9.49 231	38	9.51 435	43	10.48 565	9.97 796	4	54
7	9.49 269	39	9.51 478	42	10.48 522	9.97 792	4	53
8	9.49 308	39	9.51 520	43	10.48 480	9.97 788	4	52
9	9.49 347	38	9.51 563	43	10.48 437	9.97 784	5	51
10	9.49 385	39	9.51 606	42	10.48 394	9.97 779	4	**50**
11	9.49 424	38	9.51 648	43	10.48 352	9.97 775	4	49
12	9.49 462	38	9.51 691	43	10.48 309	9.97 771	4	48
13	9.49 500	39	9.51 734	42	10.48 266	9.97 767	4	47
14	9.49 539	38	9.51 776	43	10.48 224	9.97 763	4	46
15	9.49 577	38	9.51 819	42	10.48 181	9.97 759	5	**45**
16	9.49 615	39	9.51 861	42	10.48 139	9.97 754	4	44
17	9.49 654	38	9.51 903	43	10.48 097	9.97 750	4	43
18	9.49 692	38	9.51 946	42	10.48 054	9.97 746	4	42
19	9.49 730	38	9.51 988	43	10.48 012	9.97 742	4	41
20	9.49 768	38	9.52 031	42	10.47 969	9.97 738	4	**40**
21	9.49 806	38	9.52 073	42	10.47 927	9.97 734	5	39
22	9.49 844	38	9.52 115	42	10.47 885	9.97 729	4	38
23	9.49 882	38	9.52 157	43	10.47 843	9.97 725	4	37
24	9.49 920	38	9.52 200	42	10.47 800	9.97 721	4	36
25	9.49 958	38	9.52 242	42	10.47 758	9.97 717	4	**35**
26	9.49 996	38	9.52 284	42	10.47 716	9.97 713	5	34
27	9.50 034	38	9.52 326	42	10.47 674	9.97 708	4	33
28	9.50 072	38	9.52 368	42	10.47 632	9.97 704	4	32
29	9.50 110	38	9.52 410	42	10.47 590	9.97 700	4	31
30	9.50 148	37	9.52 452	42	10.47 548	9.97 696	5	**30**
31	9.50 185	38	9.52 494	42	10.47 506	9.97 691	4	29
32	9.50 223	38	9.52 536	42	10.47 464	9.97 687	4	28
33	9.50 261	37	9.52 578	42	10.47 422	9.97 683	4	27
34	9.50 298	38	9.52 620	41	10.47 380	9.97 679	5	26
35	9.50 336	38	9.52 661	42	10.47 339	9.97 674	4	**25**
36	9.50 374	37	9.52 703	42	10.47 297	9.97 670	4	24
37	9.50 411	38	9.52 745	42	10.47 255	9.97 666	4	23
38	9.50 449	37	9.52 787	42	10.47 213	9.97 662	5	22
39	9.50 486	37	9.52 829	41	10.47 171	9.97 657	4	21
40	9.50 523	38	9.52 870	42	10.47 130	9.97 653	4	**20**
41	9.50 561	37	9.52 912	41	10.47 088	9.97 649	4	19
42	9.50 598	37	9.52 953	42	10.47 047	9.97 645	5	18
43	9.50 635	38	9.52 995	42	10.47 005	9.97 640	4	17
44	9.50 673	37	9.53 037	41	10.46 963	9.97 636	4	16
45	9.50 710	37	9.53 078	42	10.46 922	9.97 632	4	**15**
46	9.50 747	37	9.53 120	41	10.46 880	9.97 628	5	14
47	9.50 784	37	9.53 161	41	10.46 839	9.97 623	4	13
48	9.50 821	37	9.53 202	42	10.46 798	9.97 619	4	12
49	9.50 858	38	9.53 244	41	10.46 756	9.97 615	5	11
50	9.50 896	37	9.53 285	42	10.46 715	9.97 610	4	**10**
51	9.50 933	37	9.53 327	41	10.46 673	9.97 606	4	9
52	9.50 970	37	9.53 368	41	10.46 632	9.97 602	5	8
53	9.51 007	36	9.53 409	41	10.46 591	9.97 597	4	7
54	9.51 043	37	9.53 450	42	10.46 550	9.97 593	4	6
55	9.51 080	37	9.53 492	41	10.46 508	9.97 589	5	**5**
56	9.51 117	37	9.53 533	41	10.46 467	9.97 584	4	4
57	9.51 154	37	9.53 574	41	10.46 426	9.97 580	4	3
58	9.51 191	36	9.53 615	41	10.46 385	9.97 576	5	2
59	9.51 227	37	9.53 656	41	10.46 344	9.97 571	4	1
60	9.51 264		9.53 697		10.46 303	9.97 567		**0**
	L Cos	d	L Ctn	cd	L Tan	L Sin	d	′

Prop. Pts.

	43	**42**	**41**
2	8.6	8.4	8.2
3	12.9	12.6	12.3
4	17.2	16.8	16.4
5	21.5	21.0	20.5
6	25.8	25.2	24.6
7	30.1	29.4	28.7
8	34.4	33.6	32.8
9	38.7	37.8	36.9

	39	**38**	**37**
2	7.8	7.6	7.4
3	11.7	11.4	11.1
4	15.6	15.2	14.8
5	19.5	19.0	18.5
6	23.4	22.8	22.2
7	27.3	26.6	25.9
8	31.2	30.4	29.6
9	35.1	34.2	33.3

	36	**5**	**4**
2	7.2	1.0	0.8
3	10.8	1.5	1.2
4	14.4	2.0	1.6
5	18.0	2.5	2.0
6	21.6	3.0	2.4
7	25.2	3.5	2.8
8	28.8	4.0	3.2
9	32.4	4.5	3.6

From the top:

For **18°+** or **198°+**, read as printed; for **108°+** or **288°+**, read co-function.

From the bottom:

For **71°+** or **251°+**, read as printed; for **161°+** or **341°+**, read co-function.

Prop. Pts.

19° — Logarithms of Trigonometric Functions

′	L Sin	d	L Tan	c d	L Ctn	L Cos	d	
0	9.51 264		9.53 697		10.46 303	9.97 567		60
1	9.51 301	37	9.53 738	41	10.46 262	9.97 563	4	59
2	9.51 338	37	9.53 779	41	10.46 221	9.97 558	5	58
3	9.51 374	36	9.53 820	41	10.46 180	9.97 554	4	57
4	9.51 411	37	9.53 861	41	10.46 139	9.97 550	4	56
5	9.51 447	36	9.53 902	41	10.46 098	9.97 545	5	55
6	9.51 484	37	9.53 943	41	10.46 057	9.97 541	4	54
7	9.51 520	36	9.53 984	41	10.46 016	9.97 536	5	53
8	9.51 557	37	9.54 025	41	10.45 975	9.97 532	4	52
9	9.51 593	36	9.54 065	40	10.45 935	9.97 528	4	51
10	9.51 629	36	9.54 106	41	10.45 894	9.97 523	5	50
11	9.51 666	37	9.54 147	41	10.45 853	9.97 519	4	49
12	9.51 702	36	9.54 187	40	10.45 813	9.97 515	4	48
13	9.51 738	36	9.54 228	41	10.45 772	9.97 510	5	47
14	9.51 774	36	9.54 269	41	10.45 731	9.97 506	4	46
15	9.51 811	37	9.54 309	40	10.45 691	9.97 501	5	45
16	9.51 847	36	9.54 350	41	10.45 650	9.97 497	4	44
17	9.51 883	36	9.54 390	40	10.45 610	9.97 492	5	43
18	9.51 919	36	9.54 431	41	10.45 569	9.97 488	4	42
19	9.51 955	36	9.54 471	40	10.45 529	9.97 484	4	41
20	9.51 991	36	9.54 512	41	10.45 488	9.97 479	5	40
21	9.52 027	36	9.54 552	40	10.45 448	9.97 475	4	39
22	9.52 063	36	9.54 593	41	10.45 407	9.97 470	5	38
23	9.52 099	36	9.54 633	40	10.45 367	9.97 466	4	37
24	9.52 135	36	9.54 673	40	10.45 327	9.97 461	5	36
25	9.52 171	36	9.54 714	41	10.45 286	9.97 457	4	35
26	9.52 207	36	9.54 754	40	10.45 246	9.97 453	4	34
27	9.52 242	35	9.54 794	40	10.45 206	9.97 448	5	33
28	9.52 278	36	9.54 835	41	10.45 165	9.97 444	4	32
29	9.52 314	36	9.54 875	40	10.45 125	9.97 439	5	31
30	9.52 350	36	9.54 915	40	10.45 085	9.97 435	4	30
31	9.52 385	35	9.54 955	40	10.45 045	9.97 430	5	29
32	9.52 421	36	9.54 995	40	10.45 005	9.97 426	4	28
33	9.52 456	35	9.55 035	40	10.44 965	9.97 421	5	27
34	9.52 492	36	9.55 075	40	10.44 925	9.97 417	4	26
35	9.52 527	35	9.55 115	40	10.44 885	9.97 412	5	25
36	9.52 563	36	9.55 155	40	10.44 845	9.97 408	4	24
37	9.52 598	35	9.55 195	40	10.44 805	9.97 403	5	23
38	9.52 634	36	9.55 235	40	10.44 765	9.97 399	4	22
39	9.52 669	35	9.55 275	40	10.44 725	9.97 394	5	21
40	9.52 705	36	9.55 315	40	10.44 685	9.97 390	4	20
41	9.52 740	35	9.55 355	40	10.44 645	9.97 385	5	19
42	9.52 775	35	9.55 395	40	10.44 605	9.97 381	4	18
43	9.52 811	36	9.55 434	39	10.44 566	9.97 376	5	17
44	9.52 846	35	9.55 474	40	10.44 526	9.97 372	4	16
45	9.52 881	35	9.55 514	40	10.44 486	9.97 367	5	15
46	9.52 916	35	9.55 554	40	10.44 446	9.97 363	4	14
47	9.52 951	35	9.55 593	39	10.44 407	9.97 358	5	13
48	9.52 986	35	9.55 633	40	10.44 367	9.97 353	5	12
49	9.53 021	35	9.55 673	40	10.44 327	9.97 349	4	11
50	9.53 056	35	9.55 712	39	10.44 288	9.97 344	5	10
51	9.53 092	36	9.55 752	40	10.44 248	9.97 340	4	9
52	9.53 126	34	9.55 791	39	10.44 209	9.97 335	5	8
53	9.53 161	35	9.55 831	40	10.44 169	9.97 331	4	7
54	9.53 196	35	9.55 870	39	10.44 130	9.97 326	5	6
55	9.53 231	35	9.55 910	40	10.44 090	9.97 322	4	5
56	9.53 266	35	9.55 949	39	10.44 051	9.97 317	5	4
57	9.53 301	35	9.55 989	40	10.44 011	9.97 312	5	3
58	9.53 336	35	9.56 028	39	10.43 972	9.97 308	4	2
59	9.53 370	34	9.56 067	39	10.43 933	9.97 303	5	1
60	9.53 405	35	9.56 107	40	10.43 893	9.97 299	4	0
	L Cos	d	L Ctn	c d	L Tan	L Sin	d	′

Prop. Pts.

	41	40	39
2	8.2	8.0	7.8
3	12.3	12.0	11.7
4	16.4	16.0	15.6
5	20.5	20.0	19.5
6	24.6	24.0	23.4
7	28.7	28.0	27.3
8	32.8	32.0	31.2
9	36.9	36.0	35.1

	37	36	35
2	7.4	7.2	7.0
3	11.1	10.8	10.5
4	14.8	14.4	14.0
5	18.5	18.0	17.5
6	22.2	21.6	21.0
7	25.9	25.2	24.5
8	29.6	28.8	28.0
9	33.3	32.4	31.5

	34	5	4
2	6.8	1.0	0.8
3	10.2	1.5	1.2
4	13.6	2.0	1.6
5	17.0	2.5	2.0
6	20.4	3.0	2.4
7	23.8	3.5	2.8
8	27.2	4.0	3.2
9	30.6	4.5	3.6

From the top:

For **19°+** or **199°+**, read as printed; for **109°+** or **289°+**, read co-function.

From the bottom:

For **70°+** or **250°+**, read as printed; for **160°+** or **340°+**, read co-function.

Prop. Pts.

70° — Logarithms of Trigonometric Functions

20° — Logarithms of Trigonometric Functions

′	L Sin	d	L Tan	cd	L Ctn	L Cos	d	
0	9.53 405	35	9.56 107	39	10.43 893	9.97 299	5	60
1	9.53 440	35	9.56 146	39	10.43 854	9.97 294	5	59
2	9.53 475	34	9.56 185	39	10.43 815	9.97 289	4	58
3	9.53 509	35	9.56 224	40	10.43 776	9.97 285	5	57
4	9.53 544	34	9.56 264	39	10.43 736	9.97 280	4	56
5	9.53 578	35	9.56 303	39	10.43 697	9.97 276	5	55
6	9.53 613	34	9.56 342	39	10.43 658	9.97 271	5	54
7	9.53 647	35	9.56 381	39	10.43 619	9.97 266	4	53
8	9.53 682	34	9.56 420	39	10.43 580	9.97 262	5	52
9	9.53 716	35	9.56 459	39	10.43 541	9.97 257	5	51
10	9.53 751	34	9.56 498	39	10.43 502	9.97 252	4	50
11	9.53 785	34	9.56 537	39	10.43 463	9.97 248	5	49
12	9.53 819	35	9.56 576	39	10.43 424	9.97 243	5	48
13	9.53 854	34	9.56 615	39	10.43 385	9.97 238	4	47
14	9.53 888	34	9.56 654	39	10.43 346	9.97 234	5	46
15	9.53 922	35	9.56 693	39	10.43 307	9.97 229	5	45
16	9.53 957	34	9.56 732	39	10.43 268	9.97 224	4	44
17	9.53 991	34	9.56 771	39	10.43 229	9.97 220	5	43
18	9.54 025	34	9.56 810	39	10.43 190	9.97 215	5	42
19	9.54 059	34	9.56 849	38	10.43 151	9.97 210	4	41
20	9.54 093	34	9.56 887	39	10.43 113	9.97 206	5	40
21	9.54 127	34	9.56 926	39	10.43 074	9.97 201	5	39
22	9.54 161	34	9.56 965	39	10.43 035	9.97 196	4	38
23	9.54 195	34	9.57 004	38	10.42 996	9.97 192	5	37
24	9.54 229	34	9.57 042	39	10.42 958	9.97 187	5	36
25	9.54 263	34	9.57 081	39	10.42 919	9.97 182	4	35
26	9.54 297	34	9.57 120	38	10.42 880	9.97 178	5	34
27	9.54 331	34	9.57 158	39	10.42 842	9.97 173	5	33
28	9.54 365	34	9.57 197	38	10.42 803	9.97 168	5	32
29	9.54 399	34	9.57 235	39	10.42 765	9.97 163	4	31
30	9.54 433	33	9.57 274	38	10.42 726	9.97 159	5	30
31	9.54 466	34	9.57 312	39	10.42 688	9.97 154	5	29
32	9.54 500	34	9.57 351	38	10.42 649	9.97 149	4	28
33	9.54 534	33	9.57 389	39	10.42 611	9.97 145	5	27
34	9.54 567	34	9.57 428	38	10.42 572	9.97 140	5	26
35	9.54 601	34	9.57 466	38	10.42 534	9.97 135	5	25
36	9.54 635	33	9.57 504	39	10.42 496	9.97 130	4	24
37	9.54 668	34	9.57 543	38	10.42 457	9.97 126	5	23
38	9.54 702	33	9.57 581	38	10.42 419	9.97 121	5	22
39	9.54 735	34	9.57 619	39	10.42 381	9.97 116	5	21
40	9.54 769	33	9.57 658	38	10.42 342	9.97 111	4	20
41	9.54 802	34	9.57 696	38	10.42 304	9.97 107	5	19
42	9.54 836	33	9.57 734	38	10.42 266	9.97 102	5	18
43	9.54 869	34	9.57 772	38	10.42 228	9.97 097	5	17
44	9.54 903	33	9.57 810	39	10.42 190	9.97 092	5	16
45	9.54 936	33	9.57 849	38	10.42 151	9.97 087	4	15
46	9.54 969	34	9.57 887	38	10.42 113	9.97 083	5	14
47	9.55 003	33	9.57 925	38	10.42 075	9.97 078	5	13
48	9.55 036	33	9.57 963	38	10.42 037	9.97 073	5	12
49	9.55 069	33	9.58 001	38	10.41 999	9.97 068	5	11
50	9.55 102	34	9.58 039	38	10.41 961	9.97 063	4	10
51	9.55 136	33	9.58 077	38	10.41 923	9.97 059	5	9
52	9.55 169	33	9.58 115	38	10.41 885	9.97 054	5	8
53	9.55 202	33	9.58 153	38	10.41 847	9.97 049	5	7
54	9.55 235	33	9.58 191	38	10.41 809	9.97 044	5	6
55	9.55 268	33	9.58 229	38	10.41 771	9.97 039	4	5
56	9.55 301	33	9.58 267	37	10.41 733	9.97 035	5	4
57	9.55 334	33	9.58 304	38	10.41 696	9.97 030	5	3
58	9.55 367	33	9.58 342	38	10.41 658	9.97 025	5	2
59	9.55 400	33	9.58 380	38	10.41 620	9.97 020	5	1
60	9.55 433		9.58 418		10.41 582	9.97 015		0
	L Cos	d	L Ctn	cd	L Tan	L Sin	d	′

Prop. Pts.

	40	39	38
2	8.0	7.8	7.6
3	12.0	11.7	11.4
4	16.0	15.6	15.2
5	20.0	19.5	19.0
6	24.0	23.4	22.8
7	28.0	27.3	26.6
8	32.0	31.2	30.4
9	36.0	35.1	34.2

	37	35	34
2	7.4	7.0	6.8
3	11.1	10.5	10.2
4	14.8	14.0	13.6
5	18.5	17.5	17.0
6	22.2	21.0	20.4
7	25.9	24.5	23.8
8	29.6	28.0	27.2
9	33.3	31.5	30.6

	33	5	4
2	6.6	1.0	0.8
3	9.9	1.5	1.2
4	13.2	2.0	1.6
5	16.5	2.5	2.0
6	19.8	3.0	2.4
7	23.1	3.5	2.8
8	26.4	4.0	3.2
9	29.7	4.5	3.6

From the top:

For **20°+** or **200°+**, read as printed; for **110°+** or **290°+**, read co-function.

From the bottom:

For **69°+** or **249°+**, read as printed; for **159°+** or **339°+**, read co-function.

Prop. Pts.

69° — Logarithms of Trigonometric Functions

21° — Logarithms of Trigonometric Functions

′	L Sin	d	L Tan	c d	L Ctn	L Cos	d	
0	9.55 433	33	9.58 418	37	10.41 582	9.97 015	5	60
1	9.55 466	33	9.58 455	38	10.41 545	9.97 010	5	59
2	9.55 499	33	9.58 493	38	10.41 507	9.97 005	4	58
3	9.55 532	32	9.58 531	38	10.41 469	9.97 001	5	57
4	9.55 564	33	9.58 569	37	10.41 431	9.96 996	5	56
5	9.55 597	33	9.58 606	38	10.41 394	9.96 991	5	55
6	9.55 630	33	9.58 644	37	10.41 356	9.96 986	5	54
7	9.55 663	32	9.58 681	38	10.41 319	9.96 981	5	53
8	9.55 695	33	9.58 719	38	10.41 281	9.96 976	5	52
9	9.55 728	33	9.58 757	37	10.41 243	9.96 971	5	51
10	9.55 761	32	9.58 794	38	10.41 206	9.96 966	4	50
11	9.55 793	33	9.58 832	37	10.41 168	9.96 962	5	49
12	9.55 826	32	9.58 869	38	10.41 131	9.96 957	5	48
13	9.55 858	33	9.58 907	37	10.41 093	9.96 952	5	47
14	9.55 891	32	9.58 944	37	10.41 056	9.96 947	5	46
15	9.55 923	33	9.58 981	38	10.41 019	9.96 942	5	45
16	9.55 956	32	9.59 019	37	10.40 981	9.96 937	5	44
17	9.55 988	33	9.59 056	38	10.40 944	9.96 932	5	43
18	9.56 021	32	9.59 094	37	10.40 906	9.96 927	5	42
19	9.56 053	32	9.59 131	37	10.40 869	9.96 922	5	41
20	9.56 085	33	9.59 168	37	10.40 832	9.96 917	5	40
21	9.56 118	32	9.59 205	38	10.40 795	9.96 912	5	39
22	9.56 150	32	9.59 243	37	10.40 757	9.96 907	4	38
23	9.56 182	33	9.59 280	37	10.40 720	9.96 903	5	37
24	9.56 215	32	9.59 317	37	10.40 683	9.96 898	5	36
25	9.56 247	32	9.59 354	37	10.40 646	9.96 893	5	35
26	9.56 279	32	9.59 391	38	10.40 609	9.96 888	5	34
27	9.56 311	32	9.59 429	37	10.40 571	9.96 883	5	33
28	9.56 343	32	9.59 466	37	10.40 534	9.96 878	5	32
29	9.56 375	33	9.59 503	37	10.40 497	9.96 873	5	31
30	9.56 408	32	9.59 540	37	10.40 460	9.96 868	5	30
31	9.56 440	32	9.59 577	37	10.40 423	9.96 863	5	29
32	9.56 472	32	9.59 614	37	10.40 386	9.96 858	5	28
33	9.56 504	32	9.59 651	37	10.40 349	9.96 853	5	27
34	9.56 536	32	9.59 688	37	10.40 312	9.96 848	5	26
35	9.56 568	31	9.59 725	37	10.40 275	9.96 843	5	25
36	9.56 599	32	9.59 762	37	10.40 238	9.96 838	5	24
37	9.56 631	32	9.59 799	36	10.40 201	9.96 833	5	23
38	9.56 663	32	9.59 835	37	10.40 165	9.96 828	5	22
39	9.56 695	32	9.59 872	37	10.40 128	9.96 823	5	21
40	9.56 727	32	9.59 909	37	10.40 091	9.96 818	5	20
41	9.56 759	31	9.59 946	37	10.40 054	9.96 813	5	19
42	9.56 790	32	9.59 983	36	10.40 017	9.96 808	5	18
43	9.56 822	32	9.60 019	37	10.39 981	9.96 803	5	17
44	9.56 854	32	9.60 056	37	10.39 944	9.96 798	5	16
45	9.56 886	31	9.60 093	37	10.39 907	9.96 793	5	15
46	9.56 917	32	9.60 130	36	10.39 870	9.96 788	5	14
47	9.56 949	31	9.60 166	37	10.39 834	9.96 783	5	13
48	9.56 980	32	9.60 203	37	10.39 797	9.96 778	6	12
49	9.57 012	32	9.60 240	36	10.39 760	9.96 772	5	11
50	9.57 044	31	9.60 276	37	10.39 724	9.96 767	5	10
51	9.57 075	32	9.60 313	36	10.39 687	9.96 762	5	9
52	9.57 107	31	9.60 349	37	10.39 651	9.96 757	5	8
53	9.57 138	31	9.60 386	36	10.39 614	9.96 752	5	7
54	9.57 169	32	9.60 422	37	10.39 578	9.96 747	5	6
55	9.57 201	31	9.60 459	36	10.39 541	9.96 742	5	5
56	9.57 232	32	9.60 495	37	10.39 505	9.96 737	5	4
57	9.57 264	31	9.60 532	36	10.39 468	9.96 732	5	3
58	9.57 295	31	9.60 568	37	10.39 432	9.96 727	5	2
59	9.57 326	32	9.60 605	36	10.39 395	9.96 722	5	1
60	9.57 358		9.60 641		10.39 359	9.96 717		0
	L Cos	d	L Ctn	c d	L Tan	L Sin	d	′

Prop. Pts.

	38	37	36
2	7.6	7.4	7.2
3	11.4	11.1	10.8
4	15.2	14.8	14.4
5	19.0	18.5	18.0
6	22.8	22.2	21.6
7	26.6	25.9	25.2
8	30.4	29.6	28.8
9	34.2	33.3	32.4

	33	32	31
2	6.6	6.4	6.2
3	9.9	9.6	9.3
4	13.2	12.8	12.4
5	16.5	16.0	15.5
6	19.8	19.2	18.6
7	23.1	22.4	21.7
8	26.4	25.6	24.8
9	29.7	28.8	27.9

	6	5	4
2	1.2	1.0	0.8
3	1.8	1.5	1.2
4	2.4	2.0	1.6
5	3.0	2.5	2.0
6	3.6	3.0	2.4
7	4.2	3.5	2.8
8	4.8	4.0	3.2
9	5.4	4.5	3.6

From the top:

For **21°+** or **201°+**, read as printed; for **111°+** or **291°+**, read co-function.

From the bottom:

For **68°+** or **248°+**, read as printed; for **158°+** or **338°+**, read co-function.

Prop. Pts.

68° — Logarithms of Trigonometric Functions

22° — Logarithms of Trigonometric Functions

′	L Sin	d	L Tan	c d	L Ctn	L Cos	d	
0	9.57 358	31	9.60 641	36	10.39 359	9.96 717	6	60
1	9.57 389	31	9.60 677	37	10.39 323	9.96 711	5	59
2	9.57 420	31	9.60 714	36	10.39 286	9.96 706	5	58
3	9.57 451	31	9.60 750	36	10.39 250	9.96 701	5	57
4	9.57 482	32	9.60 786	37	10.39 214	9.96 696	5	56
5	9.57 514	31	9.60 823	36	10.39 177	9.96 691	5	55
6	9.57 545	31	9.60 859	36	10.39 141	9.96 686	5	54
7	9.57 576	31	9.60 895	36	10.39 105	9.96 681	5	53
8	9.57 607	31	9.60 931	36	10.39 069	9.96 676	6	52
9	9.57 638	31	9.60 967	37	10.39 033	9.96 670	5	51
10	9.57 669	31	9.61 004	36	10.38 996	9.96 665	5	50
11	9.57 700	31	9.61 040	36	10.38 960	9.96 660	5	49
12	9.57 731	31	9.61 076	36	10.38 924	9.96 655	5	48
13	9.57 762	31	9.61 112	36	10.38 888	9.96 650	5	47
14	9.57 793	31	9.61 148	36	10.38 852	9.96 645	5	46
15	9.57 824	31	9.61 184	36	10.38 816	9.96 640	6	45
16	9.57 855	30	9.61 220	36	10.38 780	9.96 634	5	44
17	9.57 885	31	9.61 256	36	10.38 744	9.96 629	5	43
18	9.57 916	31	9.61 292	36	10.38 708	9.96 624	5	42
19	9.57 947	31	9.61 328	36	10.38 672	9.96 619	5	41
20	9.57 978	30	9.61 364	36	10.38 636	9.96 614	6	40
21	9.58 008	31	9.61 400	36	10.38 600	9.96 608	5	39
22	9.58 039	31	9.61 436	36	10.38 564	9.96 603	5	38
23	9.58 070	31	9.61 472	36	10.38 528	9.96 598	5	37
24	9.58 101	30	9.61 508	36	10.38 492	9.96 593	5	36
25	9.58 131	31	9.61 544	35	10.38 456	9.96 588	6	35
26	9.58 162	30	9.61 579	36	10.38 421	9.96 582	5	34
27	9.58 192	31	9.61 615	36	10.38 385	9.96 577	5	33
28	9.58 223	30	9.61 651	36	10.38 349	9.96 572	5	32
29	9.58 253	31	9.61 687	35	10.38 313	9.96 567	5	31
30	9.58 284	30	9.61 722	36	10.38 278	9.96 562	6	30
31	9.58 314	31	9.61 758	36	10.38 242	9.96 556	5	29
32	9.58 345	30	9.61 794	36	10.38 206	9.96 551	5	28
33	9.58 375	31	9.61 830	35	10.38 170	9.96 546	5	27
34	9.58 406	30	9.61 865	36	10.38 135	9.96 541	6	26
35	9.58 436	31	9.61 901	35	10.38 099	9.96 535	5	25
36	9.58 467	30	9.61 936	36	10.38 064	9.96 530	5	24
37	9.58 497	30	9.61 972	36	10.38 028	9.96 525	5	23
38	9.58 527	30	9.62 008	35	10.37 992	9.96 520	6	22
39	9.58 557	31	9.62 043	36	10.37 957	9.96 514	5	21
40	9.58 588	30	9.62 079	35	10.37 921	9.96 509	5	20
41	9.58 618	30	9.62 114	36	10.37 886	9.96 504	6	19
42	9.58 648	30	9.62 150	35	10.37 850	9.96 498	5	18
43	9.58 678	31	9.62 185	36	10.37 815	9.96 493	5	17
44	9.58 709	30	9.62 221	35	10.37 779	9.96 488	5	16
45	9.58 739	30	9.62 256	36	10.37 744	9.96 483	6	15
46	9.58 769	30	9.62 292	35	10.37 708	9.96 477	5	14
47	9.58 799	30	9.62 327	35	10.37 673	9.96 472	5	13
48	9.58 829	30	9.62 362	36	10.37 638	9.96 467	6	12
49	9.58 859	30	9.62 398	35	10.37 602	9.96 461	5	11
50	9.58 889	30	9.62 433	35	10.37 567	9.96 456	5	10
51	9.58 919	30	9.62 468	36	10.37 532	9.96 451	6	9
52	9.58 949	30	9.62 504	35	10.37 496	9.96 445	5	8
53	9.58 979	30	9.62 539	35	10.37 461	9.96 440	5	7
54	9.59 009	30	9.62 574	35	10.37 426	9.96 435	6	6
55	9.59 039	30	9.62 609	36	10.37 391	9.96 429	5	5
56	9.59 069	29	9.62 645	35	10.37 355	9.96 424	5	4
57	9.59 098	30	9.62 680	35	10.37 320	9.96 419	6	3
58	9.59 128	30	9.62 715	35	10.37 285	9.96 413	5	2
59	9.59 158	30	9.62 750	35	10.37 250	9.96 408	5	1
60	9.59 188		9.62 785		10.37 215	9.96 403		0
	L Cos	d	L Ctn	c d	L Tan	L Sin	d	′

Prop. Pts.

	37	36	35
2	7.4	7.2	7.0
3	11.1	10.8	10.5
4	14.8	14.4	14.0
5	18.5	18.0	17.5
6	22.2	21.6	21.0
7	25.9	25.2	24.5
8	29.6	28.8	28.0
9	33.3	32.4	31.5

	32	31	30
2	6.4	6.2	6.0
3	9.6	9.3	9.0
4	12.8	12.4	12.0
5	16.0	15.5	15.0
6	19.2	18.6	18.0
7	22.4	21.7	21.0
8	25.6	24.8	24.0
9	28.8	27.9	27.0

	29	6	5
2	5.8	1.2	1.0
3	8.7	1.8	1.5
4	11.6	2.4	2.0
5	14.5	3.0	2.5
6	17.4	3.6	3.0
7	20.3	4.2	3.5
8	23.2	4.8	4.0
9	26.1	5.4	4.5

From the top:

For **22°+** or **202°+**, read as printed; for **112°+** or **292°+**, read co-function.

From the bottom:

For **67°+** or **247°+**, read as printed; for **157°+** or **337°+**, read co-function.

67° — Logarithms of Trigonometric Functions

′	L Sin	d	L Tan	cd	L Ctn	L Cos	d	
0	9.59 188	30	9.62 785	35	10.37 215	9.96 403	6	**60**
1	9.59 218	29	9.62 820	35	10.37 180	9.96 397	5	59
2	9.59 247	30	9.62 855	35	10.37 145	9.96 392	5	58
3	9.59 277	30	9.62 890	36	10.37 110	9.96 387	6	57
4	9.59 307	29	9.62 926	35	10.37 074	9.96 381	5	56
5	9.59 336	30	9.62 961	35	10.37 039	9.96 376	6	**55**
6	9.59 366	30	9.62 996	35	10.37 004	9.96 370	5	54
7	9.59 396	29	9.63 031	35	10.36 969	9.96 365	5	53
8	9.59 425	30	9.63 066	35	10.36 934	9.96 360	6	52
9	9.59 455	29	9.63 101	34	10.36 899	9.96 354	5	51
10	9.59 484	30	9.63 135	35	10.36 865	9.96 349	6	**50**
11	9.59 514	29	9.63 170	35	10.36 830	9.96 343	5	49
12	9.59 543	30	9.63 205	35	10.36 795	9.96 338	5	48
13	9.59 573	29	9.63 240	35	10.36 760	9.96 333	6	47
14	9.59 602	30	9.63 275	35	10.36 725	9.96 327	5	46
15	9.59 632	29	9.63 310	35	10.36 690	9.96 322	6	**45**
16	9.59 661	29	9.63 345	34	10.36 655	9.96 316	5	44
17	9.59 690	30	9.63 379	35	10.36 621	9.96 311	6	43
18	9.59 720	29	9.63 414	35	10.36 586	9.96 305	5	42
19	9.59 749	29	9.63 449	35	10.36 551	9.96 300	6	41
20	9.59 778	30	9.63 484	35	10.36 516	9.96 294	5	**40**
21	9.59 808	29	9.63 519	34	10.36 481	9.96 289	5	39
22	9.59 837	29	9.63 553	35	10.36 447	9.96 284	6	38
23	9.59 866	29	9.63 588	35	10.36 412	9.96 278	5	37
24	9.59 895	29	9.63 623	34	10.36 377	9.96 273	6	36
25	9.59 924	30	9.63 657	35	10.36 343	9.96 267	5	**35**
26	9.59 954	29	9.63 692	34	10.36 308	9.96 262	6	34
27	9.59 983	29	9.63 726	35	10.36 274	9.96 256	5	33
28	9.60 012	29	9.63 761	35	10.36 239	9.96 251	6	32
29	9.60 041	29	9.63 796	34	10.36 204	9.96 245	5	31
30	9.60 070	29	9.63 830	35	10.36 170	9.96 240	6	**30**
31	9.60 099	29	9.63 865	34	10.36 135	9.96 234	5	29
32	9.60 128	29	9.63 899	35	10.36 101	9.96 229	6	28
33	9.60 157	29	9.63 934	34	10.36 066	9.96 223	5	27
34	9.60 186	29	9.63 968	35	10.36 032	9.96 218	6	26
35	9.60 215	29	9.64 003	34	10.35 997	9.96 212	5	**25**
36	9.60 244	29	9.64 037	35	10.35 963	9.96 207	6	24
37	9.60 273	29	9.64 072	34	10.35 928	9.96 201	5	23
38	9.60 302	29	9.64 106	34	10.35 894	9.96 196	6	22
39	9.60 331	28	9.64 140	35	10.35 860	9.96 190	5	21
40	9.60 359	29	9.64 175	34	10.35 825	9.96 185	6	**20**
41	9.60 388	29	9.64 209	34	10.35 791	9.96 179	5	19
42	9.60 417	29	9.64 243	35	10.35 757	9.96 174	6	18
43	9.60 446	28	9.64 278	34	10.35 722	9.96 168	6	17
44	9.60 474	29	9.64 312	34	10.35 688	9.96 162	5	16
45	9.60 503	29	9.64 346	35	10.35 654	9.96 157	6	**15**
46	9.60 532	29	9.64 381	34	10.35 619	9.96 151	5	14
47	9.60 561	28	9.64 415	34	10.35 585	9.96 146	6	13
48	9.60 589	29	9.64 449	34	10.35 551	9.96 140	5	12
49	9.60 618	28	9.64 483	34	10.35 517	9.96 135	6	11
50	9.60 646	29	9.64 517	35	10.35 483	9.96 129	6	**10**
51	9.60 675	29	9.64 552	34	10.35 448	9.96 123	5	9
52	9.60 704	28	9.64 586	34	10.35 414	9.96 118	6	8
53	9.60 732	29	9.64 620	34	10.35 380	9.96 112	5	7
54	9.60 761	28	9.64 654	34	10.35 346	9.96 107	6	6
55	9.60 789	29	9.64 688	34	10.35 312	9.96 101	6	**5**
56	9.60 818	28	9.64 722	34	10.35 278	9.96 095	5	4
57	9.60 846	29	9.64 756	34	10.35 244	9.96 090	6	3
58	9.60 875	28	9.64 790	34	10.35 210	9.96 084	5	2
59	9.60 903	28	9.64 824	34	10.35 176	9.96 079	6	1
60	9.60 931		9.64 858		10.35 142	9.96 073		**0**
	L Cos	d	L Ctn	cd	L Tan	L Sin	d	′

Prop. Pts.

	36	35
2	7.2	7.0
3	10.8	10.5
4	14.4	14.0
5	18.0	17.5
6	21.6	21.0
7	25.2	24.5
8	28.8	28.0
9	32.4	31.5

	34	30
2	6.8	6.0
3	10.2	9.0
4	13.6	12.0
5	17.0	15.0
6	20.4	18.0
7	23.8	21.0
8	27.2	24.0
9	30.6	27.0

	29	28
2	5.8	5.6
3	8.7	8.4
4	11.6	11.2
5	14.5	14.0
6	17.4	16.8
7	20.3	19.6
8	23.2	22.4
9	26.1	25.2

	6	5
2	1.2	1.0
3	1.8	1.5
4	2.4	2.0
5	3.0	2.5
6	3.6	3.0
7	4.2	3.5
8	4.8	4.0
9	5.4	4.5

From the top:

For **23°+** or **203°+**, read as printed; for **113°+** or **293°+**, read co-function.

From the bottom:

For **66°+** or **246°+**, read as printed; for **156°+** or **336°+**, read co-function.

Prop. Pts.

24° — Logarithms of Trigonometric Functions

′	L Sin	d	L Tan	c d	L Ctn	L Cos	d	
0	9.60 931	29	9.64 858	34	10.35 142	9.96 073	6	**60**
1	9.60 960	28	9.64 892	34	10.35 108	9.96 067	5	59
2	9.60 988	28	9.64 926	34	10.35 074	9.96 062	6	58
3	9.61 016	29	9.64 960	34	10.35 040	9.96 056	6	57
4	9.61 045	28	9.64 994	34	10.35 006	9.96 050	5	56
5	9.61 073	28	9.65 028	34	10.34 972	9.96 045	6	**55**
6	9.61 101	28	9.65 062	34	10.34 938	9.96 039	5	54
7	9.61 129	29	9.65 096	34	10.34 904	9.96 034	6	53
8	9.61 158	28	9.65 130	34	10.34 870	9.96 028	6	52
9	9.61 186	28	9.65 164	33	10.34 836	9.96 022	5	51
10	9.61 214	28	9.65 197	34	10.34 803	9.96 017	6	**50**
11	9.61 242	28	9.65 231	34	10.34 769	9.96 011	6	49
12	9.61 270	28	9.65 265	34	10.34 735	9.96 005	5	48
13	9.61 298	28	9.65 299	34	10.34 701	9.96 000	6	47
14	9.61 326	28	9.65 333	33	10.34 667	9.95 994	6	46
15	9.61 354	28	9.65 366	34	10.34 634	9.95 988	6	**45**
16	9.61 382	29	9.65 400	34	10.34 600	9.95 982	5	44
17	9.61 411	27	9.65 434	33	10.34 566	9.95 977	6	43
18	9.61 438	28	9.65 467	34	10.34 533	9.95 971	6	42
19	9.61 466	28	9.65 501	34	10.34 499	9.95 965	5	41
20	9.61 494	28	9.65 535	33	10.34 465	9.95 960	6	**40**
21	9.61 522	28	9.65 568	34	10.34 432	9.95 954	6	39
22	9.61 550	28	9.65 602	34	10.34 398	9.95 948	6	38
23	9.61 578	28	9.65 636	33	10.34 364	9.95 942	5	37
24	9.61 606	28	9.65 669	34	10.34 331	9.95 937	6	36
25	9.61 634	28	9.65 703	33	10.34 297	9.95 931	6	**35**
26	9.61 662	27	9.65 736	34	10.34 264	9.95 925	5	34
27	9.61 689	28	9.65 770	33	10.34 230	9.95 920	6	33
28	9.61 717	28	9.65 803	34	10.34 197	9.95 914	6	32
29	9.61 745	28	9.65 837	33	10.34 163	9.95 908	6	31
30	9.61 773	27	9.65 870	34	10.34 130	9.95 902	5	**30**
31	9.61 800	28	9.65 904	33	10.34 096	9.95 897	6	29
32	9.61 828	28	9.65 937	34	10.34 063	9.95 891	6	28
33	9.61 856	27	9.65 971	33	10.34 029	9.95 885	6	27
34	9.61 883	28	9.66 004	34	10.33 996	9.95 879	6	26
35	9.61 911	28	9.66 038	33	10.33 962	9.95 873	5	**25**
36	9.61 939	27	9.66 071	33	10.33 929	9.95 868	6	24
37	9.61 966	28	9.66 104	34	10.33 896	9.95 862	6	23
38	9.61 994	27	9.66 138	33	10.33 862	9.95 856	6	22
39	9.62 021	28	9.66 171	33	10.33 829	9.95 850	6	21
40	9.62 049	27	9.66 204	34	10.33 796	9.95 844	5	**20**
41	9.62 076	28	9.66 238	33	10.33 762	9.95 839	6	19
42	9.62 104	27	9.66 271	33	10.33 729	9.95 833	6	18
43	9.62 131	28	9.66 304	33	10.33 696	9.95 827	6	17
44	9.62 159	27	9.66 337	34	10.33 663	9.95 821	6	16
45	9.62 186	28	9.66 371	33	10.33 629	9.95 815	5	**15**
46	9.62 214	27	9.66 404	33	10.33 596	9.95 810	6	14
47	9.62 241	27	9.66 437	33	10.33 563	9.95 804	6	13
48	9.62 268	28	9.66 470	33	10.33 530	9.95 798	6	12
49	9.62 296	27	9.66 503	34	10.33 497	9.95 792	6	11
50	9.62 323	27	9.66 537	33	10.33 463	9.95 786	6	**10**
51	9.62 350	27	9.66 570	33	10.33 430	9.95 780	5	9
52	9.62 377	28	9.66 603	33	10.33 397	9.95 775	6	8
53	9.62 405	27	9.66 636	33	10.33 364	9.95 769	6	7
54	9.62 432	27	9.66 669	33	10.33 331	9.95 763	6	6
55	9.62 459	27	9.66 702	33	10.33 298	9.95 757	6	**5**
56	9.62 486	27	9.66 735	33	10.33 265	9.95 751	6	4
57	9.62 513	28	9.66 768	33	10.33 232	9.95 745	6	3
58	9.62 541	27	9.66 801	33	10.33 199	9.95 739	6	2
59	9.62 568	27	9.66 834	33	10.33 166	9.95 733	5	1
60	9.62 595		9.66 867		10.33 133	9.95 728		**0**
	L Cos	d	L Ctn	c d	L Tan	L Sin	d	′

Prop. Pts.

	34	33
2	6.8	6.6
3	10.2	9.9
4	13.6	13.2
5	17.0	16.5
6	20.4	19.8
7	23.8	23.1
8	27.2	26.4
9	30.6	29.7

	29	28
2	5.8	5.6
3	8.7	8.4
4	11.6	11.2
5	14.5	14.0
6	17.4	16.8
7	20.3	19.6
8	23.2	22.4
9	26.1	25.2

	27	6
2	5.4	1.2
3	8.1	1.8
4	10.8	2.4
5	13.5	3.0
6	16.2	3.6
7	18.9	4.2
8	21.6	4.8
9	24.3	5.4

	5
2	1.0
3	1.5
4	2.0
5	2.5
6	3.0
7	3.5
8	4.0
9	4.5

From the top:

For **24°+** or **204°+**, read as printed; for **114°+** or **294°+**, read co-function.

From the bottom:

For **65°+** or **245°+**, read as printed; for **155°+** or **335°+**, read co-function.

65° — Logarithms of Trigonometric Functions

25° — Logarithms of Trigonometric Functions

′	L Sin	d	L Tan	cd	L Ctn	L Cos	d	
0	9.62 595	27	9.66 867	33	10.33 133	9.95 728	6	60
1	9.62 622	27	9.66 900	33	10.33 100	9.95 722	6	59
2	9.62 649	27	9.66 933	33	10.33 067	9.95 716	6	58
3	9.62 676	27	9.66 966	33	10.33 034	9.95 710	6	57
4	9.62 703	27	9.66 999	33	10.33 001	9.95 704	6	56
5	9.62 730	27	9.67 032	33	10.32 968	9.95 698	6	55
6	9.62 757	27	9.67 065	33	10.32 935	9.95 692	6	54
7	9.62 784	27	9.67 098	33	10.32 902	9.95 686	6	53
8	9.62 811	27	9.67 131	32	10.32 869	9.95 680	6	52
9	9.62 838	27	9.67 163	33	10.32 837	9.95 674	6	51
10	9.62 865	27	9.67 196	33	10.32 804	9.95 668	5	50
11	9.62 892	26	9.67 229	33	10.32 771	9.95 663	6	49
12	9.62 918	27	9.67 262	33	10.32 738	9.95 657	6	48
13	9.62 945	27	9.67 295	32	10.32 705	9.95 651	6	47
14	9.62 972	27	9.67 327	33	10.32 673	9.95 645	6	46
15	9.62 999	27	9.67 360	33	10.32 640	9.95 639	6	45
16	9.63 026	26	9.67 393	33	10.32 607	9.95 633	6	44
17	9.63 052	27	9.67 426	32	10.32 574	9.95 627	6	43
18	9.63 079	27	9.67 458	33	10.32 542	9.95 621	6	42
19	9.63 106	27	9.67 491	33	10.32 509	9.95 615	6	41
20	9.63 133	26	9.67 524	32	10.32 476	9.95 609	6	40
21	9.63 159	27	9.67 556	33	10.32 444	9.95 603	6	39
22	9.63 186	27	9.67 589	33	10.32 411	9.95 597	6	38
23	9.63 213	26	9.67 622	32	10.32 378	9.95 591	6	37
24	9.63 239	27	9.67 654	33	10.32 346	9.95 585	6	36
25	9.63 266	26	9.67 687	32	10.32 313	9.95 579	6	35
26	9.63 292	27	9.67 719	33	10.32 281	9.95 573	6	34
27	9.63 319	26	9.67 752	33	10.32 248	9.95 567	6	33
28	9.63 345	27	9.67 785	32	10.32 215	9.95 561	6	32
29	9.63 372	26	9.67 817	33	10.32 183	9.95 555	6	31
30	9.63 398	27	9.67 850	32	10.32 150	9.95 549	6	30
31	9.63 425	26	9.67 882	33	10.32 118	9.95 543	6	29
32	9.63 451	27	9.67 915	32	10.32 085	9.95 537	6	28
33	9.63 478	26	9.67 947	33	10.32 053	9.95 531	6	27
34	9.63 504	27	9.67 980	32	10.32 020	9.95 525	6	26
35	9.63 531	26	9.68 012	32	10.31 988	9.95 519	6	25
36	9.63 557	26	9.68 044	33	10.31 956	9.95 513	6	24
37	9.63 583	27	9.68 077	32	10.31 923	9.95 507	7	23
38	9.63 610	26	9.68 109	33	10.31 891	9.95 500	6	22
39	9.63 636	26	9.68 142	32	10.31 858	9.95 494	6	21
40	9.63 662	27	9.68 174	32	10.31 826	9.95 488	6	20
41	9.63 689	26	9.68 206	33	10.31 794	9.95 482	6	19
42	9.63 715	26	9.68 239	32	10.31 761	9.95 476	6	18
43	9.63 741	26	9.68 271	32	10.31 729	9.95 470	6	17
44	9.63 767	27	9.68 303	33	10.31 697	9.95 464	6	16
45	9.63 794	26	9.68 336	32	10.31 664	9.95 458	6	15
46	9.63 820	26	9.68 368	32	10.31 632	9.95 452	6	14
47	9.63 846	26	9.68 400	32	10.31 600	9.95 446	6	13
48	9.63 872	26	9.68 432	33	10.31 568	9.95 440	6	12
49	9.63 898	26	9.68 465	32	10.31 535	9.95 434	7	11
50	9.63 924	26	9.68 497	32	10.31 503	9.95 427	6	10
51	9.63 950	26	9.68 529	32	10.31 471	9.95 421	6	9
52	9.63 976	26	9.68 561	32	10.31 439	9.95 415	6	8
53	9.64 002	26	9.68 593	33	10.31 407	9.95 409	6	7
54	9.64 028	26	9.68 626	32	10.31 374	9.95 403	6	6
55	9.64 054	26	9.68 658	32	10.31 342	9.95 397	6	5
56	9.64 080	26	9.68 690	32	10.31 310	9.95 391	7	4
57	9.64 106	26	9.68 722	32	10.31 278	9.95 384	6	3
58	9.64 132	26	9.68 754	32	10.31 246	9.95 378	6	2
59	9.64 158	26	9.68 786	32	10.31 214	9.95 372	6	1
60	9.64 184		9.68 818		10.31 182	9.95 366		0
	L Cos	d	L Ctn	cd	L Tan	L Sin	d	′

Prop. Pts.

	33	32
2	6.6	6.4
3	9.9	9.6
4	13.2	12.8
5	16.5	16.0
6	19.8	19.2
7	23.1	22.4
8	26.4	25.6
9	29.7	28.8

	27	26
2	5.4	5.2
3	8.1	7.8
4	10.8	10.4
5	13.5	13.0
6	16.2	15.6
7	18.9	18.2
8	21.6	20.8
9	24.3	23.4

	7	6
2	1.4	1.2
3	2.1	1.8
4	2.8	2.4
5	3.5	3.0
6	4.2	3.6
7	4.9	4.2
8	5.6	4.8
9	6.3	5.4

	5
2	1.0
3	1.5
4	2.0
5	2.5
6	3.0
7	3.5
8	4.0
9	4.5

From the top:

For **25°+** or **205°+**, read as printed; for **115°+** or **295°+**, read co-function.

From the bottom:

For **64°+** or **244°+**, read as printed; for **154°+** or **334°+**, read co-function.

64° — Logarithms of Trigonometric Functions

26° — Logarithms of Trigonometric Functions

′	L Sin	d	L Tan	cd	L Ctn	L Cos	d	
0	9.64 184	26	9.68 818	32	10.31 182	9.95 366	6	60
1	9.64 210	26	9.68 850	32	10.31 150	9.95 360	6	59
2	9.64 236	26	9.68 882	32	10.31 118	9.95 354	6	58
3	9.64 262	26	9.68 914	32	10.31 086	9.95 348	7	57
4	9.64 288	25	9.68 946	32	10.31 054	9.95 341	6	56
5	9.64 313	26	9.68 978	32	10.31 022	9.95 335	6	55
6	9.64 339	26	9.69 010	32	10.30 990	9.95 329	6	54
7	9.64 365	26	9.69 042	32	10.30 958	9.95 323	6	53
8	9.64 391	26	9.69 074	32	10.30 926	9.95 317	7	52
9	9.64 417	25	9.69 106	32	10.30 894	9.95 310	6	51
10	9.64 442	26	9.69 138	32	10.30 862	9.95 304	6	50
11	9.64 468	26	9.69 170	32	10.30 830	9.95 298	6	49
12	9.64 494	25	9.69 202	32	10.30 798	9.95 292	6	48
13	9.64 519	26	9.69 234	32	10.30 766	9.95 286	7	47
14	9.64 545	26	9.69 266	32	10.30 734	9.95 279	6	46
15	9.64 571	25	9.69 298	31	10.30 702	9.95 273	6	45
16	9.64 596	26	9.69 329	32	10.30 671	9.95 267	6	44
17	9.64 622	25	9.69 361	32	10.30 639	9.95 261	7	43
18	9.64 647	26	9.69 393	32	10.30 607	9.95 254	6	42
19	9.64 673	25	9.69 425	32	10.30 575	9.95 248	6	41
20	9.64 698	26	9.69 457	31	10.30 543	9.95 242	6	40
21	9.64 724	25	9.69 488	32	10.30 512	9.95 236	7	39
22	9.64 749	26	9.69 520	32	10.30 480	9.95 229	6	38
23	9.64 775	25	9.69 552	32	10.30 448	9.95 223	6	37
24	9.64 800	26	9.69 584	31	10.30 416	9.95 217	6	36
25	9.64 826	25	9.69 615	32	10.30 385	9.95 211	7	35
26	9.64 851	26	9.69 647	32	10.30 353	9.95 204	6	34
27	9.64 877	25	9.69 679	31	10.30 321	9.95 198	6	33
28	9.64 902	25	9.69 710	32	10.30 290	9.95 192	7	32
29	9.64 927	26	9.69 742	32	10.30 258	9.95 185	6	31
30	9.64 953	25	9.69 774	31	10.30 226	9.95 179	6	30
31	9.64 978	25	9.69 805	32	10.30 195	9.95 173	6	29
32	9.65 003	26	9.69 837	31	10.30 163	9.95 167	7	28
33	9.65 029	25	9.69 868	32	10.30 132	9.95 160	6	27
34	9.65 054	25	9.69 900	32	10.30 100	9.95 154	6	26
35	9.65 079	25	9.69 932	31	10.30 068	9.95 148	7	25
36	9.65 104	26	9.69 963	32	10.30 037	9.95 141	6	24
37	9.65 130	25	9.69 995	31	10.30 005	9.95 135	6	23
38	9.65 155	25	9.70 026	32	10.29 974	9.95 129	7	22
39	9.65 180	25	9.70 058	31	10.29 942	9.95 122	6	21
40	9.65 205	25	9.70 089	32	10.29 911	9.95 116	6	20
41	9.65 230	25	9.70 121	31	10.29 879	9.95 110	7	19
42	9.65 255	26	9.70 152	32	10.29 848	9.95 103	6	18
43	9.65 281	25	9.70 184	31	10.29 816	9.95 097	7	17
44	9.65 306	25	9.70 215	32	10.29 785	9.95 090	6	16
45	9.65 331	25	9.70 247	31	10.29 753	9.95 084	6	15
46	9.65 356	25	9.70 278	31	10.29 722	9.95 078	7	14
47	9.65 381	25	9.70 309	32	10.29 691	9.95 071	6	13
48	9.65 406	25	9.70 341	31	10.29 659	9.95 065	6	12
49	9.65 431	25	9.70 372	32	10.29 628	9.95 059	7	11
50	9.65 456	25	9.70 404	31	10.29 596	9.95 052	6	10
51	9.65 481	25	9.70 435	31	10.29 565	9.95 046	7	9
52	9.65 506	25	9.70 466	32	10.29 534	9.95 039	6	8
53	9.65 531	25	9.70 498	31	10.29 502	9.95 033	6	7
54	9.65 556	24	9.70 529	31	10.29 471	9.95 027	7	6
55	9.65 580	25	9.70 560	32	10.29 440	9.95 020	6	5
56	9.65 605	25	9.70 592	31	10.29 408	9.95 014	7	4
57	9.65 630	25	9.70 623	31	10.29 377	9.95 007	6	3
58	9.65 655	25	9.70 654	31	10.29 346	9.95 001	6	2
59	9.65 680	25	9.70 685	32	10.29 315	9.94 995	7	1
60	9.65 705		9.70 717		10.29 283	9.94 988		0
	L Cos	d	L Ctn	cd	L Tan	L Sin	d	′

Prop. Pts.

	32	31
2	6.4	6.2
3	9.6	9.3
4	12.8	12.4
5	16.0	15.5
6	19.2	18.6
7	22.4	21.7
8	25.6	24.8
9	28.8	27.9

	26	25
2	5.2	5.0
3	7.8	7.5
4	10.4	10.0
5	13.0	12.5
6	15.6	15.0
7	18.2	17.5
8	20.8	20.0
9	23.4	22.5

	24	7
2	4.8	1.4
3	7.2	2.1
4	9.6	2.8
5	12.0	3.5
6	14.4	4.2
7	16.8	4.9
8	19.2	5.6
9	21.6	6.3

	6
2	1.2
3	1.8
4	2.4
5	3.0
6	3.6
7	4.2
8	4.8
9	5.4

From the top:

For **26°+** or **206°+**, read as printed; for **116°+** or **296°+**, read co-function.

From the bottom:

For **63°+** or **243°+**, read as printed; for **153°+** or **333°+**, read co-function.

Prop. Pts.

63° — Logarithms of Trigonometric Functions

27° — Logarithms of Trigonometric Functions

′	L Sin	d	L Tan	cd	L Ctn	L Cos	d	
0	9.65 705	24	9.70 717	31	10.29 283	9.94 988	6	**60**
1	9.65 729	25	9.70 748	31	10.29 252	9.94 982	7	59
2	9.65 754	25	9.70 779	31	10.29 221	9.94 975	6	58
3	9.65 779	25	9.70 810	31	10.29 190	9.94 969	7	57
4	9.65 804	24	9.70 841	32	10.29 159	9.94 962	6	56
5	9.65 828	25	9.70 873	31	10.29 127	9.94 956	7	**55**
6	9.65 853	25	9.70 904	31	10.29 096	9.94 949	6	54
7	9.65 878	24	9.70 935	31	10.29 065	9.94 943	7	53
8	9.65 902	25	9.70 966	31	10.29 034	9.94 936	6	52
9	9.65 927	25	9.70 997	31	10.29 003	9.94 930	7	51
10	9.65 952	24	9.71 028	31	10.28 972	9.94 923	6	**50**
11	9.65 976	25	9.71 059	31	10.28 941	9.94 917	6	49
12	9.66 001	24	9.71 090	31	10.28 910	9.94 911	7	48
13	9.66 025	25	9.71 121	32	10.28 879	9.94 904	6	47
14	9.66 050	25	9.71 153	31	10.28 847	9.94 898	7	46
15	9.66 075	24	9.71 184	31	10.28 816	9.94 891	6	**45**
16	9.66 099	25	9.71 215	31	10.28 785	9.94 885	7	44
17	9.66 124	24	9.71 246	31	10.28 754	9.94 878	7	43
18	9.66 148	25	9.71 277	31	10.28 723	9.94 871	6	42
19	9.66 173	24	9.71 308	31	10.28 692	9.94 865	7	41
20	9.66 197	24	9.71 339	31	10.28 661	9.94 858	6	**40**
21	9.66 221	25	9.71 370	31	10.28 630	9.94 852	7	39
22	9.66 246	24	9.71 401	30	10.28 599	9.94 845	6	38
23	9.66 270	25	9.71 431	31	10.28 569	9.94 839	7	37
24	9.66 295	24	9.71 462	31	10.28 538	9.94 832	6	36
25	9.66 319	24	9.71 493	31	10.28 507	9.94 826	7	**35**
26	9.66 343	25	9.71 524	31	10.28 476	9.94 819	6	34
27	9.66 368	24	9.71 555	31	10.28 445	9.94 813	7	33
28	9.66 392	24	9.71 586	31	10.28 414	9.94 806	7	32
29	9.66 416	25	9.71 617	31	10.28 383	9.94 799	6	31
30	9.66 441	24	9.71 648	31	10.28 352	9.94 793	7	**30**
31	9.66 465	24	9.71 679	30	10.28 321	9.94 786	6	29
32	9.66 489	24	9.71 709	31	10.28 291	9.94 780	7	28
33	9.66 513	24	9.71 740	31	10.28 260	9.94 773	6	27
34	9.66 537	25	9.71 771	31	10.28 229	9.94 767	7	26
35	9.66 562	24	9.71 802	31	10.28 198	9.94 760	7	**25**
36	9.66 586	24	9.71 833	30	10.28 167	9.94 753	6	24
37	9.66 610	24	9.71 863	31	10.28 137	9.94 747	7	23
38	9.66 634	24	9.71 894	31	10.28 106	9.94 740	6	22
39	9.66 658	24	9.71 925	30	10.28 075	9.94 734	7	21
40	9.66 682	24	9.71 955	31	10.28 045	9.94 727	7	**20**
41	9.66 706	25	9.71 986	31	10.28 014	9.94 720	6	19
42	9.66 731	24	9.72 017	31	10.27 983	9.94 714	7	18
43	9.66 755	24	9.72 048	30	10.27 952	9.94 707	7	17
44	9.66 779	24	9.72 078	31	10.27 922	9.94 700	6	16
45	9.66 803	24	9.72 109	31	10.27 891	9.94 694	7	**15**
46	9.66 827	24	9.72 140	30	10.27 860	9.94 687	7	14
47	9.66 851	24	9.72 170	31	10.27 830	9.94 680	6	13
48	9.66 875	24	9.72 201	30	10.27 799	9.94 674	7	12
49	9.66 899	23	9.72 231	31	10.27 769	9.94 667	7	11
50	9.66 922	24	9.72 262	31	10.27 738	9.94 660	6	**10**
51	9.66 946	24	9.72 293	30	10.27 707	9.94 654	7	9
52	9.66 970	24	9.72 323	31	10.27 677	9.94 647	7	8
53	9.66 994	24	9.72 354	30	10.27 646	9.94 640	6	7
54	9.67 018	24	9.72 384	31	10.27 616	9.94 634	7	6
55	9.67 042	24	9.72 415	30	10.27 585	9.94 627	7	**5**
56	9.67 066	24	9.72 445	31	10.27 555	9.94 620	6	4
57	9.67 090	23	9.72 476	30	10.27 524	9.94 614	7	3
58	9.67 113	24	9.72 506	31	10.27 494	9.94 607	7	2
59	9.67 137	24	9.72 537	30	10.27 463	9.94 600	7	1
60	9.67 161		9.72 567		10.27 433	9.94 593		**0**
	L Cos	d	L Ctn	cd	L Tan	L Sin	d	′

Prop. Pts.

	32	31
2	6.4	6.2
3	9.6	9.3
4	12.8	12.4
5	16.0	15.5
6	19.2	18.6
7	22.4	21.7
8	25.6	24.8
9	28.8	27.9

	30	25
2	6.0	5.0
3	9.0	7.5
4	12.0	10.0
5	15.0	12.5
6	18.0	15.0
7	21.0	17.5
8	24.0	20.0
9	27.0	22.5

	24	23
2	4.8	4.6
3	7.2	6.9
4	9.6	9.2
5	12.0	11.5
6	14.4	13.8
7	16.8	16.1
8	19.2	18.4
9	21.6	20.7

	7	6
2	1.4	1.2
3	2.1	1.8
4	2.8	2.4
5	3.5	3.0
6	4.2	3.6
7	4.9	4.2
8	5.6	4.8
9	6.3	5.4

From the top:

For **27°+** or **207°+**, read as printed; for **117°+** or **297°+**, read co-function.

From the bottom:

For **62°+** or **242°+**, read as printed; for **152°+** or **332°+**, read co-function.

Prop. Pts.

62° — Logarithms of Trigonometric Functions

′	L Sin	d	L Tan	c d	L Ctn	L Cos	d	
0	9.67 161	24	9.72 567	31	10.27 433	9.94 593	6	60
1	9.67 185	23	9.72 598	30	10.27 402	9.94 587	7	59
2	9.67 208	24	9.72 628	31	10.27 372	9.94 580	7	58
3	9.67 232	24	9.72 659	30	10.27 341	9.94 573	6	57
4	9.67 256	24	9.72 689	31	10.27 311	9.94 567	7	56
5	9.67 280	23	9.72 720	30	10.27 280	9.94 560	7	55
6	9.67 303	24	9.72 750	30	10.27 250	9.94 553	7	54
7	9.67 327	23	9.72 780	31	10.27 220	9.94 546	6	53
8	9.67 350	24	9.72 811	30	10.27 189	9.94 540	7	52
9	9.67 374	24	9.72 841	31	10.27 159	9.94 533	7	51
10	9.67 398	23	9.72 872	30	10.27 128	9.94 526	7	50
11	9.67 421	24	9.72 902	30	10.27 098	9.94 519	6	49
12	9.67 445	23	9.72 932	31	10.27 068	9.94 513	7	48
13	9.67 468	24	9.72 963	30	10.27 037	9.94 506	7	47
14	9.67 492	23	9.72 993	30	10.27 007	9.94 499	7	46
15	9.67 515	24	9.73 023	31	10.26 977	9.94 492	7	45
16	9.67 539	23	9.73 054	30	10.26 946	9.94 485	6	44
17	9.67 562	24	9.73 084	30	10.26 916	9.94 479	7	43
18	9.67 586	23	9.73 114	30	10.26 886	9.94 472	7	42
19	9.67 609	24	9.73 144	31	10.26 856	9.94 465	7	41
20	9.67 633	23	9.73 175	30	10.26 825	9.94 458	7	40
21	9.67 656	24	9.73 205	30	10.26 795	9.94 451	6	39
22	9.67 680	23	9.73 235	30	10.26 765	9.94 445	7	38
23	9.67 703	23	9.73 265	30	10.26 735	9.94 438	7	37
24	9.67 726	24	9.73 295	31	10.26 705	9.94 431	7	36
25	9.67 750	23	9.73 326	30	10.26 674	9.94 424	7	35
26	9.67 773	23	9.73 356	30	10.26 644	9.94 417	7	34
27	9.67 796	24	9.73 386	30	10.26 614	9.94 410	6	33
28	9.67 820	23	9.73 416	30	10.26 584	9.94 404	7	32
29	9.67 843	23	9.73 446	30	10.26 554	9.94 397	7	31
30	9.67 866	24	9.73 476	31	10.26 524	9.94 390	7	30
31	9.67 890	23	9.73 507	30	10.26 493	9.94 383	7	29
32	9.67 913	23	9.73 537	30	10.26 463	9.94 376	7	28
33	9.67 936	23	9.73 567	30	10.26 433	9.94 369	7	27
34	9.67 959	23	9.73 597	30	10.26 403	9.94 362	7	26
35	9.67 982	24	9.73 627	30	10.26 373	9.94 355	6	25
36	9.68 006	23	9.73 657	30	10.26 343	9.94 349	7	24
37	9.68 029	23	9.73 687	30	10.26 313	9.94 342	7	23
38	9.68 052	23	9.73 717	30	10.26 283	9.94 335	7	22
39	9.68 075	23	9.73 747	30	10.26 253	9.94 328	7	21
40	9.68 098	23	9.73 777	30	10.26 223	9.94 321	7	20
41	9.68 121	23	9.73 807	30	10.26 193	9.94 314	7	19
42	9.68 144	23	9.73 837	30	10.26 163	9.94 307	7	18
43	9.68 167	23	9.73 867	30	10.26 133	9.94 300	7	17
44	9.68 190	23	9.73 897	30	10.26 103	9.94 293	7	16
45	9.68 213	24	9.73 927	30	10.26 073	9.94 286	7	15
46	9.68 237	23	9.73 957	30	10.26 043	9.94 279	6	14
47	9.68 260	23	9.73 987	30	10.26 013	9.94 273	7	13
48	9.68 283	22	9.74 017	30	10.25 983	9.94 266	7	12
49	9.68 305	23	9.74 047	30	10.25 953	9.94 259	7	11
50	9.68 328	23	9.74 077	30	10.25 923	9.94 252	7	10
51	9.68 351	23	9.74 107	30	10.25 893	9.94 245	7	9
52	9.68 374	23	9.74 137	29	10.25 863	9.94 238	7	8
53	9.68 397	23	9.74 166	30	10.25 834	9.94 231	7	7
54	9.68 420	23	9.74 196	30	10.25 804	9.94 224	7	6
55	9.68 443	23	9.74 226	30	10.25 774	9.94 217	7	5
56	9.68 466	23	9.74 256	30	10.25 744	9.94 210	7	4
57	9.68 489	23	9.74 286	30	10.25 714	9.94 203	7	3
58	9.68 512	22	9.74 316	29	10.25 684	9.94 196	7	2
59	9.68 534	23	9.74 345	30	10.25 655	9.94 189	7	1
60	9.68 557		9.74 375		10.25 625	9.94 182		0
	L Cos	d	L Ctn	c d	L Tan	L Sin	d	′

Prop. Pts.

	31	30
2	6.2	6.0
3	9.3	9.0
4	12.4	12.0
5	15.5	15.0
6	18.6	18.0
7	21.7	21.0
8	24.8	24.0
9	27.9	27.0

	29	24
2	5.8	4.8
3	8.7	7.2
4	11.6	9.6
5	14.5	12.0
6	17.4	14.4
7	20.3	16.8
8	23.2	19.2
9	26.1	21.6

	23	22
2	4.6	4.4
3	6.9	6.6
4	9.2	8.8
5	11.5	11.0
6	13.8	13.2
7	16.1	15.4
8	18.4	17.6
9	20.7	19.8

	7	6
2	1.4	1.2
3	2.1	1.8
4	2.8	2.4
5	3.5	3.0
6	4.2	3.6
7	4.9	4.2
8	5.6	4.8
9	6.3	5.4

From the top:

For **28°+** or **208°+**, read as printed; for **118°+** or **298°+**, read co-function.

From the bottom:

For **61°+** or **241°+**, read as printed; for **151°+** or **331°+**, read co-function.

Prop. Pts.

29° — Logarithms of Trigonometric Functions

′	L Sin	d	L Tan	cd	L Ctn	L Cos	d	
0	9.68 557	23	9.74 375	30	10.25 625	9.94 182	7	**60**
1	9.68 580	23	9.74 405	30	10.25 595	9.94 175	7	59
2	9.68 603	22	9.74 435	30	10.25 565	9.94 168	7	58
3	9.68 625	23	9.74 465	29	10.25 535	9.94 161	7	57
4	9.68 648	23	9.74 494	30	10.25 506	9.94 154	7	56
5	9.68 671	23	9.74 524	30	10.25 476	9.94 147	7	**55**
6	9.68 694	22	9.74 554	29	10.25 446	9.94 140	7	54
7	9.68 716	23	9.74 583	30	10.25 417	9.94 133	7	53
8	9.68 739	23	9.74 613	30	10.25 387	9.94 126	7	52
9	9.68 762	22	9.74 643	30	10.25 357	9.94 119	7	51
10	9.68 784	23	9.74 673	29	10.25 327	9.94 112	7	**50**
11	9.68 807	22	9.74 702	30	10.25 298	9.94 105	7	49
12	9.68 829	23	9.74 732	30	10.25 268	9.94 098	8	48
13	9.68 852	23	9.74 762	29	10.25 238	9.94 090	7	47
14	9.68 875	22	9.74 791	30	10.25 209	9.94 083	7	46
15	9.68 897	23	9.74 821	30	10.25 179	9.94 076	7	**45**
16	9.68 920	22	9.74 851	29	10.25 149	9.94 069	7	44
17	9.68 942	23	9.74 880	30	10.25 120	9.94 062	7	43
18	9.68 965	22	9.74 910	29	10.25 090	9.94 055	7	42
19	9.68 987	23	9.74 939	30	10.25 061	9.94 048	7	41
20	9.69 010	22	9.74 969	29	10.25 031	9.94 041	7	**40**
21	9.69 032	23	9.74 998	30	10.25 002	9.94 034	7	39
22	9.69 055	22	9.75 028	30	10.24 972	9.94 027	7	38
23	9.69 077	23	9.75 058	29	10.24 942	9.94 020	8	37
24	9.69 100	22	9.75 087	30	10.24 913	9.94 012	7	36
25	9.69 122	22	9.75 117	29	10.24 883	9.94 005	7	**35**
26	9.69 144	23	9.75 146	30	10.24 854	9.93 998	7	34
27	9.69 167	22	9.75 176	29	10.24 824	9.93 991	7	33
28	9.69 189	23	9.75 205	30	10.24 795	9.93 984	7	32
29	9.69 212	22	9.75 235	29	10.24 765	9.93 977	7	31
30	9.69 234	22	9.75 264	30	10.24 736	9.93 970	7	**30**
31	9.69 256	23	9.75 294	29	10.24 706	9.93 963	8	29
32	9.69 279	22	9.75 323	30	10.24 677	9.93 955	7	28
33	9.69 301	22	9.75 353	29	10.24 647	9.93 948	7	27
34	9.69 323	22	9.75 382	29	10.24 618	9.93 941	7	26
35	9.69 345	23	9.75 411	30	10.24 589	9.93 934	7	**25**
36	9.69 368	22	9.75 441	29	10.24 559	9.93 927	7	24
37	9.69 390	22	9.75 470	30	10.24 530	9.93 920	8	23
38	9.69 412	22	9.75 500	29	10.24 500	9.93 912	7	22
39	9.69 434	22	9.75 529	29	10.24 471	9.93 905	7	21
40	9.69 456	23	9.75 558	30	10.24 442	9.93 898	7	**20**
41	9.69 479	22	9.75 588	29	10.24 412	9.93 891	7	19
42	9.69 501	22	9.75 617	30	10.24 383	9.93 884	8	18
43	9.69 523	22	9.75 647	29	10.24 353	9.93 876	7	17
44	9.69 545	22	9.75 676	29	10.24 324	9.93 869	7	16
45	9.69 567	22	9.75 705	30	10.24 295	9.93 862	7	**15**
46	9.69 589	22	9.75 735	29	10.24 265	9.93 855	8	14
47	9.69 611	22	9.75 764	29	10.24 236	9.93 847	7	13
48	9.69 633	22	9.75 793	29	10.24 207	9.93 840	7	12
49	9.69 655	22	9.75 822	30	10.24 178	9.93 833	7	11
50	9.69 677	22	9.75 852	29	10.24 148	9.93 826	7	**10**
51	9.69 699	22	9.75 881	29	10.24 119	9.93 819	8	9
52	9.69 721	22	9.75 910	29	10.24 090	9.93 811	7	8
53	9.69 743	22	9.75 939	30	10.24 061	9.93 804	7	7
54	9.69 765	22	9.75 969	29	10.24 031	9.93 797	8	6
55	9.69 787	22	9.75 998	29	10.24 002	9.93 789	7	**5**
56	9.69 809	22	9.76 027	29	10.23 973	9.93 782	7	4
57	9.69 831	22	9.76 056	30	10.23 944	9.93 775	7	3
58	9.69 853	22	9.76 086	29	10.23 914	9.93 768	8	2
59	9.69 875	22	9.76 115	29	10.23 885	9.93 760	7	1
60	9.69 897		9.76 144		10.23 856	9.93 753		**0**
	L Cos	d	L Ctn	cd	L Tan	L Sin	d	′

Prop. Pts.

	30	29
2	6.0	5.8
3	9.0	8.7
4	12.0	11.6
5	15.0	14.5
6	18.0	17.4
7	21.0	20.3
8	24.0	23.2
9	27.0	26.1

	23	22
2	4.6	4.4
3	6.9	6.6
4	9.2	8.8
5	11.5	11.0
6	13.8	13.2
7	16.1	15.4
8	18.4	17.6
9	20.7	19.8

	8	7
2	1.6	1.4
3	2.4	2.1
4	3.2	2.8
5	4.0	3.5
6	4.8	4.2
7	5.6	4.9
8	6.4	5.6
9	7.2	6.3

From the top:

For **29°+** or **209°+**, read as printed; for **119°+** or **299°+**, read co-function.

From the bottom:

For **60°+** or **240°+**, read as printed; for **150°+** or **330°+**, read co-function.

Prop. Pts.

60° — Logarithms of Trigonometric Functions

30° — Logarithms of Trigonometric Functions

′	L Sin	d	L Tan	cd	L Ctn	L Cos	d	
0	9.69 897	22	9.76 144	29	10.23 856	9.93 753	7	**60**
1	9.69 919	22	9.76 173	29	10.23 827	9.93 746	8	59
2	9.69 941	22	9.76 202	29	10.23 798	9.93 738	7	58
3	9.69 963	21	9.76 231	30	10.23 769	9.93 731	7	57
4	9.69 984	22	9.76 261	29	10.23 739	9.93 724	7	56
5	9.70 006	22	9.76 290	29	10.23 710	9.93 717	8	**55**
6	9.70 028	22	9.76 319	29	10.23 681	9.93 709	7	54
7	9.70 050	22	9.76 348	29	10.23 652	9.93 702	7	53
8	9.70 072	21	9.76 377	29	10.23 623	9.93 695	8	52
9	9.70 093	22	9.76 406	29	10.23 594	9.93 687	7	51
10	9.70 115	22	9.76 435	29	10.23 565	9.93 680	7	**50**
11	9.70 137	22	9.76 464	29	10.23 536	9.93 673	8	49
12	9.70 159	21	9.76 493	29	10.23 507	9.93 665	7	48
13	9.70 180	22	9.76 522	29	10.23 478	9.93 658	8	47
14	9.70 202	22	9.76 551	29	10.23 449	9.93 650	7	46
15	9.70 224	21	9.76 580	29	10.23 420	9.93 643	7	**45**
16	9.70 245	22	9.76 609	30	10.23 391	9.93 636	8	44
17	9.70 267	21	9.76 639	29	10.23 361	9.93 628	7	43
18	9.70 288	22	9.76 668	29	10.23 332	9.93 621	7	42
19	9.70 310	22	9.76 697	28	10.23 303	9.93 614	8	41
20	9.70 332	21	9.76 725	29	10.23 275	9.93 606	7	**40**
21	9.70 353	22	9.76 754	29	10.23 246	9.93 599	8	39
22	9.70 375	21	9.76 783	29	10.23 217	9.93 591	7	38
23	9.70 396	22	9.76 812	29	10.23 188	9.93 584	7	37
24	9.70 418	21	9.76 841	29	10.23 159	9.93 577	8	36
25	9.70 439	22	9.76 870	29	10.23 130	9.93 569	7	**35**
26	9.70 461	21	9.76 899	29	10.23 101	9.93 562	8	34
27	9.70 482	22	9.76 928	29	10.23 072	9.93 554	7	33
28	9.70 504	21	9.76 957	29	10.23 043	9.93 547	8	32
29	9.70 525	22	9.76 986	29	10.23 014	9.93 539	7	31
30	9.70 547	21	9.77 015	29	10.22 985	9.93 532	7	**30**
31	9.70 568	22	9.77 044	29	10.22 956	9.93 525	8	29
32	9.70 590	21	9.77 073	28	10.22 927	9.93 517	7	28
33	9.70 611	22	9.77 101	29	10.22 899	9.93 510	8	27
34	9.70 633	21	9.77 130	29	10.22 870	9.93 502	7	26
35	9.70 654	21	9.77 159	29	10.22 841	9.93 495	8	**25**
36	9.70 675	22	9.77 188	29	10.22 812	9.93 487	7	24
37	9.70 697	21	9.77 217	29	10.22 783	9.93 480	8	23
38	9.70 718	21	9.77 246	28	10.22 754	9.93 472	7	22
39	9.70 739	22	9.77 274	29	10.22 726	9.93 465	8	21
40	9.70 761	21	9.77 303	29	10.22 697	9.93 457	7	**20**
41	9.70 782	21	9.77 332	29	10.22 668	9.93 450	8	19
42	9.70 803	21	9.77 361	29	10.22 639	9.93 442	7	18
43	9.70 824	22	9.77 390	28	10.22 610	9.93 435	8	17
44	9.70 846	21	9.77 418	29	10.22 582	9.93 427	7	16
45	9.70 867	21	9.77 447	29	10.22 553	9.93 420	8	**15**
46	9.70 888	21	9.77 476	29	10.22 524	9.93 412	7	14
47	9.70 909	22	9.77 505	28	10.22 495	9.93 405	8	13
48	9.70 931	21	9.77 533	29	10.22 467	9.93 397	7	12
49	9.70 952	21	9.77 562	29	10.22 438	9.93 390	8	11
50	9.70 973	21	9.77 591	28	10.22 409	9.93 382	7	**10**
51	9.70 994	21	9.77 619	29	10.22 381	9.93 375	8	9
52	9.71 015	21	9.77 648	29	10.22 352	9.93 367	7	8
53	9.71 036	22	9.77 677	29	10.22 323	9.93 360	8	7
54	9.71 058	21	9.77 706	28	10.22 294	9.93 352	8	6
55	9.71 079	21	9.77 734	29	10.22 266	9.93 344	7	**5**
56	9.71 100	21	9.77 763	28	10.22 237	9.93 337	8	4
57	9.71 121	21	9.77 791	29	10.22 209	9.93 329	7	3
58	9.71 142	21	9.77 820	29	10.22 180	9.93 322	8	2
59	9.71 163	21	9.77 849	28	10.22 151	9.93 314	7	1
60	9.71 184		9.77 877		10.22 123	9.93 307		**0**
	L Cos	d	L Ctn	cd	L Tan	L Sin	d	′

Prop. Pts.

	30	29
2	6.0	5.8
3	9.0	8.7
4	12.0	11.6
5	15.0	14.5
6	18.0	17.4
7	21.0	20.3
8	24.0	23.2
9	27.0	26.1

	28	22
2	5.6	4.4
3	8.4	6.6
4	11.2	8.8
5	14.0	11.0
6	16.8	13.2
7	19.6	15.4
8	22.4	17.6
9	25.2	19.8

	21	8
2	4.2	1.6
3	6.3	2.4
4	8.4	3.2
5	10.5	4.0
6	12.6	4.8
7	14.7	5.6
8	16.8	6.4
9	18.9	7.2

	7
2	1.4
3	2.1
4	2.8
5	3.5
6	4.2
7	4.9
8	5.6
9	6.3

From the top:

For **30°+** or **210°+**, read as printed; for **120°+** or **300°+**, read co-function.

From the bottom:

For **59°+** or **239°+**, read as printed; for **149°+** or **329°+**, read co-function.

Prop. Pts.

59° — Logarithms of Trigonometric Functions

′	L Sin	d	L Tan	c d	L Ctn	L Cos	d	
0	9.71 184	21	9.77 877	29	10.22 123	9.93 307	8	60
1	9.71 205	21	9.77 906	29	10.22 094	9.93 299	8	59
2	9.71 226	21	9.77 935	28	10.22 065	9.93 291	7	58
3	9.71 247	21	9.77 963	29	10.22 037	9.93 284	8	57
4	9.71 268	21	9.77 992	28	10.22 008	9.93 276	7	56
5	9.71 289	21	9.78 020	29	10.21 980	9.93 269	8	55
6	9.71 310	21	9.78 049	28	10.21 951	9.93 261	8	54
7	9.71 331	21	9.78 077	29	10.21 923	9.93 253	7	53
8	9.71 352	21	9.78 106	29	10.21 894	9.93 246	8	52
9	9.71 373	20	9.78 135	28	10.21 865	9.93 238	8	51
10	9.71 393	21	9.78 163	29	10.21 837	9.93 230	7	50
11	9.71 414	21	9.78 192	28	10.21 808	9.93 223	8	49
12	9.71 435	21	9.78 220	29	10.21 780	9.93 215	8	48
13	9.71 456	21	9.78 249	28	10.21 751	9.93 207	7	47
14	9.71 477	21	9.78 277	29	10.21 723	9.93 200	8	46
15	9.71 498	21	9.78 306	28	10.21 694	9.93 192	8	45
16	9.71 519	20	9.78 334	29	10.21 666	9.93 184	7	44
17	9.71 539	21	9.78 363	28	10.21 637	9.93 177	8	43
18	9.71 560	21	9.78 391	28	10.21 609	9.93 169	8	42
19	9.71 581	21	9.78 419	29	10.21 581	9.93 161	7	41
20	9.71 602	20	9.78 448	28	10.21 552	9.93 154	8	40
21	9.71 622	21	9.78 476	29	10.21 524	9.93 146	8	39
22	9.71 643	21	9.78 505	28	10.21 495	9.93 138	7	38
23	9.71 664	21	9.78 533	29	10.21 467	9.93 131	8	37
24	9.71 685	20	9.78 562	28	10.21 438	9.93 123	8	36
25	9.71 705	21	9.78 590	28	10.21 410	9.93 115	7	35
26	9.71 726	21	9.78 618	29	10.21 382	9.93 108	8	34
27	9.71 747	20	9.78 647	28	10.21 353	9.93 100	8	33
28	9.71 767	21	9.78 675	29	10.21 325	9.93 092	8	32
29	9.71 788	21	9.78 704	28	10.21 296	9.93 084	7	31
30	9.71 809	20	9.78 732	28	10.21 268	9.93 077	8	30
31	9.71 829	21	9.78 760	29	10.21 240	9.93 069	8	29
32	9.71 850	20	9.78 789	28	10.21 211	9.93 061	8	28
33	9.71 870	21	9.78 817	28	10.21 183	9.93 053	7	27
34	9.71 891	20	9.78 845	29	10.21 155	9.93 046	8	26
35	9.71 911	21	9.78 874	28	10.21 126	9.93 038	8	25
36	9.71 932	20	9.78 902	28	10.21 098	9.93 030	8	24
37	9.71 952	21	9.78 930	29	10.21 070	9.93 022	8	23
38	9.71 973	21	9.78 959	28	10.21 041	9.93 014	7	22
39	9.71 994	20	9.78 987	28	10.21 013	9.93 007	8	21
40	9.72 014	20	9.79 015	28	10.20 985	9.92 999	8	20
41	9.72 034	21	9.79 043	29	10.20 957	9.92 991	8	19
42	9.72 055	20	9.79 072	28	10.20 928	9.92 983	7	18
43	9.72 075	21	9.79 100	28	10.20 900	9.92 976	8	17
44	9.72 096	20	9.79 128	28	10.20 872	9.92 968	8	16
45	9.72 116	21	9.79 156	29	10.20 844	9.92 960	8	15
46	9.72 137	20	9.79 185	28	10.20 815	9.92 952	8	14
47	9.72 157	20	9.79 213	28	10.20 787	9.92 944	8	13
48	9.72 177	21	9.79 241	28	10.20 759	9.92 936	7	12
49	9.72 198	20	9.79 269	28	10.20 731	9.92 929	8	11
50	9.72 218	20	9.79 297	29	10.20 703	9.92 921	8	10
51	9.72 238	21	9.79 326	28	10.20 674	9.92 913	8	9
52	9.72 259	20	9.79 354	28	10.20 646	9.92 905	8	8
53	9.72 279	20	9.79 382	28	10.20 618	9.92 897	8	7
54	9.72 299	21	9.79 410	28	10.20 590	9.92 889	8	6
55	9.72 320	20	9.79 438	28	10.20 562	9.92 881	7	5
56	9.72 340	20	9.79 466	29	10.20 534	9.92 874	8	4
57	9.72 360	21	9.79 495	28	10.20 505	9.92 866	8	3
58	9.72 381	20	9.79 523	28	10.20 477	9.92 858	8	2
59	9.72 401	20	9.79 551	28	10.20 449	9.92 850	8	1
60	9.72 421		9.79 579		10.20 421	9.92 842		0
	L Cos	d	L Ctn	c d	L Tan	L Sin	d	′

Prop. Pts.

	29	28
2	5.8	5.6
3	8.7	8.4
4	11.6	11.2
5	14.5	14.0
6	17.4	16.8
7	20.3	19.6
8	23.2	22.4
9	26.1	25.2

	21	20
2	4.2	4.0
3	6.3	6.0
4	8.4	8.0
5	10.5	10.0
6	12.6	12.0
7	14.7	14.0
8	16.8	16.0
9	18.9	18.0

	8	7
2	1.6	1.4
3	2.4	2.1
4	3.2	2.8
5	4.0	3.5
6	4.8	4.2
7	5.6	4.9
8	6.4	5.6
9	7.2	6.3

From the top:

For **31°+** or **211°+**, read as printed; for **121°+** or **301°+**, read co-function.

From the bottom:

For **58°+** or **238°+**, read as printed; for **148°+** or **328°+**, read co-function.

Prop. Pts.

32° — Logarithms of Trigonometric Functions

′	L Sin	d	L Tan	cd	L Ctn	L Cos	d	′
0	9.72 421	20	9.79 579	28	10.20 421	9.92 842	8	**60**
1	9.72 441	20	9.79 607	28	10.20 393	9.92 834	8	59
2	9.72 461	21	9.79 635	28	10.20 365	9.92 826	8	58
3	9.72 482	20	9.79 663	28	10.20 337	9.92 818	8	57
4	9.72 502	20	9.79 691	28	10.20 309	9.92 810	7	56
5	9.72 522	20	9.79 719	28	10.20 281	9.92 803	8	**55**
6	9.72 542	20	9.79 747	29	10.20 253	9.92 795	8	54
7	9.72 562	20	9.79 776	28	10.20 224	9.92 787	8	53
8	9.72 582	20	9.79 804	28	10.20 196	9.92 779	8	52
9	9.72 602	20	9.79 832	28	10.20 168	9.92 771	8	51
10	9.72 622	21	9.79 860	28	10.20 140	9.92 763	8	**50**
11	9.72 643	20	9.79 888	28	10.20 112	9.92 755	8	49
12	9.72 663	20	9.79 916	28	10.20 084	9.92 747	8	48
13	9.72 683	20	9.79 944	28	10.20 056	9.92 739	8	47
14	9.72 703	20	9.79 972	28	10.20 028	9.92 731	8	46
15	9.72 723	20	9.80 000	28	10.20 000	9.92 723	8	**45**
16	9.72 743	20	9.80 028	28	10.19 972	9.92 715	8	44
17	9.72 763	20	9.80 056	28	10.19 944	9.92 707	8	43
18	9.72 783	20	9.80 084	28	10.19 916	9.92 699	8	42
19	9.72 803	20	9.80 112	28	10.19 888	9.92 691	8	41
20	9.72 823	20	9.80 140	28	10.19 860	9.92 683	8	**40**
21	9.72 843	20	9.80 168	27	10.19 832	9.92 675	8	39
22	9.72 863	20	9.80 195	28	10.19 805	9.92 667	8	38
23	9.72 883	19	9.80 223	28	10.19 777	9.92 659	8	37
24	9.72 902	20	9.80 251	28	10.19 749	9.92 651	8	36
25	9.72 922	20	9.80 279	28	10.19 721	9.92 643	8	**35**
26	9.72 942	20	9.80 307	28	10.19 693	9.92 635	8	34
27	9.72 962	20	9.80 335	28	10.19 665	9.92 627	8	33
28	9.72 982	20	9.80 363	28	10.19 637	9.92 619	8	32
29	9.73 002	20	9.80 391	28	10.19 609	9.92 611	8	31
30	9.73 022	19	9.80 419	28	10.19 581	9.92 603	8	**30**
31	9.73 041	20	9.80 447	27	10.19 553	9.92 595	8	29
32	9.73 061	20	9.80 474	28	10.19 526	9.92 587	8	28
33	9.73 081	20	9.80 502	28	10.19 498	9.92 579	8	27
34	9.73 101	20	9.80 530	28	10.19 470	9.92 571	8	26
35	9.73 121	19	9.80 558	28	10.19 442	9.92 563	8	**25**
36	9.73 140	20	9.80 586	28	10.19 414	9.92 555	9	24
37	9.73 160	20	9.80 614	28	10.19 386	9.92 546	8	23
38	9.73 180	20	9.80 642	27	10.19 358	9.92 538	8	22
39	9.73 200	19	9.80 669	28	10.19 331	9.92 530	8	21
40	9.73 219	20	9.80 697	28	10.19 303	9.92 522	8	**20**
41	9.73 239	20	9.80 725	28	10.19 275	9.92 514	8	19
42	9.73 259	19	9.80 753	28	10.19 247	9.92 506	8	18
43	9.73 278	20	9.80 781	27	10.19 219	9.92 498	8	17
44	9.73 298	20	9.80 808	28	10.19 192	9.92 490	8	16
45	9.73 318	19	9.80 836	28	10.19 164	9.92 482	9	**15**
46	9.73 337	20	9.80 864	28	10.19 136	9.92 473	8	14
47	9.73 357	20	9.80 892	27	10.19 108	9.92 465	8	13
48	9.73 377	19	9.80 919	28	10.19 081	9.92 457	8	12
49	9.73 396	20	9.80 947	28	10.19 053	9.92 449	8	11
50	9.73 416	19	9.80 975	28	10.19 025	9.92 441	8	**10**
51	9.73 435	20	9.81 003	27	10.18 997	9.92 433	8	9
52	9.73 455	19	9.81 030	28	10.18 970	9.92 425	9	8
53	9.73 474	20	9.81 058	28	10.18 942	9.92 416	8	7
54	9.73 494	19	9.81 086	27	10.18 914	9.92 408	8	6
55	9.73 513	20	9.81 113	28	10.18 887	9.92 400	8	**5**
56	9.73 533	19	9.81 141	28	10.18 859	9.92 392	8	4
57	9.73 552	20	9.81 169	27	10.18 831	9.92 384	8	3
58	9.73 572	19	9.81 196	28	10.18 804	9.92 376	9	2
59	9.73 591	20	9.81 224	28	10.18 776	9.92 367	8	1
60	9.73 611		9.81 252		10.18 748	9.92 359		**0**
	L Cos	d	L Ctn	cd	L Tan	L Sin	d	′

Prop. Pts.

	29	**28**
2	5.8	5.6
3	8.7	8.4
4	11.6	11.2
5	14.5	14.0
6	17.4	16.8
7	20.3	19.6
8	23.2	22.4
9	26.1	25.2

	27	**21**
2	5.4	4.2
3	8.1	6.3
4	10.8	8.4
5	13.5	10.5
6	16.2	12.6
7	18.9	14.7
8	21.6	16.8
9	24.3	18.9

	20	**19**
2	4.0	3.8
3	6.0	5.7
4	8.0	7.6
5	10.0	9.5
6	12.0	11.4
7	14.0	13.3
8	16.0	15.2
9	18.0	17.1

	9	**8**	**7**
2	1.8	1.6	1.4
3	2.7	2.4	2.1
4	3.6	3.2	2.8
5	4.5	4.0	3.5
6	5.4	4.8	4.2
7	6.3	5.6	4.9
8	7.2	6.4	5.6
9	8.1	7.2	6.3

From the top:

For **32°+** or **212°+**, read as printed; for **122°+** or **302°+**, read co-function.

From the bottom:

For **57°+** or **237°+**, read as printed; for **147°+** or **327°+**, read co-function.

Prop. Pts.

57° — Logarithms of Trigonometric Functions

′	L Sin	d	L Tan	cd	L Ctn	L Cos	d	
0	9.73 611	19	9.81 252	27	10.18 748	9.92 359	8	60
1	9.73 630	20	9.81 279	28	10.18 721	9.92 351	8	59
2	9.73 650	19	9.81 307	28	10.18 693	9.92 343	8	58
3	9.73 669	20	9.81 335	27	10.18 665	9.92 335	9	57
4	9.73 689	19	9.81 362	28	10.18 638	9.92 326	8	56
5	9.73 708	19	9.81 390	28	10.18 610	9.92 318	8	55
6	9.73 727	20	9.81 418	27	10.18 582	9.92 310	8	54
7	9.73 747	19	9.81 445	28	10.18 555	9.92 302	9	53
8	9.73 766	19	9.81 473	27	10.18 527	9.92 293	8	52
9	9.73 785	20	9.81 500	28	10.18 500	9.92 285	8	51
10	9.73 805	19	9.81 528	28	10.18 472	9.92 277	8	50
11	9.73 824	19	9.81 556	27	10.18 444	9.92 269	9	49
12	9.73 843	20	9.81 583	28	10.18 417	9.92 260	8	48
13	9.73 863	19	9.81 611	27	10.18 389	9.92 252	8	47
14	9.73 882	19	9.81 638	28	10.18 362	9.92 244	9	46
15	9.73 901	20	9.81 666	27	10.18 334	9.92 235	8	45
16	9.73 921	19	9.81 693	28	10.18 307	9.92 227	8	44
17	9.73 940	19	9.81 721	27	10.18 279	9.92 219	8	43
18	9.73 959	19	9.81 748	28	10.18 252	9.92 211	9	42
19	9.73 978	19	9.81 776	27	10.18 224	9.92 202	8	41
20	9.73 997	20	9.81 803	28	10.18 197	9.92 194	8	40
21	9.74 017	19	9.81 831	27	10.18 169	9.92 186	9	39
22	9.74 036	19	9.81 858	28	10.18 142	9.92 177	8	38
23	9.74 055	19	9.81 886	27	10.18 114	9.92 169	8	37
24	9.74 074	19	9.81 913	28	10.18 087	9.92 161	9	36
25	9.74 093	20	9.81 941	27	10.18 059	9.92 152	8	35
26	9.74 113	19	9.81 968	28	10.18 032	9.92 144	8	34
27	9.74 132	19	9.81 996	27	10.18 004	9.92 136	9	33
28	9.74 151	19	9.82 023	28	10.17 977	9.92 127	8	32
29	9.74 170	19	9.82 051	27	10.17 949	9.92 119	8	31
30	9.74 189	19	9.82 078	28	10.17 922	9.92 111	9	30
31	9.74 208	19	9.82 106	27	10.17 894	9.92 102	8	29
32	9.74 227	19	9.82 133	28	10.17 867	9.92 094	8	28
33	9.74 246	19	9.82 161	27	10.17 839	9.92 086	9	27
34	9.74 265	19	9.82 188	27	10.17 812	9.92 077	8	26
35	9.74 284	19	9.82 215	28	10.17 785	9.92 069	9	25
36	9.74 303	19	9.82 243	27	10.17 757	9.92 060	8	24
37	9.74 322	19	9.82 270	28	10.17 730	9.92 052	8	23
38	9.74 341	19	9.82 298	27	10.17 702	9.92 044	9	22
39	9.74 360	19	9.82 325	27	10.17 675	9.92 035	8	21
40	9.74 379	19	9.82 352	28	10.17 648	9.92 027	9	20
41	9.74 398	19	9.82 380	27	10.17 620	9.92 018	8	19
42	9.74 417	19	9.82 407	28	10.17 593	9.92 010	8	18
43	9.74 436	19	9.82 435	27	10.17 565	9.92 002	9	17
44	9.74 455	19	9.82 462	27	10.17 538	9.91 993	8	16
45	9.74 474	19	9.82 489	28	10.17 511	9.91 985	9	15
46	9.74 493	19	9.82 517	27	10.17 483	9.91 976	8	14
47	9.74 512	19	9.82 544	27	10.17 456	9.91 968	9	13
48	9.74 531	18	9.82 571	28	10.17 429	9.91 959	8	12
49	9.74 549	19	9.82 599	27	10.17 401	9.91 951	9	11
50	9.74 568	19	9.82 626	27	10.17 374	9.91 942	8	10
51	9.74 587	19	9.82 653	28	10.17 347	9.91 934	9	9
52	9.74 606	19	9.82 681	27	10.17 319	9.91 925	8	8
53	9.74 625	19	9.82 708	27	10.17 292	9.91 917	9	7
54	9.74 644	18	9.82 735	27	10.17 265	9.91 908	8	6
55	9.74 662	19	9.82 762	28	10.17 238	9.91 900	9	5
56	9.74 681	19	9.82 790	27	10.17 210	9.91 891	8	4
57	9.74 700	19	9.82 817	27	10.17 183	9.91 883	9	3
58	9.74 719	18	9.82 844	27	10.17 156	9.91 874	8	2
59	9.74 737	19	9.82 871	28	10.17 129	9.91 866	9	1
60	9.74 756		9.82 899		10.17 101	9.91 857		0
	L Cos	d	L Ctn	cd	L Tan	L Sin	d	′

Prop. Pts.

	28	27
2	5.6	5.4
3	8.4	8.1
4	11.2	10.8
5	14.0	13.5
6	16.8	16.2
7	19.6	18.9
8	22.4	21.6
9	25.2	24.3

	20	19
2	4.0	3.8
3	6.0	5.7
4	8.0	7.6
5	10.0	9.5
6	12.0	11.4
7	14.0	13.3
8	16.0	15.2
9	18.0	17.1

	18	9
2	3.6	1.8
3	5.4	2.7
4	7.2	3.6
5	9.0	4.5
6	10.8	5.4
7	12.6	6.3
8	14.4	7.2
9	16.2	8.1

	8
2	1.6
3	2.4
4	3.2
5	4.0
6	4.8
7	5.6
8	6.4
9	7.2

From the top:

For **33°+** or **213°+**, read as printed; for **123°+** or **303°+**, read co-function.

From the bottom:

For **56°+** or **236°+**, read as printed; for **146°+** or **326°+**, read co-function.

Prop. Pts.

56° — Logarithms of Trigonometric Functions

34° — Logarithms of Trigonometric Functions

′	L Sin	d	L Tan	c d	L Ctn	L Cos	d	
0	9.74 756	19	9.82 899	27	10.17 101	9.91 857	8	60
1	9.74 775	19	9.82 926	27	10.17 074	9.91 849	9	59
2	9.74 794	18	9.82 953	27	10.17 047	9.91 840	8	58
3	9.74 812	19	9.82 980	28	10.17 020	9.91 832	9	57
4	9.74 831	19	9.83 008	27	10.16 992	9.91 823	8	56
5	9.74 850	18	9.83 035	27	10.16 965	9.91 815	9	55
6	9.74 868	19	9.83 062	27	10.16 938	9.91 806	8	54
7	9.74 887	19	9.83 089	28	10.16 911	9.91 798	9	53
8	9.74 906	18	9.83 117	27	10.16 883	9.91 789	8	52
9	9.74 924	19	9.83 144	27	10.16 856	9.91 781	9	51
10	9.74 943	18	9.83 171	27	10.16 829	9.91 772	9	50
11	9.74 961	19	9.83 198	27	10.16 802	9.91 763	8	49
12	9.74 980	19	9.83 225	27	10.16 775	9.91 755	9	48
13	9.74 999	18	9.83 252	28	10.16 748	9.91 746	8	47
14	9.75 017	19	9.83 280	27	10.16 720	9.91 738	9	46
15	9.75 036	18	9.83 307	27	10.16 693	9.91 729	9	45
16	9.75 054	19	9.83 334	27	10.16 666	9.91 720	8	44
17	9.75 073	18	9.83 361	27	10.16 639	9.91 712	9	43
18	9.75 091	19	9.83 388	27	10.16 612	9.91 703	8	42
19	9.75 110	18	9.83 415	27	10.16 585	9.91 695	9	41
20	9.75 128	19	9.83 442	28	10.16 558	9.91 686	9	40
21	9.75 147	18	9.83 470	27	10.16 530	9.91 677	8	39
22	9.75 165	19	9.83 497	27	10.16 503	9.91 669	9	38
23	9.75 184	18	9.83 524	27	10.16 476	9.91 660	9	37
24	9.75 202	19	9.83 551	27	10.16 449	9.91 651	8	36
25	9.75 221	18	9.83 578	27	10.16 422	9.91 643	9	35
26	9.75 239	19	9.83 605	27	10.16 395	9.91 634	9	34
27	9.75 258	18	9.83 632	27	10.16 368	9.91 625	8	33
28	9.75 276	18	9.83 659	27	10.16 341	9.91 617	9	32
29	9.75 294	19	9.83 686	27	10.16 314	9.91 608	9	31
30	9.75 313	18	9.83 713	27	10.16 287	9.91 599	8	30
31	9.75 331	19	9.83 740	28	10.16 260	9.91 591	9	29
32	9.75 350	18	9.83 768	27	10.16 232	9.91 582	9	28
33	9.75 368	18	9.83 795	27	10.16 205	9.91 573	8	27
34	9.75 386	19	9.83 822	27	10.16 178	9.91 565	9	26
35	9.75 405	18	9.83 849	27	10.16 151	9.91 556	9	25
36	9.75 423	18	9.83 876	27	10.16 124	9.91 547	9	24
37	9.75 441	18	9.83 903	27	10.16 097	9.91 538	8	23
38	9.75 459	19	9.83 930	27	10.16 070	9.91 530	9	22
39	9.75 478	18	9.83 957	27	10.16 043	9.91 521	9	21
40	9.75 496	18	9.83 984	27	10.16 016	9.91 512	8	20
41	9.75 514	19	9.84 011	27	10.15 989	9.91 504	9	19
42	9.75 533	18	9.84 038	27	10.15 962	9.91 495	9	18
43	9.75 551	18	9.84 065	27	10.15 935	9.91 486	9	17
44	9.75 569	18	9.84 092	27	10.15 908	9.91 477	8	16
45	9.75 587	18	9.84 119	27	10.15 881	9.91 469	9	15
46	9.75 605	19	9.84 146	27	10.15 854	9.91 460	9	14
47	9.75 624	18	9.84 173	27	10.15 827	9.91 451	9	13
48	9.75 642	18	9.84 200	27	10.15 800	9.91 442	9	12
49	9.75 660	18	9.84 227	27	10.15 773	9.91 433	8	11
50	9.75 678	18	9.84 254	26	10.15 746	9.91 425	9	10
51	9.75 696	18	9.84 280	27	10.15 720	9.91 416	9	9
52	9.75 714	19	9.84 307	27	10.15 693	9.91 407	9	8
53	9.75 733	18	9.84 334	27	10.15 666	9.91 398	9	7
54	9.75 751	18	9.84 361	27	10.15 639	9.91 389	8	6
55	9.75 769	18	9.84 388	27	10.15 612	9.91 381	9	5
56	9.75 787	18	9.84 415	27	10.15 585	9.91 372	9	4
57	9.75 805	18	9.84 442	27	10.15 558	9.91 363	9	3
58	9.75 823	18	9.84 469	27	10.15 531	9.91 354	9	2
59	9.75 841	18	9.84 496	27	10.15 504	9.91 345	9	1
60	9.75 859		9.84 523		10.15 477	9.91 336		0
	L Cos	d	L Ctn	c d	L Tan	L Sin	d	′

Prop. Pts.

	28	27
2	5.6	5.4
3	8.4	8.1
4	11.2	10.8
5	14.0	13.5
6	16.8	16.2
7	19.6	18.9
8	22.4	21.6
9	25.2	24.3

	26	19
2	5.2	3.8
3	7.8	5.7
4	10.4	7.6
5	13.0	9.5
6	15.6	11.4
7	18.2	13.3
8	20.8	15.2
9	23.4	17.1

	18	9
2	3.6	1.8
3	5.4	2.7
4	7.2	3.6
5	9.0	4.5
6	10.8	5.4
7	12.6	6.3
8	14.4	7.2
9	16.2	8.1

	8
2	1.6
3	2.4
4	3.2
5	4.0
6	4.8
7	5.6
8	6.4
9	7.2

From the top:

For **34°+** or **214°+**, read as printed; for **124°+** or **304°+**, read co-function.

From the bottom:

For **55°+** or **235°+**, read as printed; for **145°+** or **325°+**, read co-function.

Prop. Pts.

55° — Logarithms of Trigonometric Functions

′	L Sin	d	L Tan	cd	L Ctn	L Cos	d	
0	9.75 859	18	9.84 523	27	10.15 477	9.91 336	8	60
1	9.75 877	18	9.84 550	26	10.15 450	9.91 328	9	59
2	9.75 895	18	9.84 576	27	10.15 424	9.91 319	9	58
3	9.75 913	18	9.84 603	27	10.15 397	9.91 310	9	57
4	9.75 931	18	9.84 630	27	10.15 370	9.91 301	9	56
5	9.75 949	18	9.84 657	27	10.15 343	9.91 292	9	55
6	9.75 967	18	9.84 684	27	10.15 316	9.91 283	9	54
7	9.75 985	18	9.84 711	27	10.15 289	9.91 274	8	53
8	9.76 003	18	9.84 738	26	10.15 262	9.91 266	9	52
9	9.76 021	18	9.84 764	27	10.15 236	9.91 257	9	51
10	9.76 039	18	9.84 791	27	10.15 209	9.91 248	9	50
11	9.76 057	18	9.84 818	27	10.15 182	9.91 239	9	49
12	9.76 075	18	9.84 845	27	10.15 155	9.91 230	9	48
13	9.76 093	18	9.84 872	27	10.15 128	9.91 221	9	47
14	9.76 111	18	9.84 899	26	10.15 101	9.91 212	9	46
15	9.76 129	17	9.84 925	27	10.15 075	9.91 203	9	45
16	9.76 146	18	9.84 952	27	10.15 048	9.91 194	9	44
17	9.76 164	18	9.84 979	27	10.15 021	9.91 185	9	43
18	9.76 182	18	9.85 006	27	10.14 994	9.91 176	9	42
19	9.76 200	18	9.85 033	26	10.14 967	9.91 167	9	41
20	9.76 218	18	9.85 059	27	10.14 941	9.91 158	9	40
21	9.76 236	17	9.85 086	27	10.14 914	9.91 149	8	39
22	9.76 253	18	9.85 113	27	10.14 887	9.91 141	9	38
23	9.76 271	18	9.85 140	26	10.14 860	9.91 132	9	37
24	9.76 289	18	9.85 166	27	10.14 834	9.91 123	9	36
25	9.76 307	17	9.85 193	27	10.14 807	9.91 114	9	35
26	9.76 324	18	9.85 220	27	10.14 780	9.91 105	9	34
27	9.76 342	18	9.85 247	26	10.14 753	9.91 096	9	33
28	9.76 360	18	9.85 273	27	10.14 727	9.91 087	9	32
29	9.76 378	17	9.85 300	27	10.14 700	9.91 078	9	31
30	9.76 395	18	9.85 327	27	10.14 673	9.91 069	9	30
31	9.76 413	18	9.85 354	26	10.14 646	9.91 060	9	29
32	9.76 431	17	9.85 380	27	10.14 620	9.91 051	9	28
33	9.76 448	18	9.85 407	27	10.14 593	9.91 042	9	27
34	9.76 466	18	9.85 434	26	10.14 566	9.91 033	10	26
35	9.76 484	17	9.85 460	27	10.14 540	9.91 023	9	25
36	9.76 501	18	9.85 487	27	10.14 513	9.91 014	9	24
37	9.76 519	18	9.85 514	26	10.14 486	9.91 005	9	23
38	9.76 537	17	9.85 540	27	10.14 460	9.90 996	9	22
39	9.76 554	18	9.85 567	27	10.14 433	9.90 987	9	21
40	9.76 572	18	9.85 594	26	10.14 406	9.90 978	9	20
41	9.76 590	17	9.85 620	27	10.14 380	9.90 969	9	19
42	9.76 607	18	9.85 647	27	10.14 353	9.90 960	9	18
43	9.76 625	17	9.85 674	26	10.14 326	9.90 951	9	17
44	9.76 642	18	9.85 700	27	10.14 300	9.90 942	9	16
45	9.76 660	17	9.85 727	27	10.14 273	9.90 933	9	15
46	9.76 677	18	9.85 754	26	10.14 246	9.90 924	9	14
47	9.76 695	17	9.85 780	27	10.14 220	9.90 915	9	13
48	9.76 712	18	9.85 807	27	10.14 193	9.90 906	10	12
49	9.76 730	17	9.85 834	26	10.14 166	9.90 896	9	11
50	9.76 747	18	9.85 860	27	10.14 140	9.90 887	9	10
51	9.76 765	17	9.85 887	26	10.14 113	9.90 878	9	9
52	9.76 782	18	9.85 913	27	10.14 087	9.90 869	9	8
53	9.76 800	17	9.85 940	27	10.14 060	9.90 860	9	7
54	9.76 817	18	9.85 967	26	10.14 033	9.90 851	9	6
55	9.76 835	17	9.85 993	27	10.14 007	9.90 842	10	5
56	9.76 852	18	9.86 020	26	10.13 980	9.90 832	9	4
57	9.76 870	17	9.86 046	27	10.13 954	9.90 823	9	3
58	9.76 887	17	9.86 073	27	10.13 927	9.90 814	9	2
59	9.76 904	18	9.86 100	26	10.13 900	9.90 805	9	1
60	9.76 922		9.86 126		10.13 874	9.90 796		0
	L Cos	d	L Ctn	cd	L Tan	L Sin	d	′

Prop. Pts.

	27	26
2	5.4	5.2
3	8.1	7.8
4	10.8	10.4
5	13.5	13.0
6	16.2	15.6
7	18.9	18.2
8	21.6	20.8
9	24.3	23.4

	18	17
2	3.6	3.4
3	5.4	5.1
4	7.2	6.8
5	9.0	8.5
6	10.8	10.2
7	12.6	11.9
8	14.4	13.6
9	16.2	15.3

	10	9
2	2.0	1.8
3	3.0	2.7
4	4.0	3.6
5	5.0	4.5
6	6.0	5.4
7	7.0	6.3
8	8.0	7.2
9	9.0	8.1

	8
2	1.6
3	2.4
4	3.2
5	4.0
6	4.8
7	5.6
8	6.4
9	7.2

From the top:

For **35°+** or **215°+**, read as printed; for **125°+** or **305°+**, read co-function.

From the bottom:

For **54°+** or **234°+**, read as printed; for **144°+** or **324°+**, read co-function.

Prop. Pts.

′	L Sin	d	L Tan	cd	L Ctn	L Cos	d	
0	9.76 922	17	9.86 126	27	10.13 874	9.90 796	9	60
1	9.76 939	18	9.86 153	26	10.13 847	9.90 787	10	59
2	9.76 957	17	9.86 179	27	10.13 821	9.90 777	9	58
3	9.76 974	17	9.86 206	26	10.13 794	9.90 768	9	57
4	9.76 991	18	9.86 232	27	10.13 768	9.90 759	9	56
5	9.77 009	17	9.86 259	26	10.13 741	9.90 750	9	55
6	9.77 026	17	9.86 285	27	10.13 715	9.90 741	10	54
7	9.77 043	18	9.86 312	26	10.13 688	9.90 731	9	53
8	9.77 061	17	9.86 338	27	10.13 662	9.90 722	9	52
9	9.77 078	17	9.86 365	27	10.13 635	9.90 713	9	51
10	9.77 095	17	9.86 392	26	10.13 608	9.90 704	10	50
11	9.77 112	18	9.86 418	27	10.13 582	9.90 694	9	49
12	9.77 130	17	9.86 445	26	10.13 555	9.90 685	9	48
13	9.77 147	17	9.86 471	27	10.13 529	9.90 676	9	47
14	9.77 164	17	9.86 498	26	10.13 502	9.90 667	10	46
15	9.77 181	18	9.86 524	27	10.13 476	9.90 657	9	45
16	9.77 199	17	9.86 551	26	10.13 449	9.90 648	9	44
17	9.77 216	17	9.86 577	26	10.13 423	9.90 639	9	43
18	9.77 233	17	9.86 603	27	10.13 397	9.90 630	10	42
19	9.77 250	18	9.86 630	26	10.13 370	9.90 620	9	41
20	9.77 268	17	9.86 656	27	10.13 344	9.90 611	9	40
21	9.77 285	17	9.86 683	26	10.13 317	9.90 602	10	39
22	9.77 302	17	9.86 709	27	10.13 291	9.90 592	9	38
23	9.77 319	17	9.86 736	26	10.13 264	9.90 583	9	37
24	9.77 336	17	9.86 762	27	10.13 238	9.90 574	9	36
25	9.77 353	17	9.86 789	26	10.13 211	9.90 565	10	35
26	9.77 370	17	9.86 815	27	10.13 185	9.90 555	9	34
27	9.77 387	18	9.86 842	26	10.13 158	9.90 546	9	33
28	9.77 405	17	9.86 868	26	10.13 132	9.90 537	10	32
29	9.77 422	17	9.86 894	27	10.13 106	9.90 527	9	31
30	9.77 439	17	9.86 921	26	10.13 079	9.90 518	9	30
31	9.77 456	17	9.86 947	27	10.13 053	9.90 509	10	29
32	9.77 473	17	9.86 974	26	10.13 026	9.90 499	9	28
33	9.77 490	17	9.87 000	27	10.13 000	9.90 490	10	27
34	9.77 507	17	9.87 027	26	10.12 973	9.90 480	9	26
35	9.77 524	17	9.87 053	26	10.12 947	9.90 471	9	25
36	9.77 541	17	9.87 079	27	10.12 921	9.90 462	10	24
37	9.77 558	17	9.87 106	26	10.12 894	9.90 452	9	23
38	9.77 575	17	9.87 132	26	10.12 868	9.90 443	9	22
39	9.77 592	17	9.87 158	27	10.12 842	9.90 434	10	21
40	9.77 609	17	9.87 185	26	10.12 815	9.90 424	9	20
41	9.77 626	17	9.87 211	27	10.12 789	9.90 415	10	19
42	9.77 643	17	9.87 238	26	10.12 762	9.90 405	9	18
43	9.77 660	17	9.87 264	26	10.12 736	9.90 396	10	17
44	9.77 677	17	9.87 290	27	10.12 710	9.90 386	9	16
45	9.77 694	17	9.87 317	26	10.12 683	9.90 377	9	15
46	9.77 711	17	9.87 343	26	10.12 657	9.90 368	10	14
47	9.77 728	16	9.87 369	27	10.12 631	9.90 358	9	13
48	9.77 744	17	9.87 396	26	10.12 604	9.90 349	10	12
49	9.77 761	17	9.87 422	26	10.12 578	9.90 339	9	11
50	9.77 778	17	9.87 448	27	10.12 552	9.90 330	10	10
51	9.77 795	17	9.87 475	26	10.12 525	9.90 320	9	9
52	9.77 812	17	9.87 501	26	10.12 499	9.90 311	10	8
53	9.77 829	17	9.87 527	27	10.12 473	9.90 301	9	7
54	9.77 846	16	9.87 554	26	10.12 446	9.90 292	10	6
55	9.77 862	17	9.87 580	26	10.12 420	9.90 282	9	5
56	9.77 879	17	9.87 606	27	10.12 394	9.90 273	10	4
57	9.77 896	17	9.87 633	26	10.12 367	9.90 263	9	3
58	9.77 913	17	9.87 659	26	10.12 341	9.90 254	10	2
59	9.77 930	16	9.87 685	26	10.12 315	9.90 244	9	1
60	9.77 946		9.87 711		10.12 289	9.90 235		0
	L Cos	d	L Ctn	cd	L Tan	L Sin	d	′

Prop. Pts.

	27	26
2	5.4	5.2
3	8.1	7.8
4	10.8	10.4
5	13.5	13.0
6	16.2	15.6
7	18.9	18.2
8	21.6	20.8
9	24.3	23.4

	18	17
2	3.6	3.4
3	5.4	5.1
4	7.2	6.8
5	9.0	8.5
6	10.8	10.2
7	12.6	11.9
8	14.4	13.6
9	16.2	15.3

	16	10
2	3.2	2.0
3	4.8	3.0
4	6.4	4.0
5	8.0	5.0
6	9.6	6.0
7	11.2	7.0
8	12.8	8.0
9	14.4	9.0

	9
2	1.8
3	2.7
4	3.6
5	4.5
6	5.4
7	6.3
8	7.2
9	8.1

From the top:

For **36°+** or **216°+**, read as printed; for **126°+** or **306°+**, read co-function.

From the bottom:

For **53°+** or **233°+**, read as printed; for **143°+** or **323°+**, read co-function.

Prop. Pts.

37° — Logarithms of Trigonometric Functions

′	L Sin	d	L Tan	cd	L Ctn	L Cos	d	′
0	9.77 946	17	9.87 711	27	10.12 289	9.90 235	10	60
1	9.77 963	17	9.87 738	26	10.12 262	9.90 225	9	59
2	9.77 980	17	9.87 764	26	10.12 236	9.90 216	10	58
3	9.77 997	16	9.87 790	27	10.12 210	9.90 206	9	57
4	9.78 013	17	9.87 817	26	10.12 183	9.90 197	10	56
5	9.78 030	17	9.87 843	26	10.12 157	9.90 187	9	55
6	9.78 047	16	9.87 869	26	10.12 131	9.90 178	10	54
7	9.78 063	17	9.87 895	27	10.12 105	9.90 168	9	53
8	9.78 080	17	9.87 922	26	10.12 078	9.90 159	10	52
9	9.78 097	16	9.87 948	26	10.12 052	9.90 149	10	51
10	9.78 113	17	9.87 974	26	10.12 026	9.90 139	9	50
11	9.78 130	17	9.88 000	27	10.12 000	9.90 130	10	49
12	9.78 147	16	9.88 027	26	10.11 973	9.90 120	9	48
13	9.78 163	17	9.88 053	26	10.11 947	9.90 111	10	47
14	9.78 180	17	9.88 079	26	10.11 921	9.90 101	10	46
15	9.78 197	16	9.88 105	26	10.11 895	9.90 091	9	45
16	9.78 213	17	9.88 131	27	10.11 869	9.90 082	10	44
17	9.78 230	16	9.88 158	26	10.11 842	9.90 072	9	43
18	9.78 246	17	9.88 184	26	10.11 816	9.90 063	10	42
19	9.78 263	17	9.88 210	26	10.11 790	9.90 053	10	41
20	9.78 280	16	9.88 236	26	10.11 764	9.90 043	9	40
21	9.78 296	17	9.88 262	27	10.11 738	9.90 034	10	39
22	9.78 313	16	9.88 289	26	10.11 711	9.90 024	10	38
23	9.78 329	17	9.88 315	26	10.11 685	9.90 014	9	37
24	9.78 346	16	9.88 341	26	10.11 659	9.90 005	10	36
25	9.78 362	17	9.88 367	26	10.11 633	9.89 995	10	35
26	9.78 379	16	9.88 393	27	10.11 607	9.89 985	9	34
27	9.78 395	17	9.88 420	26	10.11 580	9.89 976	10	33
28	9.78 412	16	9.88 446	26	10.11 554	9.89 966	10	32
29	9.78 428	17	9.88 472	26	10.11 528	9.89 956	9	31
30	9.78 445	16	9.88 498	26	10.11 502	9.89 947	10	30
31	9.78 461	17	9.88 524	26	10.11 476	9.89 937	10	29
32	9.78 478	16	9.88 550	27	10.11 450	9.89 927	9	28
33	9.78 494	16	9.88 577	26	10.11 423	9.89 918	10	27
34	9.78 510	17	9.88 603	26	10.11 397	9.89 908	10	26
35	9.78 527	16	9.88 629	26	10.11 371	9.89 898	10	25
36	9.78 543	17	9.88 655	26	10.11 345	9.89 888	9	24
37	9.78 560	16	9.88 681	26	10.11 319	9.89 879	10	23
38	9.78 576	16	9.88 707	26	10.11 293	9.89 869	10	22
39	9.78 592	17	9.88 733	26	10.11 267	9.89 859	10	21
40	9.78 609	16	9.88 759	27	10.11 241	9.89 849	9	20
41	9.78 625	17	9.88 786	26	10.11 214	9.89 840	10	19
42	9.78 642	16	9.88 812	26	10.11 188	9.89 830	10	18
43	9.78 658	16	9.88 838	26	10.11 162	9.89 820	10	17
44	9.78 674	17	9.88 864	26	10.11 136	9.89 810	9	16
45	9.78 691	16	9.88 890	26	10.11 110	9.89 801	10	15
46	9.78 707	16	9.88 916	26	10.11 084	9.89 791	10	14
47	9.78 723	16	9.88 942	26	10.11 058	9.89 781	10	13
48	9.78 739	17	9.88 968	26	10.11 032	9.89 771	10	12
49	9.78 756	16	9.88 994	26	10.11 006	9.89 761	9	11
50	9.78 772	16	9.89 020	26	10.10 980	9.89 752	10	10
51	9.78 788	17	9.89 046	27	10.10 954	9.89 742	10	9
52	9.78 805	16	9.89 073	26	10.10 927	9.89 732	10	8
53	9.78 821	16	9.89 099	26	10.10 901	9.89 722	10	7
54	9.78 837	16	9.89 125	26	10.10 875	9.89 712	10	6
55	9.78 853	16	9.89 151	26	10.10 849	9.89 702	9	5
56	9.78 869	17	9.89 177	26	10.10 823	9.89 693	10	4
57	9.78 886	16	9.89 203	26	10.10 797	9.89 683	10	3
58	9.78 902	16	9.89 229	26	10.10 771	9.89 673	10	2
59	9.78 918	16	9.89 255	26	10.10 745	9.89 663	10	1
60	9.78 934		9.89 281		10.10 719	9.89 653		0
	L Cos	d	L Ctn	cd	L Tan	L Sin	d	′

Prop. Pts.

	27	26
2	5.4	5.2
3	8.1	7.8
4	10.8	10.4
5	13.5	13.0
6	16.2	15.6
7	18.9	18.2
8	21.6	20.8
9	24.3	23.4

	17	16
2	3.4	3.2
3	5.1	4.8
4	6.8	6.4
5	8.5	8.0
6	10.2	9.6
7	11.9	11.2
8	13.6	12.8
9	15.3	14.4

	10	9
2	2.0	1.8
3	3.0	2.7
4	4.0	3.6
5	5.0	4.5
6	6.0	5.4
7	7.0	6.3
8	8.0	7.2
9	9.0	8.1

From the top:

For **37°+** or **217°+**, read as printed; for **127°+** or **307°+**, read co-function.

From the bottom:

For **52°+** or **232°+**, read as printed; for **142°+** or **322°+**, read co-function.

Prop. Pts.

52° — Logarithms of Trigonometric Functions

′	L Sin	d	L Tan	cd	L Ctn	L Cos	d	
0	9.78 934	16	9.89 281	26	10.10 719	9.89 653	10	**60**
1	9.78 950	17	9.89 307	26	10.10 693	9.89 643	10	59
2	9.78 967	16	9.89 333	26	10.10 667	9.89 633	9	58
3	9.78 983	16	9.89 359	26	10.10 641	9.89 624	10	57
4	9.78 999	16	9.89 385	26	10.10 615	9.89 614	10	56
5	9.79 015	16	9.89 411	26	10.10 589	9.89 604	10	**55**
6	9.79 031	16	9.89 437	26	10.10 563	9.89 594	10	54
7	9.79 047	16	9.89 463	26	10.10 537	9.89 584	10	53
8	9.79 063	16	9.89 489	26	10.10 511	9.89 574	10	52
9	9.79 079	16	9.89 515	26	10.10 485	9.89 564	10	51
10	9.79 095	16	9.89 541	26	10.10 459	9.89 554	10	**50**
11	9.79 111	17	9.89 567	26	10.10 433	9.89 544	10	49
12	9.79 128	16	9.89 593	26	10.10 407	9.89 534	10	48
13	9.79 144	16	9.89 619	26	10.10 381	9.89 524	10	47
14	9.79 160	16	9.89 645	26	10.10 355	9.89 514	10	46
15	9.79 176	16	9.89 671	26	10.10 329	9.89 504	9	**45**
16	9.79 192	16	9.89 697	26	10.10 303	9.89 495	10	44
17	9.79 208	16	9.89 723	26	10.10 277	9.89 485	10	43
18	9.79 224	16	9.89 749	26	10.10 251	9.89 475	10	42
19	9.79 240	16	9.89 775	26	10.10 225	9.89 465	10	41
20	9.79 256	16	9.89 801	26	10.10 199	9.89 455	10	**40**
21	9.79 272	16	9.89 827	26	10.10 173	9.89 445	10	39
22	9.79 288	16	9.89 853	26	10.10 147	9.89 435	10	38
23	9.79 304	15	9.89 879	26	10.10 121	9.89 425	10	37
24	9.79 319	16	9.89 905	26	10.10 095	9.89 415	10	36
25	9.79 335	16	9.89 931	26	10.10 069	9.89 405	10	**35**
26	9.79 351	16	9.89 957	26	10.10 043	9.89 395	10	34
27	9.79 367	16	9.89 983	26	10.10 017	9.89 385	10	33
28	9.79 383	16	9.90 009	26	10.09 991	9.89 375	11	32
29	9.79 399	16	9.90 035	26	10.09 965	9.89 364	10	31
30	9.79 415	16	9.90 061	25	10.09 939	9.89 354	10	**30**
31	9.79 431	16	9.90 086	26	10.09 914	9.89 344	10	29
32	9.79 447	16	9.90 112	26	10.09 888	9.89 334	10	28
33	9.79 463	15	9.90 138	26	10.09 862	9.89 324	10	27
34	9.79 478	16	9.90 164	26	10.09 836	9.89 314	10	26
35	9.79 494	16	9.90 190	26	10.09 810	9.89 304	10	**25**
36	9.79 510	16	9.90 216	26	10.09 784	9.89 294	10	24
37	9.79 526	16	9.90 242	26	10.09 758	9.89 284	10	23
38	9.79 542	16	9.90 268	26	10.09 732	9.89 274	10	22
39	9.79 558	15	9.90 294	26	10.09 706	9.89 264	10	21
40	9.79 573	16	9.90 320	26	10.09 680	9.89 254	10	**20**
41	9.79 589	16	9.90 346	25	10.09 654	9.89 244	11	19
42	9.79 605	16	9.90 371	26	10.09 629	9.89 233	10	18
43	9.79 621	15	9.90 397	26	10.09 603	9.89 223	10	17
44	9.79 636	16	9.90 423	26	10.09 577	9.89 213	10	16
45	9.79 652	16	9.90 449	26	10.09 551	9.89 203	10	**15**
46	9.79 668	16	9.90 475	26	10.09 525	9.89 193	10	14
47	9.79 684	15	9.90 501	26	10.09 499	9.89 183	10	13
48	9.79 699	16	9.90 527	26	10.09 473	9.89 173	11	12
49	9.79 715	16	9.90 553	25	10.09 447	9.89 162	10	11
50	9.79 731	15	9.90 578	26	10.09 422	9.89 152	10	**10**
51	9.79 746	16	9.90 604	26	10.09 396	9.89 142	10	9
52	9.79 762	16	9.90 630	26	10.09 370	9.89 132	10	8
53	9.79 778	15	9.90 656	26	10.09 344	9.89 122	10	7
54	9.79 793	16	9.90 682	26	10.09 318	9.89 112	11	6
55	9.79 809	16	9.90 708	26	10.09 292	9.89 101	10	**5**
56	9.79 825	15	9.90 734	25	10.09 266	9.89 091	10	4
57	9.79 840	16	9.90 759	26	10.09 241	9.89 081	10	3
58	9.79 856	16	9.90 785	26	10.09 215	9.89 071	11	2
59	9.79 872	15	9.90 811	26	10.09 189	9.89 060	10	1
60	9.79 887		9.90 837		10.09 163	9.89 050		**0**
	L Cos	d	L Ctn	cd	L Tan	L Sin	d	′

Prop. Pts.

	26	25
2	5.2	5.0
3	7.8	7.5
4	10.4	10.0
5	13.0	12.5
6	15.6	15.0
7	18.2	17.5
8	20.8	20.0
9	23.4	22.5

	17	16
2	3.4	3.2
3	5.1	4.8
4	6.8	6.4
5	8.5	8.0
6	10.2	9.6
7	11.9	11.2
8	13.6	12.8
9	15.3	14.4

	15	11
2	3.0	2.2
3	4.5	3.3
4	6.0	4.4
5	7.5	5.5
6	9.0	6.6
7	10.5	7.7
8	12.0	8.8
9	13.5	9.9

	10	9
2	2.0	1.8
3	3.0	2.7
4	4.0	3.6
5	5.0	4.5
6	6.0	5.4
7	7.0	6.3
8	8.0	7.2
9	9.0	8.1

From the top:

For **38°+** or **218°+**, read as printed; for **128°+** or **308°+**, read co-function.

From the bottom:

For **51°+** or **231°+**, read as printed; for **141°+** or **321°+**, read co-function.

Prop. Pts.

39° — Logarithms of Trigonometric Functions

′	L Sin	d	L Tan	cd	L Ctn	L Cos	d	
0	9.79 887	16	9.90 837	26	10.09 163	9.89 050	10	**60**
1	9.79 903	15	9.90 863	26	10.09 137	9.89 040	10	59
2	9.79 918	16	9.90 889	25	10.09 111	9.89 030	10	58
3	9.79 934	16	9.90 914	26	10.09 086	9.89 020	11	57
4	9.79 950	15	9.90 940	26	10.09 060	9.89 009	10	56
5	9.79 965	16	9.90 966	26	10.09 034	9.88 999	10	**55**
6	9.79 981	15	9.90 992	26	10.09 008	9.88 989	11	54
7	9.79 996	16	9.91 018	25	10.08 982	9.88 978	10	53
8	9.80 012	15	9.91 043	26	10.08 957	9.88 968	10	52
9	9.80 027	16	9.91 069	26	10.08 931	9.88 958	10	51
10	9.80 043	15	9.91 095	26	10.08 905	9.88 948	11	**50**
11	9.80 058	16	9.91 121	26	10.08 879	9.88 937	10	49
12	9.80 074	15	9.91 147	25	10.08 853	9.88 927	10	48
13	9.80 089	16	9.91 172	26	10.08 828	9.88 917	11	47
14	9.80 105	15	9.91 198	26	10.08 802	9.88 906	10	46
15	9.80 120	16	9.91 224	26	10.08 776	9.88 896	10	**45**
16	9.80 136	15	9.91 250	26	10.08 750	9.88 886	11	44
17	9.80 151	15	9.91 276	25	10.08 724	9.88 875	10	43
18	9.80 166	16	9.91 301	26	10.08 699	9.88 865	10	42
19	9.80 182	15	9.91 327	26	10.08 673	9.88 855	11	41
20	9.80 197	16	9.91 353	26	10.08 647	9.88 844	10	**40**
21	9.80 213	15	9.91 379	25	10.08 621	9.88 834	10	39
22	9.80 228	16	9.91 404	26	10.08 596	9.88 824	11	38
23	9.80 244	15	9.91 430	26	10.08 570	9.88 813	10	37
24	9.80 259	15	9.91 456	26	10.08 544	9.88 803	10	36
25	9.80 274	16	9.91 482	25	10.08 518	9.88 793	11	**35**
26	9.80 290	15	9.91 507	26	10.08 493	9.88 782	10	34
27	9.80 305	15	9.91 533	26	10.08 467	9.88 772	11	33
28	9.80 320	16	9.91 559	26	10.08 441	9.88 761	10	32
29	9.80 336	15	9.91 585	25	10.08 415	9.88 751	10	31
30	9.80 351	15	9.91 610	26	10.08 390	9.88 741	11	**30**
31	9.80 366	16	9.91 636	26	10.08 364	9.88 730	10	29
32	9.80 382	15	9.91 662	26	10.08 338	9.88 720	11	28
33	9.80 397	15	9.91 688	25	10.08 312	9.88 709	10	27
34	9.80 412	16	9.91 713	26	10.08 287	9.88 699	11	26
35	9.80 428	15	9.91 739	26	10.08 261	9.88 688	10	**25**
36	9.80 443	15	9.91 765	26	10.08 235	9.88 678	10	24
37	9.80 458	15	9.91 791	25	10.08 209	9.88 668	11	23
38	9.80 473	16	9.91 816	26	10.08 184	9.88 657	10	22
39	9.80 489	15	9.91 842	26	10.08 158	9.88 647	11	21
40	9.80 504	15	9.91 868	25	10.08 132	9.88 636	10	**20**
41	9.80 519	15	9.91 893	26	10.08 107	9.88 626	11	19
42	9.80 534	16	9.91 919	26	10.08 081	9.88 615	10	18
43	9.80 550	15	9.91 945	26	10.08 055	9.88 605	11	17
44	9.80 565	15	9.91 971	25	10.08 029	9.88 594	10	16
45	9.80 580	15	9.91 996	26	10.08 004	9.88 584	11	**15**
46	9.80 595	15	9.92 022	26	10.07 978	9.88 573	10	14
47	9.80 610	15	9.92 048	25	10.07 952	9.88 563	11	13
48	9.80 625	16	9.92 073	26	10.07 927	9.88 552	10	12
49	9.80 641	15	9.92 099	26	10.07 901	9.88 542	11	11
50	9.80 656	15	9.92 125	25	10.07 875	9.88 531	10	**10**
51	9.80 671	15	9.92 150	26	10.07 850	9.88 521	11	9
52	9.80 686	15	9.92 176	26	10.07 824	9.88 510	11	8
53	9.80 701	15	9.92 202	25	10.07 798	9.88 499	10	7
54	9.80 716	15	9.92 227	26	10.07 773	9.88 489	11	6
55	9.80 731	15	9.92 253	26	10.07 747	9.88 478	10	**5**
56	9.80 746	16	9.92 279	25	10.07 721	9.88 468	11	4
57	9.80 762	15	9.92 304	26	10.07 696	9.88 457	10	3
58	9.80 777	15	9.92 330	26	10.07 670	9.88 447	11	2
59	9.80 792	15	9.92 356	25	10.07 644	9.88 436	11	1
60	9.80 807		9.92 381		10.07 619	9.88 425		**0**
	L Cos	d	L Ctn	cd	L Tan	L Sin	d	′

Prop. Pts.

	26	25
2	5.2	5.0
3	7.8	7.5
4	10.4	10.0
5	13.0	12.5
6	15.6	15.0
7	18.2	17.5
8	20.8	20.0
9	23.4	22.5

	16	15
2	3.2	3.0
3	4.8	4.5
4	6.4	6.0
5	8.0	7.5
6	9.6	9.0
7	11.2	10.5
8	12.8	12.0
9	14.4	13.5

	11	10
2	2.2	2.0
3	3.3	3.0
4	4.4	4.0
5	5.5	5.0
6	6.6	6.0
7	7.7	7.0
8	8.8	8.0
9	9.9	9.0

From the top:

For **39°+** or **219°+**, read as printed; for **129°+** or **309°+**, read co-function.

From the bottom:

For **50°+** or **230°+**, read as printed; for **140°+** or **320°+**, read co-function.

Prop. Pts.

50° — Logarithms of Trigonometric Functions

40° — Logarithms of Trigonometric Functions

′	L Sin	d	L Tan	cd	L Ctn	L Cos	d	
0	9.80 807	15	9.92 381	26	10.07 619	9.88 425	10	60
1	9.80 822	15	9.92 407	26	10.07 593	9.88 415	11	59
2	9.80 837	15	9.92 433	25	10.07 567	9.88 404	10	58
3	9.80 852	15	9.92 458	26	10.07 542	9.88 394	11	57
4	9.80 867	15	9.92 484	26	10.07 516	9.88 383	11	56
5	9.80 882	15	9.92 510	25	10.07 490	9.88 372	10	55
6	9.80 897	15	9.92 535	26	10.07 465	9.88 362	11	54
7	9.80 912	15	9.92 561	26	10.07 439	9.88 351	11	53
8	9.80 927	15	9.92 587	25	10.07 413	9.88 340	10	52
9	9.80 942	15	9.92 612	26	10.07 388	9.88 330	11	51
10	9.80 957	15	9.92 638	25	10.07 362	9.88 319	11	50
11	9.80 972	15	9.92 663	26	10.07 337	9.88 308	10	49
12	9.80 987	15	9.92 689	26	10.07 311	9.88 298	11	48
13	9.81 002	15	9.92 715	25	10.07 285	9.88 287	11	47
14	9.81 017	15	9.92 740	26	10.07 260	9.88 276	10	46
15	9.81 032	15	9.92 766	26	10.07 234	9.88 266	11	45
16	9.81 047	14	9.92 792	25	10.07 208	9.88 255	11	44
17	9.81 061	15	9.92 817	26	10.07 183	9.88 244	10	43
18	9.81 076	15	9.92 843	25	10.07 157	9.88 234	11	42
19	9.81 091	15	9.92 868	26	10.07 132	9.88 223	11	41
20	9.81 106	15	9.92 894	26	10.07 106	9.88 212	11	40
21	9.81 121	15	9.92 920	25	10.07 080	9.88 201	10	39
22	9.81 136	15	9.92 945	26	10.07 055	9.88 191	11	38
23	9.81 151	15	9.92 971	25	10.07 029	9.88 180	11	37
24	9.81 166	14	9.92 996	26	10.07 004	9.88 169	11	36
25	9.81 180	15	9.93 022	26	10.06 978	9.88 158	10	35
26	9.81 195	15	9.93 048	25	10.06 952	9.88 148	11	34
27	9.81 210	15	9.93 073	26	10.06 927	9.88 137	11	33
28	9.81 225	15	9.93 099	25	10.06 901	9.88 126	11	32
29	9.81 240	14	9.93 124	26	10.06 876	9.88 115	10	31
30	9.81 254	15	9.93 150	25	10.06 850	9.88 105	11	30
31	9.81 269	15	9.93 175	26	10.06 825	9.88 094	11	29
32	9.81 284	15	9.93 201	26	10.06 799	9.88 083	11	28
33	9.81 299	15	9.93 227	25	10.06 773	9.88 072	11	27
34	9.81 314	14	9.93 252	26	10.06 748	9.88 061	10	26
35	9.81 328	15	9.93 278	25	10.06 722	9.88 051	11	25
36	9.81 343	15	9.93 303	26	10.06 697	9.88 040	11	24
37	9.81 358	14	9.93 329	25	10.06 671	9.88 029	11	23
38	9.81 372	15	9.93 354	26	10.06 646	9.88 018	11	22
39	9.81 387	15	9.93 380	26	10.06 620	9.88 007	11	21
40	9.81 402	15	9.93 406	25	10.06 594	9.87 996	11	20
41	9.81 417	14	9.93 431	26	10.06 569	9.87 985	10	19
42	9.81 431	15	9.93 457	25	10.06 543	9.87 975	11	18
43	9.81 446	15	9.93 482	26	10.06 518	9.87 964	11	17
44	9.81 461	14	9.93 508	25	10.06 492	9.87 953	11	16
45	9.81 475	15	9.93 533	26	10.06 467	9.87 942	11	15
46	9.81 490	15	9.93 559	25	10.06 441	9.87 931	11	14
47	9.81 505	14	9.93 584	26	10.06 416	9.87 920	11	13
48	9.81 519	15	9.93 610	26	10.06 390	9.87 909	11	12
49	9.81 534	15	9.93 636	25	10.06 364	9.87 898	11	11
50	9.81 549	14	9.93 661	26	10.06 339	9.87 887	10	10
51	9.81 563	15	9.93 687	25	10.06 313	9.87 877	11	9
52	9.81 578	14	9.93 712	26	10.06 288	9.87 866	11	8
53	9.81 592	15	9.93 738	25	10.06 262	9.87 855	11	7
54	9.81 607	15	9.93 763	26	10.06 237	9.87 844	11	6
55	9.81 622	14	9.93 789	25	10.06 211	9.87 833	11	5
56	9.81 636	15	9.93 814	26	10.06 186	9.87 822	11	4
57	9.81 651	14	9.93 840	25	10.06 160	9.87 811	11	3
58	9.81 665	15	9.93 865	26	10.06 135	9.87 800	11	2
59	9.81 680	14	9.93 891	25	10.06 109	9.87 789	11	1
60	9.81 694		9.93 916		10.06 084	9.87 778		0
	L Cos	d	L Ctn	cd	L Tan	L Sin	d	′

Prop. Pts.

	26	25
2	5.2	5.0
3	7.8	7.5
4	10.4	10.0
5	13.0	12.5
6	15.6	15.0
7	18.2	17.5
8	20.8	20.0
9	23.4	22.5

	15	14
2	3.0	2.8
3	4.5	4.2
4	6.0	5.6
5	7.5	7.0
6	9.0	8.4
7	10.5	9.8
8	12.0	11.2
9	13.5	12.6

	11	10
2	2.2	2.0
3	3.3	3.0
4	4.4	4.0
5	5.5	5.0
6	6.6	6.0
7	7.7	7.0
8	8.8	8.0
9	9.9	9.0

From the top:

For **40°+** or **220°+**, read as printed; for **130°+** or **310°+**, read co-function.

From the bottom:

For **49°+** or **229°+**, read as printed; for **139°+** or **319°+**, read co-function.

Prop. Pts.

49° — Logarithms of Trigonometric Functions

′	L Sin	d	L Tan	cd	L Ctn	L Cos	d	
0	9.81 694	15	9.93 916	26	10.06 084	9.87 778	11	60
1	9.81 709	14	9.93 942	25	10.06 058	9.87 767	11	59
2	9.81 723	15	9.93 967	26	10.06 033	9.87 756	11	58
3	9.81 738	14	9.93 993	25	10.06 007	9.87 745	11	57
4	9.81 752	15	9.94 018	26	10.05 982	9.87 734	11	56
5	9.81 767	14	9.94 044	25	10.05 956	9.87 723	11	55
6	9.81 781	15	9.94 069	26	10.05 931	9.87 712	11	54
7	9.81 796	14	9.94 095	25	10.05 905	9.87 701	11	53
8	9.81 810	15	9.94 120	26	10.05 880	9.87 690	11	52
9	9.81 825	14	9.94 146	25	10.05 854	9.87 679	11	51
10	9.81 839	15	9.94 171	26	10.05 829	9.87 668	11	50
11	9.81 854	14	9.94 197	25	10.05 803	9.87 657	11	49
12	9.81 868	14	9.94 222	26	10.05 778	9.87 646	11	48
13	9.81 882	15	9.94 248	25	10.05 752	9.87 635	11	47
14	9.81 897	14	9.94 273	26	10.05 727	9.87 624	11	46
15	9.81 911	15	9.94 299	25	10.05 701	9.87 613	12	45
16	9.81 926	14	9.94 324	26	10.05 676	9.87 601	11	44
17	9.81 940	15	9.94 350	25	10.05 650	9.87 590	11	43
18	9.81 955	14	9.94 375	26	10.05 625	9.87 579	11	42
19	9.81 969	14	9.94 401	25	10.05 599	9.87 568	11	41
20	9.81 983	15	9.94 426	26	10.05 574	9.87 557	11	40
21	9.81 998	14	9.94 452	25	10.05 548	9.87 546	11	39
22	9.82 012	14	9.94 477	26	10.05 523	9.87 535	11	38
23	9.82 026	15	9.94 503	25	10.05 497	9.87 524	11	37
24	9.82 041	14	9.94 528	26	10.05 472	9.87 513	12	36
25	9.82 055	14	9.94 554	25	10.05 446	9.87 501	11	35
26	9.82 069	15	9.94 579	25	10.05 421	9.87 490	11	34
27	9.82 084	14	9.94 604	26	10.05 396	9.87 479	11	33
28	9.82 098	14	9.94 630	25	10.05 370	9.87 468	11	32
29	9.82 112	14	9.94 655	26	10.05 345	9.87 457	11	31
30	9.82 126	15	9.94 681	25	10.05 319	9.87 446	12	30
31	9.82 141	14	9.94 706	26	10.05 294	9.87 434	11	29
32	9.82 155	14	9.94 732	25	10.05 268	9.87 423	11	28
33	9.82 169	15	9.94 757	26	10.05 243	9.87 412	11	27
34	9.82 184	14	9.94 783	25	10.05 217	9.87 401	11	26
35	9.82 198	14	9.94 808	26	10.05 192	9.87 390	12	25
36	9.82 212	14	9.94 834	25	10.05 166	9.87 378	11	24
37	9.82 226	14	9.94 859	25	10.05 141	9.87 367	11	23
38	9.82 240	15	9.94 884	26	10.05 116	9.87 356	11	22
39	9.82 255	14	9.94 910	25	10.05 090	9.87 345	11	21
40	9.82 269	14	9.94 935	26	10.05 065	9.87 334	12	20
41	9.82 283	14	9.94 961	25	10.05 039	9.87 322	11	19
42	9.82 297	14	9.94 986	26	10.05 014	9.87 311	11	18
43	9.82 311	15	9.95 012	25	10.04 988	9.87 300	12	17
44	9.82 326	14	9.95 037	25	10.04 963	9.87 288	11	16
45	9.82 340	14	9.95 062	26	10.04 938	9.87 277	11	15
46	9.82 354	14	9.95 088	25	10.04 912	9.87 266	11	14
47	9.82 368	14	9.95 113	26	10.04 887	9.87 255	12	13
48	9.82 382	14	9.95 139	25	10.04 861	9.87 243	11	12
49	9.82 396	14	9.95 164	26	10.04 836	9.87 232	11	11
50	9.82 410	14	9.95 190	25	10.04 810	9.87 221	12	10
51	9.82 424	15	9.95 215	25	10.04 785	9.87 209	11	9
52	9.82 439	14	9.95 240	26	10.04 760	9.87 198	11	8
53	9.82 453	14	9.95 266	25	10.04 734	9.87 187	12	7
54	9.82 467	14	9.95 291	26	10.04 709	9.87 175	11	6
55	9.82 481	14	9.95 317	25	10.04 683	9.87 164	11	5
56	9.82 495	14	9.95 342	26	10.04 658	9.87 153	12	4
57	9.82 509	14	9.95 368	25	10.04 632	9.87 141	11	3
58	9.82 523	14	9.95 393	25	10.04 607	9.87 130	11	2
59	9.82 537	14	9.95 418	26	10.04 582	9.87 119	12	1
60	9.82 551		9.95 444		10.04 556	9.87 107		0
	L Cos	d	L Ctn	cd	L Tan	L Sin	d	′

Prop. Pts.

	26	25
2	5.2	5.0
3	7.8	7.5
4	10.4	10.0
5	13.0	12.5
6	15.6	15.0
7	18.2	17.5
8	20.8	20.0
9	23.4	22.5

	15	14
2	3.0	2.8
3	4.5	4.2
4	6.0	5.6
5	7.5	7.0
6	9.0	8.4
7	10.5	9.8
8	12.0	11.2
9	13.5	12.6

	12	11
2	2.4	2.2
3	3.6	3.3
4	4.8	4.4
5	6.0	5.5
6	7.2	6.6
7	8.4	7.7
8	9.6	8.8
9	10.8	9.9

From the top: For **41°+** or **221°+**, read as printed; for **131°+** or **311°+**, read co-function.

From the bottom: For **48°+** or **228°+**, read as printed; for **138°+** or **318°+**, read co-function.

Prop. Pts.

′	L Sin	d	L Tan	cd	L Ctn	L Cos	d	
0	9.82 551		9.95 444		10.04 556	9.87 107		60
1	9.82 565	14	9.95 469	25	10.04 531	9.87 096	11	59
2	9.82 579	14	9.95 495	26	10.04 505	9.87 085	11	58
3	9.82 593	14	9.95 520	25	10.04 480	9.87 073	12	57
4	9.82 607	14	9.95 545	25	10.04 455	9.87 062	11	56
5	9.82 621	14	9.95 571	26	10.04 429	9.87 050	12	55
6	9.82 635	14	9.95 596	25	10.04 404	9.87 039	11	54
7	9.82 649	14	9.95 622	26	10.04 378	9.87 028	11	53
8	9.82 663	14	9.95 647	25	10.04 353	9.87 016	12	52
9	9.82 677	14	9.95 672	25	10.04 328	9.87 005	11	51
10	9.82 691	14	9.95 698	26	10.04 302	9.86 993	12	50
11	9.82 705	14	9.95 723	25	10.04 277	9.86 982	11	49
12	9.82 719	14	9.95 748	25	10.04 252	9.86 970	12	48
13	9.82 733	14	9.95 774	26	10.04 226	9.86 959	11	47
14	9.82 747	14	9.95 799	25	10.04 201	9.86 947	12	46
15	9.82 761	14	9.95 825	26	10.04 175	9.86 936	11	45
16	9.82 775	14	9.95 850	25	10.04 150	9.86 924	12	44
17	9.82 788	13	9.95 875	25	10.04 125	9.86 913	11	43
18	9.82 802	14	9.95 901	26	10.04 099	9.86 902	11	42
19	9.82 816	14	9.95 926	25	10.04 074	9.86 890	12	41
20	9.82 830	14	9.95 952	26	10.04 048	9.86 879	11	40
21	9.82 844	14	9.95 977	25	10.04 023	9.86 867	12	39
22	9.82 858	14	9.96 002	25	10.03 998	9.86 855	12	38
23	9.82 872	14	9.96 028	26	10.03 972	9.86 844	11	37
24	9.82 885	13	9.96 053	25	10.03 947	9.86 832	12	36
25	9.82 899	14	9.96 078	25	10.03 922	9.86 821	11	35
26	9.82 913	14	9.96 104	26	10.03 896	9.86 809	12	34
27	9.82 927	14	9.96 129	25	10.03 871	9.86 798	11	33
28	9.82 941	14	9.96 155	26	10.03 845	9.86 786	12	32
29	9.82 955	14	9.96 180	25	10.03 820	9.86 775	11	31
30	9.82 968	13	9.96 205	25	10.03 795	9.86 763	12	30
31	9.82 982	14	9.96 231	26	10.03 769	9.86 752	11	29
32	9.82 996	14	9.96 256	25	10.03 744	9.86 740	12	28
33	9.83 010	14	9.96 281	25	10.03 719	9.86 728	12	27
34	9.83 023	13	9.96 307	26	10.03 693	9.86 717	11	26
35	9.83 037	14	9.96 332	25	10.03 668	9.86 705	12	25
36	9.83 051	14	9.96 357	25	10.03 643	9.86 694	11	24
37	9.83 065	14	9.96 383	26	10.03 617	9.86 682	12	23
38	9.83 078	13	9.96 408	25	10.03 592	9.86 670	12	22
39	9.83 092	14	9.96 433	25	10.03 567	9.86 659	11	21
40	9.83 106	14	9.96 459	26	10.03 541	9.86 647	12	20
41	9.83 120	14	9.96 484	25	10.03 516	9.86 635	12	19
42	9.83 133	13	9.96 510	26	10.03 490	9.86 624	11	18
43	9.83 147	14	9.96 535	25	10.03 465	9.86 612	12	17
44	9.83 161	14	9.96 560	25	10.03 440	9.86 600	12	16
45	9.83 174	13	9.96 586	26	10.03 414	9.86 589	11	15
46	9.83 188	14	9.96 611	25	10.03 389	9.86 577	12	14
47	9.83 202	14	9.96 636	25	10.03 364	9.86 565	12	13
48	9.83 215	13	9.96 662	26	10.03 338	9.86 554	11	12
49	9.83 229	14	9.96 687	25	10.03 313	9.86 542	12	11
50	9.83 242	13	9.96 712	25	10.03 288	9.86 530	12	10
51	9.83 256	14	9.96 738	26	10.03 262	9.86 518	12	9
52	9.83 270	14	9.96 763	25	10.03 237	9.86 507	11	8
53	9.83 283	13	9.96 788	25	10.03 212	9.86 495	12	7
54	9.83 297	14	9.96 814	26	10.03 186	9.86 483	12	6
55	9.83 310	13	9.96 839	25	10.03 161	9.86 472	11	5
56	9.83 324	14	9.96 864	25	10.03 136	9.86 460	12	4
57	9.83 338	14	9.96 890	26	10.03 110	9.86 448	12	3
58	9.83 351	13	9.96 915	25	10.03 085	9.86 436	12	2
59	9.83 365	14	9.96 940	25	10.03 060	9.86 425	11	1
60	9.83 378	13	9.96 966	26	10.03 034	9.86 413	12	0
	L Cos	d	L Ctn	cd	L Tan	L Sin	d	′

Prop. Pts.

	26	25
2	5.2	5.0
3	7.8	7.5
4	10.4	10.0
5	13.0	12.5
6	15.6	15.0
7	18.2	17.5
8	20.8	20.0
9	23.4	22.5

	14	13
2	2.8	2.6
3	4.2	3.9
4	5.6	5.2
5	7.0	6.5
6	8.4	7.8
7	9.8	9.1
8	11.2	10.4
9	12.6	11.7

	12	11
2	2.4	2.2
3	3.6	3.3
4	4.8	4.4
5	6.0	5.5
6	7.2	6.6
7	8.4	7.7
8	9.6	8.8
9	10.8	9.9

From the top:

For **42°+** or **222°+**, read as printed; for **132°+** or **312°+**, read co-function.

From the bottom:

For **47°+** or **227°+**, read as printed; for **137°+** or **317°+**, read co-function.

Prop. Pts.

43° — Logarithms of Trigonometric Functions

′	L Sin	d	L Tan	cd	L Ctn	L Cos	d	
0	9.83 378	14	9.96 966	25	10.03 034	9.86 413	12	**60**
1	9.83 392	13	9.96 991	25	10.03 009	9.86 401	12	59
2	9.83 405	14	9.97 016	26	10.02 984	9.86 389	12	58
3	9.83 419	13	9.97 042	25	10.02 958	9.86 377	11	57
4	9.83 432	14	9.97 067	25	10.02 933	9.86 366	12	56
5	9.83 446	13	9.97 092	26	10.02 908	9.86 354	12	**55**
6	9.83 459	14	9.97 118	25	10.02 882	9.86 342	12	54
7	9.83 473	13	9.97 143	25	10.02 857	9.86 330	12	53
8	9.83 486	14	9.97 168	25	10.02 832	9.86 318	12	52
9	9.83 500	13	9.97 193	26	10.02 807	9.86 306	11	51
10	9.83 513	14	9.97 219	25	10.02 781	9.86 295	12	**50**
11	9.83 527	13	9.97 244	25	10.02 756	9.86 283	12	49
12	9.83 540	14	9.97 269	26	10.02 731	9.86 271	12	48
13	9.83 554	13	9.97 295	25	10.02 705	9.86 259	12	47
14	9.83 567	14	9.97 320	25	10.02 680	9.86 247	12	46
15	9.83 581	13	9.97 345	26	10.02 655	9.86 235	12	**45**
16	9.83 594	14	9.97 371	25	10.02 629	9.86 223	12	44
17	9.83 608	13	9.97 396	25	10.02 604	9.86 211	11	43
18	9.83 621	13	9.97 421	26	10.02 579	9.86 200	12	42
19	9.83 634	14	9.97 447	25	10.02 553	9.86 188	12	41
20	9.83 648	13	9.97 472	25	10.02 528	9.86 176	12	**40**
21	9.83 661	13	9.97 497	26	10.02 503	9.86 164	12	39
22	9.83 674	14	9.97 523	25	10.02 477	9.86 152	12	38
23	9.83 688	13	9.97 548	25	10.02 452	9.86 140	12	37
24	9.83 701	14	9.97 573	25	10.02 427	9.86 128	12	36
25	9.83 715	13	9.97 598	26	10.02 402	9.86 116	12	**35**
26	9.83 728	13	9.97 624	25	10.02 376	9.86 104	12	34
27	9.83 741	14	9.97 649	25	10.02 351	9.86 092	12	33
28	9.83 755	13	9.97 674	26	10.02 326	9.86 080	12	32
29	9.83 768	13	9.97 700	25	10.02 300	9.86 068	12	31
30	9.83 781	14	9.97 725	25	10.02 275	9.86 056	12	**30**
31	9.83 795	13	9.97 750	26	10.02 250	9.86 044	12	29
32	9.83 808	13	9.97 776	25	10.02 224	9.86 032	12	28
33	9.83 821	13	9.97 801	25	10.02 199	9.86 020	12	27
34	9.83 834	14	9.97 826	25	10.02 174	9.86 008	12	26
35	9.83 848	13	9.97 851	26	10.02 149	9.85 996	12	**25**
36	9.83 861	13	9.97 877	25	10.02 123	9.85 984	12	24
37	9.83 874	13	9.97 902	25	10.02 098	9.85 972	12	23
38	9.83 887	14	9.97 927	26	10.02 073	9.85 960	12	22
39	9.83 901	13	9.97 953	25	10.02 047	9.85 948	12	21
40	9.83 914	13	9.97 978	25	10.02 022	9.85 936	12	**20**
41	9.83 927	13	9.98 003	26	10.01 997	9.85 924	12	19
42	9.83 940	14	9.98 029	25	10.01 971	9.85 912	12	18
43	9.83 954	13	9.98 054	25	10.01 946	9.85 900	12	17
44	9.83 967	13	9.98 079	25	10.01 921	9.85 888	12	16
45	9.83 980	13	9.98 104	26	10.01 896	9.85 876	12	**15**
46	9.83 993	13	9.98 130	25	10.01 870	9.85 864	13	14
47	9.84 006	14	9.98 155	25	10.01 845	9.85 851	12	13
48	9.84 020	13	9.98 180	26	10.01 820	9.85 839	12	12
49	9.84 033	13	9.98 206	25	10.01 794	9.85 827	12	11
50	9.84 046	13	9.98 231	25	10.01 769	9.85 815	12	**10**
51	9.84 059	13	9.98 256	25	10.01 744	9.85 803	12	9
52	9.84 072	13	9.98 281	26	10.01 719	9.85 791	12	8
53	9.84 085	13	9.98 307	25	10.01 693	9.85 779	13	7
54	9.84 098	14	9.98 332	25	10.01 668	9.85 766	12	6
55	9.84 112	13	9.98 357	26	10.01 643	9.85 754	12	**5**
56	9.84 125	13	9.98 383	25	10.01 617	9.85 742	12	4
57	9.84 138	13	9.98 408	25	10.01 592	9.85 730	12	3
58	9.84 151	13	9.98 433	25	10.01 567	9.85 718	12	2
59	9.84 164	13	9.98 458	26	10.01 542	9.85 706	13	1
60	9.84 177		9.98 484		10.01 516	9.85 693		**0**
	L Cos	d	L Ctn	cd	L Tan	L Sin	d	′

Prop. Pts.

	26	25
2	5.2	5.0
3	7.8	7.5
4	10.4	10.0
5	13.0	12.5
6	15.6	15.0
7	18.2	17.5
8	20.8	20.0
9	23.4	22.5

	14	13
2	2.8	2.6
3	4.2	3.9
4	5.6	5.2
5	7.0	6.5
6	8.4	7.8
7	9.8	9.1
8	11.2	10.4
9	12.6	11.7

	12	11
2	2.4	2.2
3	3.6	3.3
4	4.8	4.4
5	6.0	5.5
6	7.2	6.6
7	8.4	7.7
8	9.6	8.8
9	10.8	9.9

From the top:

For **43°+** or **223°+**, read as printed; for **133°+** or **313°+**, read co-function.

From the bottom:

For **46°+** or **226°+**, read as printed; for **136°+** or **316°+**, read co-function.

Prop. Pts.

46° — Logarithms of Trigonometric Functions

44° — Logarithms of Trigonometric Functions

′	L Sin	d	L Tan	cd	L Ctn	L Cos	d	
0	9.84 177	13	9.98 484	25	10.01 516	9.85 693	12	**60**
1	9.84 190	13	9.98 509	25	10.01 491	9.85 681	12	59
2	9.84 203	13	9.98 534	26	10.01 466	9.85 669	12	58
3	9.84 216	13	9.98 560	25	10.01 440	9.85 657	12	57
4	9.84 229	13	9.98 585	25	10.01 415	9.85 645	13	56
5	9.84 242	13	9.98 610	25	10.01 390	9.85 632	12	**55**
6	9.84 255	14	9.98 635	26	10.01 365	9.85 620	12	54
7	9.84 269	13	9.98 661	25	10.01 339	9.85 608	12	53
8	9.84 282	13	9.98 686	25	10.01 314	9.85 596	13	52
9	9.84 295	13	9.98 711	26	10.01 289	9.85 583	12	51
10	9.84 308	13	9.98 737	25	10.01 263	9.85 571	12	**50**
11	9.84 321	13	9.98 762	25	10.01 238	9.85 559	12	49
12	9.84 334	13	9.98 787	25	10.01 213	9.85 547	13	48
13	9.84 347	13	9.98 812	26	10.01 188	9.85 534	12	47
14	9.84 360	13	9.98 838	25	10.01 162	9.85 522	12	46
15	9.84 373	12	9.98 863	25	10.01 137	9.85 510	13	**45**
16	9.84 385	13	9.98 888	25	10.01 112	9.85 497	12	44
17	9.84 398	13	9.98 913	26	10.01 087	9.85 485	12	43
18	9.84 411	13	9.98 939	25	10.01 061	9.85 473	13	42
19	9.84 424	13	9.98 964	25	10.01 036	9.85 460	12	41
20	9.84 437	13	9.98 989	26	10.01 011	9.85 448	12	**40**
21	9.84 450	13	9.99 015	25	10.00 985	9.85 436	13	39
22	9.84 463	13	9.99 040	25	10.00 960	9.85 423	12	38
23	9.84 476	13	9.99 065	25	10.00 935	9.85 411	12	37
24	9.84 489	13	9.99 090	26	10.00 910	9.85 399	13	36
25	9.84 502	13	9.99 116	25	10.00 884	9.85 386	12	**35**
26	9.84 515	13	9.99 141	25	10.00 859	9.85 374	13	34
27	9.84 528	12	9.99 166	25	10.00 834	9.85 361	12	33
28	9.84 540	13	9.99 191	26	10.00 809	9.85 349	12	32
29	9.84 553	13	9.99 217	25	10.00 783	9.85 337	13	31
30	9.84 566	13	9.99 242	25	10.00 758	9.85 324	12	**30**
31	9.84 579	13	9.99 267	26	10.00 733	9.85 312	13	29
32	9.84 592	13	9.99 293	25	10.00 707	9.85 299	12	28
33	9.84 605	13	9.99 318	25	10.00 682	9.85 287	13	27
34	9.84 618	12	9.99 343	25	10.00 657	9.85 274	12	26
35	9.84 630	13	9.99 368	26	10.00 632	9.85 262	12	**25**
36	9.84 643	13	9.99 394	25	10.00 606	9.85 250	13	24
37	9.84 656	13	9.99 419	25	10.00 581	9.85 237	12	23
38	9.84 669	13	9.99 444	25	10.00 556	9.85 225	13	22
39	9.84 682	12	9.99 469	26	10.00 531	9.85 212	12	21
40	9.84 694	13	9.99 495	25	10.00 505	9.85 200	13	**20**
41	9.84 707	13	9.99 520	25	10.00 480	9.85 187	12	19
42	9.84 720	13	9.99 545	25	10.00 455	9.85 175	13	18
43	9.84 733	12	9.99 570	26	10.00 430	9.85 162	12	17
44	9.84 745	13	9.99 596	25	10.00 404	9.85 150	13	16
45	9.84 758	13	9.99 621	25	10.00 379	9.85 137	12	**15**
46	9.84 771	13	9.99 646	26	10.00 354	9.85 125	13	14
47	9.84 784	12	9.99 672	25	10.00 328	9.85 112	12	13
48	9.84 796	13	9.99 697	25	10.00 303	9.85 100	13	12
49	9.84 809	13	9.99 722	25	10.00 278	9.85 087	13	11
50	9.84 822	13	9.99 747	26	10.00 253	9.85 074	12	**10**
51	9.84 835	12	9.99 773	25	10.00 227	9.85 062	13	9
52	9.84 847	13	9.99 798	25	10.00 202	9.85 049	12	8
53	9.84 860	13	9.99 823	25	10.00 177	9.85 037	13	7
54	9.84 873	12	9.99 848	26	10.00 152	9.85 024	12	6
55	9.84 885	13	9.99 874	25	10.00 126	9.85 012	13	**5**
56	9.84 898	13	9.99 899	25	10.00 101	9.84 999	13	4
57	9.84 911	12	9.99 924	25	10.00 076	9.84 986	12	3
58	9.84 923	13	9.99 949	26	10.00 051	9.84 974	13	2
59	9.84 936	13	9.99 975	25	10.00 025	9.84 961	12	1
60	9.84 949		10.0000		10.00 000	9.84 949		**0**
	L Cos	d	L Ctn	cd	L Tan	L Sin	d	′

Prop. Pts.

	26	**25**
2	5.2	5.0
3	7.8	7.5
4	10.4	10.0
5	13.0	12.5
6	15.6	15.0
7	18.2	17.5
8	20.8	20.0
9	23.4	22.5

	14	**13**
2	2.8	2.6
3	4.2	3.9
4	5.6	5.2
5	7.0	6.5
6	8.4	7.8
7	9.8	9.1
8	11.2	10.4
9	12.6	11.7

	12
2	2.4
3	3.6
4	4.8
5	6.0
6	7.2
7	8.4
8	9.6
9	10.8

From the top:

For **44°+** or **224°+**, read as printed; for **134°+** or **314°+**, read co-function.

From the bottom:

For **45°+** or **225°+**, read as printed; for **135°+** or **315°+**, read co-function.

Prop. Pts.

45° — Logarithms of Trigonometric Functions

VI. Compound Interest

Compound Interest: $(1 + r)^n$

AMOUNT OF ONE DOLLAR PRINCIPAL AT COMPOUND INTEREST AFTER n YEARS

n	2 %	2½ %	3 %	3½ %	4 %	4½ %	5 %	6 %	7 %
1	1.0200	1.0250	1.0300	1.0350	1.0400	1.0450	1.0500	1.0600	1.0700
2	1.0404	1.0506	1.0609	1.0712	1.0816	1.0920	1.1025	1.1236	1.1449
3	1.0612	1.0769	1.0927	1.1087	1.1249	1.1412	1.1576	1.1910	1.2250
4	1.0824	1.1038	1.1255	1.1475	1.1699	1.1925	1.2155	1.2625	1.3108
5	1.1041	1.1314	1.1593	1.1877	1.2167	1.2462	1.2763	1.3382	1.4026
6	1.1262	1.1597	1.1941	1.2293	1.2653	1.3023	1.3401	1.4185	1.5007
7	1.1487	1.1887	1.2299	1.2723	1.3159	1.3609	1.4071	1.5036	1.6058
8	1.1717	1.2184	1.2668	1.3168	1.3686	1.4221	1.4775	1.5938	1.7182
9	1.1951	1.2489	1.3048	1.3629	1.4233	1.4861	1.5513	1.6895	1.8385
10	1.2190	1.2801	1.3439	1.4106	1.4802	1.5530	1.6289	1.7908	1.9672
11	1.2434	1.3121	1.3842	1.4600	1.5395	1.6229	1.7103	1.8983	2.1049
12	1.2682	1.3449	1.4258	1.5111	1.6010	1.6959	1.7959	2.0122	2.2522
13	1.2936	1.3785	1.4685	1.5640	1.6651	1.7722	1.8856	2.1329	2.4098
14	1.3195	1.4130	1.5126	1.6187	1.7317	1.8519	1.9799	2.2609	2.5785
15	1.3459	1.4483	1.5580	1.6753	1.8009	1.9353	2.0789	2.3966	2.7590
16	1.3728	1.4845	1.6047	1.7340	1.8730	2.0224	2.1829	2.5404	2.9522
17	1.4002	1.5216	1.6528	1.7947	1.9479	2.1134	2.2920	2.6928	3.1588
18	1.4282	1.5597	1.7024	1.8575	2.0258	2.2085	2.4066	2.8543	3.3799
19	1.4568	1.5987	1.7535	1.9225	2.1068	2.3079	2.5270	3.0256	3.6165
20	1.4859	1.6386	1.8061	1.9898	2.1911	2.4117	2.6533	3.2071	3.8697
21	1.5157	1.6796	1.8603	2.0594	2.2788	2.5202	2.7860	3.3996	4.1406
22	1.5460	1.7216	1.9161	2.1315	2.3699	2.6337	2.9253	3.6035	4.4304
23	1.5769	1.7646	1.9736	2.2061	2.4647	2.7522	3.0715	3.8197	4.7405
24	1.6084	1.8087	2.0328	2.2833	2.5633	2.8760	3.2251	4.0489	5.0724
25	1.6406	1.8539	2.0938	2.3632	2.6658	3.0054	3.3864	4.2919	5.4274
26	1.6734	1.9003	2.1566	2.4460	2.7725	3.1407	3.5557	4.5494	5.8074
27	1.7069	1.9478	2.2213	2.5316	2.8834	3.2820	3.7335	4.8223	6.2139
28	1.7410	1.9965	2.2879	2.6202	2.9987	3.4297	3.9201	5.1117	6.6488
29	1.7758	2.0464	2.3566	2.7119	3.1187	3.5840	4.1161	5.4184	7.1143
30	1.8114	2.0976	2.4273	2.8068	3.2434	3.7453	4.3219	5.7435	7.6123
31	1.8476	2.1500	2.5001	2.9050	3.3731	3.9139	4.5380	6.0881	8.1451
32	1.8845	2.2038	2.5751	3.0067	3.5081	4.0900	4.7649	6.4534	8.7153
33	1.9222	2.2589	2.6523	3.1119	3.6484	4.2740	5.0032	6.8406	9.3253
34	1.9607	2.3153	2.7319	3.2209	3.7943	4.4664	5.2533	7.2510	9.9781
35	1.9999	2.3732	2.8139	3.3336	3.9461	4.6673	5.5160	7.6861	10.6766
36	2.0399	2.4325	2.8983	3.4503	4.1039	4.8774	5.7918	8.1473	11.4239
37	2.0807	2.4933	2.9852	3.5710	4.2681	5.0969	6.0814	8.6361	12.2236
38	2.1223	2.5557	3.0748	3.6960	4.4388	5.3262	6.3855	9.1543	13.0793
39	2.1647	2.6196	3.1670	3.8254	4.6164	5.5659	6.7048	9.7035	13.9948
40	2.2080	2.6851	3.2620	3.9593	4.8010	5.8164	7.0400	10.2857	14.9745
41	2.2522	2.7522	3.3599	4.0978	4.9931	6.0781	7.3920	10.9029	16.0227
42	2.2972	2.8210	3.4607	4.2413	5.1928	6.3516	7.7616	11.5570	17.1443
43	2.3432	2.8915	3.5645	4.3897	5.4005	6.6374	8.1497	12.2505	18.3444
44	2.3901	2.9638	3.6715	4.5433	5.6165	6.9361	8.5572	12.9855	19.6285
45	2.4379	3.0379	3.7816	4.7024	5.8412	7.2482	8.9850	13.7646	21.0025
46	2.4866	3.1139	3.8950	4.8669	6.0748	7.5744	9.4343	14.5905	22.4726
47	2.5363	3.1917	4.0119	5.0373	6.3178	7.9153	9.9060	15.4659	24.0457
48	2.5871	3.2715	4.1323	5.2136	6.5705	8.2715	10.4013	16.3939	25.7289
49	2.6388	3.3533	4.2562	5.3961	6.8333	8.6437	10.9213	17.3775	27.5299
50	2.6916	3.4371	4.3839	5.5849	7.1067	9.0326	11.4674	18.4202	29.4570

VII. Weights and Measures: Conversion Ratios

WEIGHTS AND MEASURES*

Tables of United States Customary Weights and Measures

Linear Measure

12 inches (in.)	= 1 foot (ft.)
3 feet	= 1 yard (yd.)
$5^1/_2$ yards	= 1 rod (rd.), pole, or perch ($16^1/_2$ ft.)
40 rods	= 1 furlong (fur.) = 220 yards = 660 feet
8 furlongs	= 1 statute mile (mi.) = 1760 yards = 5280 feet
3 miles	= 1 league = 5280 yards = 15,840 feet
5280 feet	= 1 statute or land mile
6076.11549 feet	= 1 international nautical mile

Area Measure

Squares and cubes of units are sometimes abbreviated by using "superior" figures. For example, ft^2 means square foot, and ft^3 means cubic foot.

144 square inches	= 1 square foot (sq. ft.)
9 square feet	= 1 square yard (sq. yd.) = 1296 square inches
$30^1/_4$ square yards	= 1 square rod (sq. rd.) = $272^1/_4$ square feet
160 square rods	= 1 acre = 4840 square yards = 43,560 square feet
640 acres	= 1 square mile (sq. mi.)
1 mile square	= 1 section (of land)
6 miles square	= 1 township = 36 sections = 36 square miles

Cubic Measure

1728 cubic inches (cu. in.)	= 1 cubic foot (cu. ft.)
27 cubic feet	= 1 cubic yard (cu. yd.)

Gunter's or Surveyor's Chain Measure

7.92 inches (in.)	= 1 link (li.)
100 links	= 1 chain (ch.) = 4 rods = 66 feet
80 chains	= 1 statute mile (mi.) = 320 rods = 5280 feet

Liquid Measure

When necessary to distinguish the liquid pint or quart from the dry pint or quart, the word "liquid" or the abbreviation "liq" should be used in combination with the name or abbreviation of the liquid unit.

4 gills (gi.)	= 1 pint (pt.) (= 28.875 cubic inches)
2 pints	= 1 quart (qt.) (= 57.75 cubic inches)
4 quarts	= 1 gallon (gal.) (= 231 cubic inches) = 8 pints = 32 gills

* Source: National Bureau of Standards, U.S. Department of Commerce.

Apothecaries' Fluid Measure

60 minims (min.) = 1 fluid dram (fl. dr.) (= 0.2256 cubic inch)
8 fluid drams = 1 fluid ounce (fl. oz.) (= 1.8047 cubic inches)
16 fluid ounces = 1 pint (pt.) (= 28.875 cubic inches)
= 128 fluid drams
2 pints = 1 quart (qt.) (= 57.75 cubic inches)
= 32 fluid ounces = 256 fluid drams
4 quarts = 1 gallon (gal.) (= 231 cubic inches) = 128 fluid ounces = 1024 fluid drams

Dry Measure

When necessary to distinguish the dry pint or quart from the liquid pint or quart, the word "dry" should be used in combination with the name or abbreviation of the dry unit.

2 pints (pt.) = 1 quart (qt.) (= 67.2006 cubic inches)
8 quarts = 1 peck (pk.) (= 537.605 cubic inches) = 16 pints
4 pecks = 1 bushel (bu.) (= 2150.42 cubic inches) = 32 quarts

Avoirdupois Weight

When necessary to distinguish the avoirdupois dram from the apothecaries' dram, or to distinguish the avoirdupois dram or ounce from the fluid dram or ounce, or to distinguish the avoirdupois ounce or pound from the troy or apothecaries' ounce or pound, the word "avoirdupois" or the abbreviation "avdp" should be used in combination with the name or abbreviation of the avoirdupois unit.

(The "grain" is the same in avoirdupois, troy, and apothecaries' weight.)

$27^{11}/_{32}$ grains = 1 dram (dr.)
16 drams = 1 ounce (oz.) = $437^{1}/_{2}$ grains
16 ounces = 1 pound (lb.) = 256 drams = 7000 grains
100 pounds = 1 hundredweight (cwt.)†
20 hundredweights = 1 ton (tn.) = 2000 pounds†

In "gross" or "long" measure, the following values are recognized:

112 pounds = 1 gross or long hundredweight†
20 gross or long hundredweights = 1 gross or long ton = 2240 pounds†

† When the terms "hundredweight" and "ton" are used unmodified, they are commonly understood to mean the 100-pound hundredweight and the 2,000-pound ton, respectively; these units may be designated "net" or "short" when necessary to distinguish them from the corresponding units in gross or long measure.

Troy Weight

24 grains = 1 pennyweight (dwt.)
20 pennyweights = 1 ounce troy (oz. t.) = 480 grains
12 ounces troy = 1 pound troy (lb. t.) = 240 pennyweights
= 5760 grains

Apothecaries' Weight

20 grains	= scruple (s. ap.)
3 scruples	= 1 dram apothecaries' (dr. ap.) = 60 grains
8 drams apothecaries'	= 1 ounce apothecaries' (oz. ap.) = 24 scruples = 480 grains
12 ounces apothecaries'	= 1 pound apothecaries' (lb. ap.) = 96 drams apothecaries' = 288 scruples = 5760 grains

Tables of Metric Weights and Measures

Linear Measure

10 millimeters (mm.)	= 1 centimeter (cm.)
10 centimeters	= 1 decimeter (dm.) = 100 millimeters
10 decimeters	= 1 meter (m.) = 1000 millimeters
10 meters	= 1 dekameter (dkm.)
10 dekameters	= 1 hectometer (hm.) = 100 meters
10 hectometers	= 1 kilometer (km.) = 1000 meters

Area Measure

100 square millimeters (mm^2)	= 1 square centimeter (cm^2)
10,000 square centimeters	= 1 square meter (m^2) = 1,000,000 square millimeters
100 square meters	= 1 are (a.)
100 ares	= 1 hectare (ha.) = 10,000 square meters
100 hectares	= 1 square kilometer (km^2) = 1,000,000 square meters

Volume Measure

10 milliliters (ml.)	= 1 centiliter (cl.)
10 centiliters	= 1 deciliter (dl.) = 100 milliliters
10 deciliters	= 1 liter‡ (l.) = 1000 milliliters
10 liters	= 1 dekaliter (dkl.)
10 dekaliters	= 1 hectoliter (hl.) = 100 liters
10 hectoliters	= 1 kiloliter (kl.) = 1000 liters

‡ The liter is defined as the volume occupied, under standard conditions, by a quantity of pure water having a mass of 1 kilogram. This volume is very nearly equal to 1000 cubic centimeters or 1 cubic decimeter; the actual metric equivalent is, 1 liter = 1.000028 cubic decimeters. Thus the milliliter and the liter are larger than the cubic centimeter and the cubic decimeter, respectively, by 28 parts in 1,000,000.

Cubic Measure

1000 cubic millimeters (mm^3)	= 1 cubic centimeter (cm^3)
1000 cubic centimeters	= 1 cubic decimeter (dm^3) = 1,000,000 cubic millimeters
1000 cubic decimeters	= 1 cubic meter (m^3) = 1 stere = 1,000,000 cubic centimeters = 1,000,000,000 cubic millimeters

Weight

10 milligrams (mg.)	= 1 centigram (cg.)
10 centigrams	= 1 decigram (dg.) = 100 milligrams
10 decigrams	= 1 gram (g.) = 1000 milligrams
10 grams	= 1 dekagram (dkg.)
10 dekagrams	= 1 hectogram (hg.) = 100 grams
10 hectograms	= 1 kilogram (kg.) = 1000 grams
1000 kilograms	= 1 metric ton (t.)

Tables of Equivalents

When the name of a unit is enclosed in brackets thus: [1 hand], this indicates (1) that the unit is not in general current use in the United States, or (2) that the unit is believed to be based on "custom and usage" rather than on formal definition.

Equivalents involving decimals are, in most instances, rounded off to the third decimal place except where they are exact, in which cases these exact equivalents are so designated.

Lengths

1 Angstrom (A.)	0.1 millimicron (exactly) 0.0001 micron (exactly) 0.0000001 millimeter (exactly) 0.000000004 inch
1 cable's length	120 fathoms 720 feet 219.456 meters (exactly)
1 centimeter (cm.)	0.3937 inch
1 chain (ch.) (Gunter's or surveyor's)	66 feet 20.1168 meters (exactly)
1 chain (engineer's)	100 feet 30.48 meters (exactly)
1 decimeter (dm.)	3.937 inches
1 dekameter (dkm.)	32,808 feet
1 fathom	6 feet 1.8288 meters (exactly)
1 foot (ft.)	0.3048 meters (exactly)
1 furlong (fur.)	10 chains (surveyor's) 660 feet 220 yards 1/8 statute mile 201.168 meters
[1 hand]	4 inches
1 inch (in.)	2.54 centimeters (exactly)
1 kilometer (km.)	0.621 mile
1 league (land)	3 statute miles 4.828 kilometers
1 link (li.) (Gunter's or surveyor's)	7.92 inches 0.201 meter
1 link (li.) (engineer's)	1 foot 0.305 meter

1 meter (m.)	39.37 inches 1.094 yards
1 micron (μ [the Greek letter mu])	0.001 millimeter (exactly) 0.00003937 inch
1 mil	0.001 inch (exactly) 0.0254 millimeter (exactly)
1 mile (mi.) (statute or land)	5280 feet 1.609 kilometers
1 mile (mi.) (nautical, international, and new U.S. value)	1.852 kilometers (exactly) 1.150779 statute miles 6076.11549 feet
1 millimeter (mm.)	0.03937 inch
1 millimicron (mμ [the English letter *m* in combination with the Greek letter mu])	0.001 micron (exactly) 0.00000003937 inch (exactly)
1 point (typography)	0.013837 inch (exactly) 0.351 millimeter
1 rod (rd.), pole, or perch	16 1/2 feet 5 1/2 yards 5.029 meters
1 yard (yd.)	0.9144 meter (exactly)

Areas or Surfaces

1 acre	43,560 square feet 4840 square yards 0.405 hectare
1 are (a.)	119.599 square yards 0.025 acre
1 hectare (ha.)	2.471 acres
[1 square (building)]	100 square feet
1 square centimeter (cm^2)	0.155 square inch
1 square decimeter (dm^2)	15.500 square inches
1 square foot (sq. ft.)	929.030 square centimeters
1 square inch (sq. in.)	6.452 square centimeters
1 square kilometer (km^2)	247.105 acres 0.386 square mile
1 square meter (m^2)	1.196 square yards 10.764 square feet
1 square mile (sq. mi.)	258.999 hectares
1 square millimeter (mm^2)	0.002 square inch
1 square rod (sq. rd.), sq. pole, or sq. perch	25.293 square meters
1 square yard (sq. yd.)	0.836 square meter

Capacities or Volumes

1 barrel (bbl.), liquid	31 to 42 gallons*
1 barrel (bbl.), standard, for fruits, vegetables, and other dry commodities except cranberries	7056 cubic inches 105 dry quarts 3.281 bushels, struck measure

* There are a variety of "barrels," established by law or usage. For example, federal taxes on fermented liquors are based on a barrel of 31 gallons; many state laws fix the "barrel for liquids" at 31 1/2 gallons; one state fixes a 36-gallon barrel for cistern measurement; federal law recognizes a 40-gallon barrel for "proof spirits"; by custom, 42 gallons comprise a barrel of crude oil or petroleum products for statistical purposes, and this equivalent is recognized "for liquids" by four states.

1 barrel (bbl.), standard, cranberry	5826 cubic inches $86^{45}/_{64}$ dry quarts 2.709 bushels, struck measure
1 bushel (bu.) (U.S.) (struck measure)	2150.42 cubic inches (exactly) 35.238 liters
[1 bushel, heaped (U.S.)]	2747.715 cubic inches 1.278 bushels, struck measure†

† Frequently recognized as $1^1/_4$ bushels, struck measure.

[1 bushel (bu.) (British Imperial) (struck measure)]	1.032 U.S. bushels, struck measure 2219.36 cubic inches
1 cord (cd.) (firewood)	128 cubic feet
1 cubic centimeter (cm³)	0.061 cubic inch
1 cubic decimeter (dm³)	61.023 cubic inches
1 cubic foot (cu. ft.)	7.481 gallons 28.317 cubic decimeters
1 cubic inch (cu. in.)	0.554 fluid ounce 4.433 fluid drams 16.387 cubic centimeters
1 cubic meter (m³)	1.308 cubic yards
1 cubic yard (cu. yd.)	0.765 cubic meter
1 cup, measuring	8 fluid ounces $^1/_2$ liquid pint
1 dekaliter (dkl.)	2.642 gallons 1.135 pecks
1 dram, fluid (or liquid) (fl. dr.) (U.S.)	$^1/_8$ fluid ounce 0.226 cubic inch 3.697 milliliters
[1 dram, fluid (fl. dr.) (British)]	0.961 U.S. fluid dram 0.217 cubic inch 3.552 milliliters
1 gallon (gal.) (U.S.)	231 cubic inches 3.785 liters 0.833 British gallon 128 U.S. fluid ounces
[1 gallon (gal.) (British Imperial)]	277.42 cubic inches 1.201 U.S. gallons 4.546 liters 160 British fluid ounces
1 gill (gi.)	7.219 cubic inches 4 fluid ounces 0.118 liter
1 hectoliter (hl.)	26.418 gallons 2.838 bushels
1 liter	1.057 liquid quarts 0.908 dry quart 61.025 cubic inches
1 milliliter (ml.)	0.271 fluid dram 16.231 minims 0.061 cubic inch
1 ounce, fluid (or liquid) (fl. oz.) (U.S.)	1.805 cubic inches 29.573 milliliters 1.041 British fluid ounces

[1 ounce, fluid (fl. oz.) (British)]	0.961 U.S. fluid ounce
	1.734 cubic inches
	28.412 milliliters
1 peck (pk.)	8.810 liters
1 pint (pt.), dry	33.600 cubic inches
	0.551 liter
1 pint (pt.), liquid	28.875 cubic inches (exactly)
	0.473 liter
1 quart (qt.), dry (U.S.)	67.201 cubic inches
	1.101 liters
	0.969 British quart
1 quart (qt.), liquid (U.S.)	57.75 cubic inches (exactly)
	0.946 liter
	0.833 British quart
[1 quart (qt.) (British)]	69.354 cubic inches
	1.032 U.S. dry quarts
	1.201 U.S. liquid quarts
1 tablespoon	3 teaspoons‡
	4 fluid drams
	$^{1}/_{2}$ fluid ounce
1 teaspoon	$^{1}/_{3}$ tablespoon‡
	$1^{1}/_{3}$ fluid drams‡

‡ The equivalent "1 teaspoon = $1^{1}/_{3}$ fluid drams" has been found by the Bureau to correspond more closely with the actual capacities of "measuring" and silver teaspoons than the equivalent "1 teaspoon = 1 fluid dram" which is given by a number of dictionaries.

Weights or Masses

1 assay ton* (AT)	29.167 grams

* Used in assaying. The assay ton bears the same relation to the milligram that a ton of 2000 pounds avoirdupois bears to the ounce troy; hence the weight in milligrams of precious metal obtained from one assay ton of ore gives directly the number of troy ounces to the net ton.

1 carat (c.)	200 milligrams 3.086 grains
1 dram. apothecaries' (dr. ap.)	60 grains 3.888 grams
1 dram. avoirdupois (dr. avdp.)	$27^{11}/_{32}$ (= 27.344) grains 1.772 grams
gamma, *see* microgram	
1 grain	64.799 milligrams
1 gram (g.)	15.432 grains 0.035 ounce, avoirdupois
1 hundredweight, gross or long† (gross cwt.)	112 pounds 50.802 kilograms

† The gross or long ton and hundredweight are used commercially in the United States to only a limited extent, usually in restricted industrial fields. These units are the same as the British "ton" and "hundredweight."

1 hundredweight, net or short (cwt. or net cwt.)	100 pounds 45.359 kilograms
1 kilogram (kg.)	2.205 pounds
1 microgram (γ [the Greek letter gamma])	0.000001 gram (exactly)
1 milligram (mg.)	0.015 grain
1 ounce, avoirdupois (oz. avdp.)	437.5 grains (exactly) 0.911 troy or apothecaries' ounce 28.350 grams
1 ounce, troy or apothecaries' (oz. t. or oz. ap.)	480 grains 1.097 avoirdupois ounces 31.103 grams
1 pennyweight (dwt.)	1.555 grams
1 pound, avoirdupois (lb. avdp.)	7000 grains 1.215 troy or apothecaries' pounds 453.59237 grams (exactly)
1 pound, troy or apothecaries' (lb. t. or lb. ap.)	5760 grains 0.823 avoirdupois pound 373.242 grams
1 scruple (s. ap.)	20 grains 1.296 grams
1 ton, gross or long† (gross tn.)	2240 pounds 1.12 net tons (exactly) 1.016 metric tons
1 ton, metric (t.)	2204.623 pounds 0.984 gross ton 1.102 net tons
1 ton, net or short (tn. or net tn.)	2000 pounds 0.893 gross ton 0.907 metric ton

Tables of Interrelation of Units of Measurement

Bold face type indicates exact values

Units of Length

Units	Inches	Links	Feet	Yards	Rods	Chains	Miles	Cm.	Meters
1 inch =	**1**	0.126 333	0.083 333	0.027 778	0.005 051	0.001 263	0.000 016	**2.54**	**0.025 4**
1 link =	**7.92**	**1**	**0.66**	**0.22**	**0.04**	**0.01**	**0.000 125**	20.117	**0.201 168**
1 foot =	**12**	1.515 152	**1**	0.333 333	0.060 606	0.015 152	0.000 189	**30.48**	**0.304 8**
1 yard =	**36**	4.545 45	**3**	**1**	0.181 818	0.045 455	0.000 568	**91.44**	**0.914 4**
1 rod =	**198**	**25**	**16.5**	**5.5**	**1**	**0.25**	**0.003 125**	**502.92**	**5.029 2**
1 chain =	**792**	**100**	**66**	**22**	**4**	**1**	**0.012 5**	**2011.68**	**20.116 8**
1 mile =	**63 360**	**8000**	**5280**	**1760**	**320**	**80**	**1**	**160 934.4**	**1609.344**
1 cm. =	0.3937	0.049 710	0.032 808	0.010 936	0.001 988	0.000 497	0.000 006	**1**	**0.01**
1 meter =	39.37	4.970 970	3.280 840	1.093 613	0.198 839	0.049 710	0.000 621	**100**	**1**

Units of Area

Units		Square inches	Square links	Square feet	Square yards	Square rods	Square chains
1 sq. inch	=	1	.015 942 3	0.006 944	0.000 771 605	0.000 025 5	0.000 001 594
1 sq. link	=	**62.726 4**	1	**0.435 6**	**0.0484**	**0.0016**	**0.000 1**
1 sq. foot	=	**144**	2.295 684	1	0.111 111 1	0.003 673 09	0.000 229 568
1 sq. yard	=	**1296**	20.661 16	**9**	1	0.033 057 85	0.002 066 12
1 sq. rod	=	**39 204**	**625**	**272.25**	**30.25**	1	**0.062 5**
1 sq. chain	=	**627 264**	**10 000**	**4356**	**484**	**16**	1
1 acre	=	**6 272 640**	**100 000**	**43 560**	**4840**	**160**	**10**
1 sq. mile	=	**4 014 489 600**	**64 000 000**	**27 878 400**	**3 097 600**	**102 400**	**6400**
1 sq. cm.	=	0.155 000 3	0.002 471 05	0.001 076	0.000 119 599	0.000 003 954	0.000 000 247
1 sq. meter	=	1550.003	24.710 54	10.763 91	1.195 990	0.039 536 86	0.002 471 054
1 hectare	=	15 500 031	247 105	107 639.1	11 959.90	395.368 6	24.710 54

Units		Acres	Square miles	Square centimeters	Square meters	Hectares
1 sq. inch	=	0.000 000 159 423	0.000 000 000 249 10	**6.451 6**	**0.000 645 16**	0.000 000 065
1 sq. link	=	**0.000 01**	**0.000 000 015 625**	**404.685 642 24**	0.040 468 56	0.000 004 047
1 sq. foot	=	0.000 022 956 84	0.000 000 035 870 06	**929.030 4**	**0.092 903 04**	0.000 009 290
1 sq. yard	=	0.000 206 611 6	0.000 000 322 830 6	**8 361.273 6**	**0.836 127 36**	0.000 083 613
1 sq. rod	=	**0.006 25**	**0.000 009 765 625**	**252 928.526 4**	**25.292 852 64**	0.002 529 285
1 sq. chain	=	**0.1**	**0.000 156 25**	4 046 856	**404.685 642 24**	0.040 468 564
1 acre	=	1	**0.001 562 5**	40 468 654	**4046.856 422 4**	0.404 685 642
1 sq. mile	=	**640**	1	25 899 881 103	2 589 988.11	258.998 811 034
1 sq. cm.	=	0.000 000 024 711	0.000 000 000 038 610	1	**0.0001**	**0.000 000 01**
1 sq. meter	=	0.000 247 105 4	0.000 000 386 102 2	**10 000**	1	**0.0001**
1 hectare	=	2.471 054	0.003 861 022	**100 000 000**	**10 000**	1

Units of Volume

Units		Cubic inches	Cubic feet	Cubic yards	Cubic centimeters	Cubic decimeters	Cubic meters
1 cubic inch	=	**1**	0.000 578 704	0.000 021 433	**16.387 064**	0.016 387	0.000 016 387
1 cubic foot	=	**1728**	**1**	0.037 037 04	**28 316.846 592**	28.316 847	0.028 316 847
1 cubic yard	=	**46 656**	**27**	**1**	**764 554.857 984**	764.554 858	0.764 554 858
1 cubic cm.	=	0.061 023 74	0.000 035 315	0.000 001 308	**1**	**0.001**	**0.000 001**
1 cubic dm.	=	61.023 74	0.035 314 67	0.001 307 951	**1000**	**1**	**0.001**
1 cubic meter	=	61 023.74	35.314 67	1.307 951	**1 000 000**	**1000**	**1**

Units of Capacity (Liquid Measure)

Units		Minims	Fluid drams	Fluid ounces	Gills	Liquid pints
1 minim	=	**1**	0.016 666 7	0.002 083 33	0.000 520 833	0.000 130 208
1 fluid dram	=	**60**	**1**	**0.125**	**0.031 25**	**0.007 812 5**
1 fluid ounce	=	**480**	**8**	**1**	**0.25**	**0.062 5**
1 gill	=	**1920**	**32**	**4**	**1**	**0.25**
1 liquid pint	=	**7680**	**128**	**16**	**4**	**1**
1 liquid quart	=	**15 360**	**256**	**32**	**8**	**2**
1 gallon	=	**61 440**	**1024**	**128**	**32**	**8**
1 milliliter	=	16.231	0.270 519 8	0.033 814 97	0.008 453 742	0.002 113 436
1 liter	=	16 231.19	270.519 8	33.814 97	8.453 742	2.113 436
1 cubic inch	=	265.974	4.432 900	0.554 112 6	0.138 528 1	0.034 632 03
1 cubic foot	=	459 603.1	7660.052	957.506 5	239.376 6	59.844 16

Units of Capacity (Liquid Measure) Continued. **Bold face** type indicates exact values

Units		Liquid quarts	Gallons	Milliliters	Liters	Cubic inches	Cubic feet
1 minim	=	0.000 065 104	0.000 016 276	0.061 610	0.000 061 610	0.003 760	0.000 002 176
1 fluid dram	=	**0.003 906 25**	0.000 976 562	3.696 588	0.003 696 588	0.225 586	0.000 130 547
1 fluid ounce	=	**0.031 25**	**0.007 812 5**	29.572 70	0.029 572 7	1.804 687	0.001 044 379
1 gill	=	**0.125**	**0.031 25**	118.290 8	0.118 290 8	**7.218 75**	0.004 177 517
1 liquid pint	=	**0.5**	**0.125**	473.163 2	0.473 163 2	**28.875**	0.016 710 07
1 liquid quart	=	**1**	**0.25**	946.326 4	0.946 326 4	**57.75**	0.033 420 14
1 gallon	=	**4**	**1**	3785.306	3.785 306	**231**	0.133 680 6
1 milliliter	=	0.001 056 718	0.000 264 179	**1**	**0.001**	0.061 025	0.000 035 316
1 liter	=	1.056 718	0.264 179 4	**1000**	**1**	61.025 45	0.035 315 66
1 cubic inch	=	0.017 316 02	0.004 329 004	16.386 61	0.016 386 61	**1**	0.000 578 704
1 cubic foot	=	29.922 08	7.480 519	28 316.05	28.316 05	**1728**	**1**

Units of Capacity (Dry Measure)

Units		Dry pints	Dry quarts	Pecks	Bushels	Liters	Dekaliters	Cubic inches
1 dry pint	=	**1**	**0.5**	**0.062 5**	**0.015 625**	0.550 595	0.055 060	**33.600 312 5**
1 dry quart	=	**2**	**1**	**0.125**	**0.031 25**	1.101 190	0.110 119	**67.200 625**
1 peck	=	**16**	**8**	**1**	**0.25**	8.809 521	0.880 952	**537.605**
1 bushel	=	**64**	**32**	**4**	**1**	35.238 08	3.523 808	**2150.42**
1 liter	=	1.816 217	0.908 108	0.113 514	0.028 378	**1**	**0.1**	61.025 45
1 dekaliter	=	18.162 17	9.081 084	1.135 136	0.283 784	**10**	**1**	610.254 5
1 cubic inch	=	0.029 762	0.014 881	0.001 860	0.000 465	0.016 386	0.001 639	**1**

Units of Mass not Greater than Pounds and Kilograms

Units		Grains	Apothecaries' scruples	Pennyweights	Avoirdupois drams	Apothecaries' drams	Avoirdupois ounces
1 grain	=	**1**	**0.05**	0.041 666 67	0.036 571 43	0.016 666 67	0.002 285 71
1 scruple	=	**20**	**1**	0.833 333 3	0.731 428 6	0.333 333 3	0.045 714 29
1 pennyweight	=	**24**	**1.2**	**1**	0.877 714 3	**0.4**	0.054 857 14
1 dram avdp.	=	**27.343 75**	**1.367 187 5**	1.139 323	**1**	0.455 729 2	**0.062 5**
1 dram ap.	=	**60**	**3**	**2.5**	2.194 286	**1**	0.137 142 9
1 oz. avdp.	=	**437.5**	**21.875**	18.229 17	**16**	7.291 667	**1**
1 oz. ap. or t.	=	**480**	**24**	**20**	17.554 29	**8**	1.097 143
1 lb. ap. or t.	=	**5760**	**288**	**240**	210.651 4	**96**	13.165 71
1 lb. avdp.	=	**7000**	**350**	291.666 7	**256**	116.666 7	**16**
1 milligram	=	0.015 432	0.000 771 618	0.000 643 015	0.000 564 383	0.000 257 206	0.000 035 274
1 gram	=	15.432 36	0.771 617 9	0.643 014 9	0.564 383 4	0.257 206 0	0.035 273 96
1 kilogram	=	15 432.36	771.617 9	643.014 9	564.383 4	257.206 0	35.273 96

Units		Apothecaries' or troy ounces	Apothecaries' or troy pounds	Avoirdupois pounds	Milligrams	Grams	Kilograms
1 grain	=	0.002 083 33	0.000 173 611	0.000 142 857	**64.798 91**	**0.064 798 91**	0.000 064 799
1 scruple	=	0.041 666 67	0.003 472 222	0.002 857 143	**1295.978 2**	**1.295 978 2**	0.001 295 978
1 pennyweight	=	**0.05**	0.004 166 667	0.003 428 571	**1555.173 84**	**1.555 173 84**	0.001 555 174
1 dram avdp.	=	0.056 966 15	0.004 747 179	0.003 906 25	1771.845 195	1.771 845 195	0.001 771 845
1 dram ap.	=	**0.125**	0.010 416 67	0.008 571 429	**3887.934 6**	**3.887 934 6**	0.003 887 935
1 oz. avdp.	=	0.911 458 3	0.075 954 86	**0.062 5**	**28 349.523 125**	**28.349 523 125**	0.028 349 52
1 oz. ap. or t.	=	**1**	0.083 333 333	0.068 571 43	**31 103.476 8**	**31.103 476 8**	0.031 103 47
1 lb. ap. or t.	=	**12**	**1**	0.822 857 1	**373 241.721 6**	**373.241 721 6**	0.373 241 722
1 lb. avdp.	=	14.583 33	1.215 278	**1**	**453 592.37**	**453.592 37**	**0.453 592 37**
1 milligram	=	0.000 032 151	0.000 002 679	0.000 002 205	**1**	**0.001**	**0.000 001**
1 gram	=	0.032 150 75	0.002 679 229	0.002 204 623	**1000**	**1**	**0.001**
1 kilogram	=	32.150 75	2.679 229	2.204 623	**1 000 000**	**1000**	**1**

Units of Mass not Less than Avoirdupois Ounces

Units		Avoirdupois ounces	Avoirdupois pounds	Short hundredweights	Short tons	Long tons	Kilograms	Metric tons
1 oz. avdp.	=	**1**	**0.0625**	**0.000 625**	**0.000 031 25**	0.000 027 902	0.028 349 523	0.000 028 350
1 lb. avdp.	=	**16**	**1**	**0.01**	**0.0005**	0.000 446 429	**0.453 592 37**	0.000 453 592
1 short cwt.	=	**1600**	**100**	**1**	**0.05**	0.044 642 86	**45.359 237**	**0.045 359 237**
1 short ton	=	**32 000**	**2000**	**20**	**1**	0.892 857 1	**907.184 74**	**0.907 184 74**
1 long ton	=	**35 840**	**2240**	**22.4**	**1.12**	**1**	**1016.046 908 8**	1.016 046 909
1 kilogram	=	35.273 96	2.204 623	0.022 046 23	0.001 102 311	0.000 094 207	**1**	**0.001**
1 metric ton	=	35 273.96	2204.623	22.046 23	1.102 311	0.984 206 5	**1000**	**1**

VIII. Decimal Equivalents of Common Fractions

8ths	16ths	32ds	64ths		8ths	16ths	32ds	64ths	
			1	.015625				33	.515625
		1	2	.03125			17	34	.53125
			3	.046875				35	.546875
	1	2	4	.0625		9	18	36	.5625
			5	.078125				37	.578125
		3	6	.09375			19	38	.59375
			7	.109375				39	.609375
1	2	4	8	.125	5	10	20	40	.625
			9	.140625				41	.640625
		5	10	.15625			21	42	.65625
			11	.171875				43	.671875
	3	6	12	.1875		11	22	44	.6875
			13	.203125				45	.703125
		7	14	.21875			23	46	.71875
			15	.234375				47	.734375
2	4	8	16	.25	6	12	24	48	.75
			17	.265625				49	.765625
		9	18	.28125			25	50	.78125
			19	.296875				51	.796875
	5	10	20	.3125		13	26	52	.8125
			21	.328125				53	.828125
		11	22	.34375			27	54	.84375
			23	.359375				55	.859375
3	6	12	24	.375	7	14	28	56	.875
			25	.390625				57	.890625
		13	26	.40625			29	58	.90625
			27	.421875				59	.921875
	7	14	28	.4375		15	30	60	.9375
			29	.453125				61	.953125
		15	30	.46875			31	62	.96875
			31	.484375				63	.984375
4	8	16	32	.5	8	16	32	64	1

IX. Greek Alphabet; Roman Numerals

GREEK ALPHABET

Α	α	alpha	Ι	ι	iota	Ρ	ρ	rho
Β	β	beta	Κ	κ	kappa	Σ	σ	sigma
Γ	γ	gamma	Λ	λ	lambda	Τ	τ	tau
Δ	δ	delta	Μ	μ	mu	Υ	υ	upsilon
Ε	ε	epsilon	Ν	ν	nu	Φ	φ	phi
Ζ	ζ	zeta	Ξ	ξ	xi	Χ	χ	chi
Η	η	eta	Ο	ο	omicron	Ψ	ψ	psi
Θ	θ	theta	Π	π	pi	Ω	ω	omega

ROMAN NUMERALS

I	1	XI	11	XXX	30	CD	400
II	2	XII	12	XL	40	D	500
III	3	XIII	13	L	50	DC	600
IV	4	XIV	14	LX	60	DCC	700
V	5	XV	15	LXX	70	DCCC	800
VI	6	XVI	16	LXXX	80	CM	900
VII	7	XVII	17	XC	90	M	1,000
VIII	8	XVIII	18	C	100	MCM	1,900
IX	9	XIX	19	CC	200	MM	2,000
X	10	XX	20	CCC	300	$\overline{\mathrm{V}}$	5,000

A dash line over a numeral multiplies the value by 1,000: thus, $\overline{\mathrm{X}}$ = 10,000; $\overline{\mathrm{L}}$ = 50,000; $\overline{\mathrm{C}}$ = 100,000; $\overline{\mathrm{D}}$ = 500,000; $\overline{\mathrm{M}}$ = 1,000,000; $\overline{\mathrm{CLIX}}$ = 159,000; $\overline{\mathrm{DLIX}}$ = 559,000.

Other general rules for Roman numerals are as follows: (1) Repeating a letter repeats its value: XX = 20; CCC = 300. (2) A letter placed after one of greater value adds thereto: VI = 6; DC = 600. (3) A letter placed before one of greater value subtracts therefrom: IV = 4.